Instructor's Manual for

Human Sexuality, Second Edition

Instructor's Manual for

Masters, Johnson, and Kolodny's

Human Sexuality, Second Edition

Prepared by

Nancy J. Kolodny, M.A., M.S.W.

Little, Brown and Company

Boston   Toronto

ISBN 0-316-54996-7

5   4   3   2   1

MV

Published simultaneously in Canada
by Little, Brown & Company (Canada) Limited

Printed in the United States of America

PREFACE

This manual provides a concise planning guide for college instructors using the second edition of Masters, Johnson, and Kolodny's Human Sexuality. Recognizing the great diversity of ways in which sexuality courses are taught, we have aimed for coverage that has a broad applicability and a high degree of practical usefulness. As a preamble, the organization of this manual will be briefly discussed.

INTRODUCTION

The introductory essay gives an overview of the challenges implicit in teaching a college course on sexuality. After initial consideration of course goals from both students' and instructors' viewpoints, a section on implementation of course goals discusses various ways of using the text -- including alternate plans for revised course sequences and abridgements suitable for one-quarter courses. This is followed by a series of suggestions regarding lectures, classroom discussions, and the use of ancillary aids such as movies and guest lecturers. The introduction concludes with a thought-provoking section on potential pitfalls that is aimed to help prevent, circumvent, or minimize problems an instructor might encounter.

GENERAL RESOURCES

This section provides instructors with a wide range of materials useful in planning their courses. An annotated guide to sexuality films (and a listing of film distributors) is supplemented by up-to-date lists of journals and newsletters dealing with sexuality, organizations in the field, and as a unique convenience, a listing of special bibliographies that cover thousands of publications on specific topics in sexology.

CHAPTER LISTINGS

Each of the twenty-four chapters in the text has a corresponding chapter in this manual which is organized with the following components:

Overview

A concise synopsis of the chapter contents is followed by a list of significant issues that students should consider while reading the chapter.

Learning Objectives

Taken directly from the Student Study Guide, these objectives indicate the core content of each chapter for which students will be held responsible. (The student objectives can also be used as additional test material.)

Teaching Strategies

Specific suggestions are tailored to each chapter for presenting lecture material in a lively fashion, supplementing the textbook content, and leading class discussions. In addition, potential difficulties that students commonly encounter are discussed.

Student Projects

Designed to encourage further involvement by students in understanding the conceptual material of the text, these projects span a broad range of activities from library research to field trips or interviews to the design of mini-research projects.

Personal Reflections Questions

Designed as a thought-provoking way of helping students personalize the meaning of the material in each chapter, these questions help students deal with issues of aesthetics, values, and speculation about their own sexual lives.

Test Items

A detailed set of 25 multiple choice questions (with the first five in each set being general comprehension questions), 15 true-false, and 15 fill-in-the blanks are provided for each chapter. They vary in difficulty within each chapter and test recall of factual material as well as comprehension of broader concepts. More than 1000 individual questions are presented in this manual.

Discussion/Essay Questions

Discussion/essay questions suitable either for use in examinations or for focused classroom dialogue follow the fill-in-the-blanks and vary in number per chapter.

A <u>Student Study Guide</u>, prepared by Professor Marvin R. Levy of Temple University, is also available as an ancillary teaching aid to Masters, Johnson, and Kolodny's <u>Human Sexuality, Second Edition.</u>

CONTENTS

INTRODUCTION

Teaching a course about human sexuality is an extremely challenging task. To begin with, the instructor is likely to be faced with a sizable number of students who believe that they are already "expert" in their knowledge on the basis of personal experiences. At the same time, other students may have registered for the course because they were aware of their <u>lack</u> of sexual knowledge. Similarly, there is likely to be considerable diversity in the sexual values of the students, with an intermingling of religious backgrounds, varying degrees of conservatism and liberalism, and philosophies about interpersonal behavior and responsibility. In addition to these cross-currents -- which are more likely to be expressed in a sexuality course than in a course on the 19th Century English Novel or Botany 101 -- the instructor must also deal with the sex education students receive from sources outside the classroom, including X-rated movies, popular magazines, personal advice columns in newspapers, and best-selling books. Separating fact from fiction and science from sensationalism is not always easy.

Students in a sexuality course are also more likely to be personally touched by the subject matter and the instructor's style of teaching than in other courses. Discussions about sexuality can provoke feelings of insecurity, embarrassment, guilt, or shock in some students in ways that are often unpredictable. A seemingly off-hand remark by the instructor, an attempt at humor, or a statement of opinion may have far greater emotional impact than might be anticipated. Therefore, it is crucial that the instructor of a sexuality course blends competent knowledge of the subject matter with a sensitivity to the needs and reactions of students while presenting a lively, thought-provoking, objective course in an atmosphere of safety and good taste. This <u>Instructor's Manual</u> is aimed at helping the teacher achieve this goal.

GOALS OF A HUMAN SEXUALITY COURSE

While each college instructor is likely to have some personal priorities and predilections in planning and implementing a course about sexuality, most instructors would probably agree that three aspects of the teaching plan are most central to their objectives: to enhance knowledge, to engender comfort, to allow choice. For the student, learning about sexuality not only includes mastering the fundamental body of knowledge of sexology accepted as "fact" today but learning how to ask questions, how to develop a healthy skepticism, and how to be willing to admit that "I don't know" or "I'm uncertain." Knowledge by itself, however, is not as likely to be useful to the student as is knowledge integrated with comfort and choice.

It's one thing to know, but quite another to be comfortable with what one knows -- particularly in terms of self-perception, tolerance for others whose values, practices, or beliefs differ from one's own, and the ability to translate one's intellectual knowledge into the reality of personal relationships. In much the same vein, for the course to be successful, helping students gain knowledge and comfort about the subject of sex is not quite enough. It must include a framework in which students can learn to choose what is right for themselves, and responsible rather than exploitive, in their dealings with others.

While such goals won't be fully attained with each and every student, the instructor can make a sizable impact on a large percentage of students by keeping these goals in mind as the course progresses. They are, in fact, reasonable and attainable.

In order to move realistically toward the transformation of these goals from abstractions to concrete processes, the instructor needs to pursue a set of specific aims in teaching a sexuality course. For example, enhancing knowledge entails the following components: (1) correcting misinformation or mistaken assumptions that students bring to the course; (2) providing new information across a broad range of topics; (3) helping students develop a conceptual framework for integrating and understanding what they can learn; and (4) catalyzing the process wherein students can personalize their knowledge and apply it to their own lives. Similarly, each instructor will need to develop specific objectives that involve the educational emphasis in his or her course. For example, one instructor may choose to teach a course stressing the sociological aspects of sexuality, another may place greatest emphasis on biological topics, and another may highlight psychological themes. Curriculum design and classroom discussions must be structured to supplement the text accordingly.

STUDENT GOALS

Students enroll in a course about sexuality for a variety of reasons. Some are majoring in areas such as psychology, biology, or sociology and see the study of sex as an important adjunct to their academic interests. Many others sign up because of personal fascination with the subject and the idea that "this is one class that won't be boring." Others are searching for the keys to personal happiness, solutions to personal problems, or for a "how to" course that will turn them into proficient, desired lovers in one semester. Some students enroll hoping that the class will help them find compatible sex partners (or any willing sex partners), and still others believe they are already so knowledgeable about sexuality that the course will prove to be easy.

Given this diversity, the instructor's approach to motivating students must necessarily rely on more than the nature of the subject alone. For this reason, it is often helpful if the first session of the class includes some specific discussion of the goals of the course, the reasons behind the goals, and a detailed look at the components of the course such as textbook readings, class lectures and discussions, use of ancillary resources such as films, guest speakers, field trips, and examinations and grading practices. In fact, a major theme that is stressed throughout this manual is that one of the best ways to motivate students is to make the reading and lecture material have personal relevance and fascination for them. One sure way is to offer creative classroom presentations.

IMPLEMENTING THE COURSE GOALS

Use of the Text

Masters, Johnson, and Kolodny's Human Sexuality, Second Edition was carefully organized with an eye to the differing needs of a broad range of college sexuality courses. While the book is structured sequentially in a fashion designed for a smooth, logical flow of topics, each chapter is relatively self-contained so that instructors can choose either a different sequence of material or can omit specific chapters or sections of chapters in order to fit the needs of their courses. Several alternate plans for the use of Masters, Johnson, and Kolodny's Human Sexuality, Second Edition are presented below.

Plan #1: Revised sequence emphasizing cultural aspects of sexuality early in the course. Have students read Ch. 1 and then move immediately to Ch. 22 ("Sexual Themes in Popular Culture"), Ch. 23 ("Religious and Ethical Perspectives on Sexuality"), and Ch. 24 ("Sexuality in Cross-Cultural Perspective). The remainder of the course can be taught following the sequence of textbook Chapters 2-21.
The advantage of this revised sequence is that cultural aspects of sexuality have a very immediate accessibility to students and can provide a useful persepctive for viewing all subsequent material. In classes with a large number of students who may have been away from an academic environment for a number of years, this sequence provides a way to ease the student back into the learning process, because the material in Chapters 22, 23, and 24 is not as technically demanding as is the material in the biological chapters.
For shorter courses where this emphasis is desirable, and where the instructor's intention is to reduce the student's need to digest research or biologically-oriented chapters, the following portions of the text could be omitted: Ch. 2 ("Sex Research: An Overview"), Ch. 5 ("Human Reproduction"), Ch. 7 ("Developmental Sexuality: A Biological View"), and Ch. 20 ("Sexual Disorders and Sexual Health"). The materials in Ch. 6 ("Birth Control") and Ch. 21 ("Sexually Transmitted Diseases") can also be abridged in this plan if desired, although we believe that all college level students should be familiarized with these topics.

3

Plan #2: Revised sequence emphasizing psychosocial aspects of sexuality early in the course. Have students first read Ch. 1 and Ch. 2 and then skip ahead to Ch. 8 ("Childhood and Adolescent Sexuality"). Proceed with Chapters 9-19 in order, and then have students read Chapters 3-7, followed by Chapters 20-24.

This sequence places its initial emphasis on psychosocial aspects of sexuality and reduces the chance that students will be overwhelmed by or unduly impressed with the importance of biological issues before they have gotten a broader grasp of the course material. However, if the instructor completely ignores biological elements in the first two-thirds of the course, there is a risk of dichotomizing and distoring the students' conceptual grasp of the interacting dimensions of sexuality.

For shorter courses where this sequential approach is desirable, several or all of the following chapters could be omitted: Ch. 5 ("Human Reproduction"), Ch. 6 ("Birth Control"), Ch. 7 ("Developmental Sexuality: A Biological View"), Ch. 20 ("Sexual Disorders and Sexual Health"), Ch. 21 ("Sexually Transmitted Diseases"), Ch. 22 ("Sexual Themes in Popular Culture"), Ch. 23 ("Religious and Ethical Perspectives on Sexuality"), and Ch. 24 ("Sexuality in Cross-Cultural Perspective").

Plan #3: Abridging the text for a one-quarter course emphasizing biological aspects of sexuality. Assign Chapters 2-9 sequentially. Then cover Ch. 12 ("Intimacy and Communication Skills"), Ch. 15 ("Heterosexuality"), Ch. 16 ("Homosexuality and Bisexuality"), Ch. 20 ("Sexual Disorders and Sexual Health") and Ch. 21 ("Sexually Transmitted Diseases"). Discussions of topics such as masturbation, gender roles, sex therapy, coercive sex, and cultural aspects of sexuality will have to be integrated into the lecture material by the instructor or can be partially covered by the use of films if desired.

Plan #4: Abridging the text for a one-quarter course emphasizing behavioral aspects of sexuality. After beginning with Ch. 1 ("Perspectives on Sexuality"), devote one class lecture to fundamental aspects of sexual anatomy and physiology, assigning selected portions of Chapters 3 ("Sexual Anatomy") and 4 ("Sexual Physiology") for students to read (for example, the sections on "Hormonal Regulation of Sexual Function" and "Menstruation" can be omitted from Ch. 4). Next, assign all of Ch. 8 ("Childhood and Adolescent Sexuality") and Ch. 9 ("Adult Sexuality"), selected portions of Ch.10 ("Gender Roles") (only the first half of the chapter, concluding with the section on androgyny), and all of Ch. 11 ("Loving and Being Loved") and Ch. 12 ("Intimacy and Communication Skills"). Conclude the course by assigning Chapters 14 through 18 in sequence. If desired, material on cross-cultural aspects of sexual behavior and on sexual dysfunctions can be integrated into lectures without assigning specific readings on these topics.

In addition, instructors faced with time constraints may find it useful to include a lecture toward the end of the course sequence titled "Timely Topics in Human Sexuality" in which they touch on a variety of issues they haven't addressed in the mainstream of their lectures. Thus, an instructor who has taught a course emphasizing the psychosocial aspects of sexuality may want to make brief, but informative, mention of topics as diverse as premenstrual syndrome, the G-spot controversy, the latest developments in legislation related to sexual behavior, and new findings about AIDS all in one "pot pourri" course finale.

Instructors teaching a one-quarter course or others who are forced by time constraints to omit several chapters of the text from assigned readings may wish to give "extra credit" to students for reading the "optional" chapters. This can be accomplished by having students hand in short papers or completed sections of the Student Study Guide to document their extra work.

Use of the Classroom

Most instructors of college sexuality courses choose to use a mixture of lectures, class discussions, and ancillary aids (such as guest speakers, films, student reports, and so on) on a regular basis to provide balance, variety, and liveliness to their teaching. In each chapter of this Instructor's Manual, specific suggestions regarding teaching strategies will be given to provide a number of options for consideration. Here, we present some general ideas about lectures, classroom discussions, and ancillary aids to assist the instructor in planning a sexuality course.

Lectures

While lectures present an opportunity to cover a great deal of information in an organized fashion and to integrate concepts in a manner that students may not have achieved by the textbook readings alone, lectures also may become dry, boring, or pedantic unless specific measures are taken to balance this tendency. Try to avoid lectures that simply repeat the text; instead, supplement material in the text by examples drawn from your own work, by the use of items recently in the news, and by lectures that address the particular concerns of your students and campus. For instance, if you've done any sex counseling or sex therapy, brief case profiles may dramatically illustrate many principles you'd like your students to understand. If there's a referendum in your vicinity on gay rights, present the particulars to your students (and, depending on the point you'd like to emphasize, use this opportunity to cover historical or legal concepts too).

The lecture format runs the risk of being overwhelming to some students. You can guard against this by good pacing and by using a variety of techniques to prevent your lectures from sounding too austere or too mechanical. For instance, try to balance the scientific side of your talks with a humanistic perspective. "Dry" lecture material, such as coverage of sexual anatomy or physiology, can be humanized (or humorized) by ploys such as intermingled readings of brief erotic passages from 19th and 20th century novels. Almost any lecture topic can be enhanced by using well-selected cross-cultural comparisons. Examining the political ramifications of a topic -- such as the American Psychiatric Association's decision to drop homosexuality from their official classification of mental disorders -- can also be used to highlight controversy or make a seemingly less accessible topic "come to life." Introducing up-to-the-minute statistics from government reports (on matters ranging from divorce figures to national rates of gonorrhea) or from public opinion surveys or national magazine surveys can also be used profitably to hold students' interest during a lecture.

Class Discussions

Many instructors feel that the caliber and spontaneity of classroom discussions are among the principal ingredients in determining the success of a college sexuality course. In contrast to the largely passive role forced on students as lecture-listeners, class discussions encourage students to become active participants in the course in a variety of ways. Students can voice their own opinions, challenge the views of the instructor (or their classmates), ask practical questions, and "let off steam" in a way that can help themselves as well as assist the instructor in developing a sense of how people in the class are internalizing the subject matter.

In our experience, it is difficult to generate meaningful classroom discussion in classes with thirty or more students. While it may be possible to have plenty of talking occur so that the allotted time is used up, rarely will it be possible for a class of this size to develop a style of group discussion in which, over a number of weeks of continued dialogue, students discover a peer support network, a forum for informal debate, and a sense of shared intellectual closeness. Instructors faced with this problem may wish to divide their class into two or three discussion sections and either find a colleague or teaching assistant to share group discussion leadership or meet personally with each discussion group at a separate time. Another option is to train a selected group of students who have previously completed the course in strategies of group discussion leaders and allow them to meet with student groups (while regularly reporting back to the instructor on the progress and problems of each group).

In smaller classes, students can quickly develop a sense of comfort in discussing sensitive, value-laden issues if a realistic course is set by the instructor. While it is important to encourage the consideration of a number of (sometimes conflicting) beliefs or positions, it is also important to realize that a college class is not group therapy and that inappropriate self-disclosure may be destructive to the individual and injurious to the class. The instructor is responsible for giving direct and indirect messages to students about the appropriate amount and type of disclosure of personal information; and the instructor must also be circumspect in his or her personal confessions.

Ancillary Aids

Movies or videotapes. The large number of audiovisual products now available on the subject of sexuality can supplement lectures and assigned readings in important ways. Some of these films are likely to have a striking emotional impact on students because they

6

personalize a theme and pack a gut-level wallop (films about sex and disability; films about victims of rape or incest). Other films document the natural wonder of biologic processes (films showing ovulation, films of swimming sperm, films showing the physiologic changes of the sexual response cycle) in ways a textbook cannot hope to match. Many other films or tapes are useful because they can simultaneously disseminate information, hold students' interest, and serve as a potent stimulus for class discussions.

Films about sexuality can also function as "desensitizers," but it is far from certain as to just how reliable or lasting this effect may be. Indeed, sexually explicit films can also provoke different types of anxieties, ranging from the obvious concerns about body image and attractiveness that college students are likely to have, to anxieties of a more subtle nature. For example, students may become anxious if they find themselves getting sexually aroused while viewing a movie depicting something that conflicts with their religious or personal values. Yet, because instructors cannot talk individually with each student to assess his or her reaction to a film and because some students (in particular, anxious students) may be reticent in group discussions about a movie, the anxieties of such students may not only go undetected but may actually magnify over time. Because of this sort of problem, instructors need to be especially careful in preparing their classes for movie viewing (we suggest, in fact, that this is best handled as an optional activity) and in discussing reactions to the movie or tape in a sensitive way that gives students "permission" to have experienced it differently from the majority of their classmates.

While an annotated list of films is presented elsewhere in this manual, one other word of caution is in order here. Among the hundreds of films and tapes available on the subject of sexuality, many are of very poor quality. Not only are there many films that are cinematically substandard (blurred focus, poor editing, washed-out colors, and so on), many others are uneven (or worse) from the point-of-view of content. Never use a film or video-tape in class without having first previewed it yourself to judge its production quality, its intellectual soundness, and its compatability with your teaching objectives. Consult several of the journals and newsletters listed in the General Resources section for relatively up-to-date reviews of audiovisual materials that may be well-suited to your needs.

Guest lecturers. Finding a midwife to speak to your class about childbirth, or a law enforcement officer to talk about prostitution or rape, or a minister involved in the gay rights movement to address the issue of homosexuality is certain to gain the rapt attention of your students.

Guest lecturers can provide a good change of tempo and can meaningfully augment areas of the instructor's expertise, but careful planning is required to be sure this strategy does not backfire. Whenever possible, invite only guest speakers you've heard before. A boring guest lecturer is no asset, no matter how "authoritative" his or her credentials may seem. Be specific in outlining the ground you'd like your guests to cover, and be sure that they understand the time allotted for their talks, the positioning of their talks in the course sequence (so that they don't mistakenly assume that students will be familiar with a topic that won't come up for several more weeks), and the particular style in which you wish your class to be conducted. A guest who uses street language to describe sexual acts may shock students rather than educate them if your course is taught with a more scientific vocabulary. At the other extreme, a lecturer who spouts nothing but professional jargon will quickly lose a class of college students.

POTENTIAL PITFALLS

In planning to teach a human sexuality course, the instructor should be aware of a number of possible problems that are commonly encountered as the course unfolds. Being alert to these potential pitfalls is not always enough to prevent or eliminate them, but in most instances it will help the instructor maximize the learning experience for his or her students. Our intent here is not to be encyclopedic either by listing all potential pitfalls or by discussing them exhaustively; instead, this section is intended as a practical checklist to be of assistance to both the classroom veteran and the instructor teaching a course in sexuality for the first time.

One early set of potential pitfalls derives from the basic expectations students may have about a course in sexuality and how this should differ from other college courses. First, those who expect an easy course -- "we'll just watch some films and rap about them" -- will be unlikely to come to class having completed their assigned textbook readings, which means that they will have little or no conceptual or informational framework in which to place the lecture material or to serve as the basis for class discussion. Second, those who expect a "personal confessions" course or an "experiential learning" course will not only be unlikely to complete the reading assignments but will also propel class discussions in an unproductive direction. Third, those who expect a "how to" course -- a sort of "Cordon Bleu School of Sexual Techniques" -- will avidly tackle the textbook and diligently take notes during lectures, but will quickly lose interest once they realize that the course isn't geared to meeting their expectations. Each of these potential problems is most easily avoided by discussing the goals and requirements of the course in the first class session and specifically addressing these issues.

Another set of potential problems involves the objectivity and nonjudgmentalism of the instructor. While no sexuality instructor is able to be completely objective and unbiased by personal opinion or personal experiences, the learning dynamics of the course are likely to suffer if the instructor persistently takes dogmatic or moralistic positions. This does not mean, of course, that an amoral approach to teaching sexuality is advisable; it does suggest, however, that intellectual flexibility and refraining from offering gratuitous value judgments to students are in order.

Several offshoots of the issues of objectivity and nonjudgmentalism are worth examining more closely. The first item has to do with interpreting research findings to students, since this will occur at many points during the course. The various professional disciplines that each contribute to sexology (such as sociology, psychology, physiology, and anthropology) are not always in agreement in reaching conclusions about the validity or meaning of research data, just as the members of a particular discipline do not always agree with each other. These legitimate differences of opinion may be quite confusing to students unless the instructor reminds them periodically of the rapidly changing nature of a young field of science as it progresses by replacing old theories with new information.

In sexology, controversy surrounds many basic issues: What are the most important factors in gender identity development? How effective is sex therapy? Can men have multiple orgasms? What proof is there that sex education works? Is transsexual surgery helpful or not? This type of controversy can be exciting to students as long as they realize that their opinions are only one perspective on a complicated issue. Furthermore, unless students are reminded periodically that the instructor's way of thinking is not necessarily the "right" way or the only way of assessing the facts, students may be so much in awe of the instructor's superior knowledge and presumed expertise that they lose their sense of intellectual skepticism and become more concerned with memorizing the instructor's words than with understanding the underlying concepts and the reasons for controversy.

A second important aspect of problems related to professional objectivity and nonjudgmentalism is that an instructor with strong professional biases about a particular issue who tries to appear objective often winds up sending contradictory messages to the students. Students are usually able to sense the difference between an authentically held viewpoint and an artificially articulated stance taken for the sake of intellectual balance and fairness. The instructor can overcome this dilemma by alerting students to his or her professional (or personal) biases early in the course and reminding students of these leanings at key junctures as the course goes on. Another way of minimizing the problems of distorted objectivity that sometimes occur is to co-teach the course with a colleague whose training and areas of expertise complement your own.

A third matter related to the objectivity-nonjudgmentalism realm is that some students are apt to have radical or dogmatic viewpoints on feminism, abortion, homosexuality, premarital sex, and other similar issues. These viewpoints may lead to lively classroom discussion, but there is a risk that such discussions can deteriorate into heated emotional arguments that serve no educational purpose and are uncomfortable for the majority of the class. The instructor's role here is to exert enough anticipatory control over discussions to minimize the chance of this sort of exchange and to recognize the early signs of potential discussion problems (escalating voice volume, one student interrupting another, ad hominem attacks, impassioned cries of "how do you know if you've never tried it?" or "that's crazy" and so on) so that the discussion can be steered in another direction. It should also be noted here that a student may sometimes pinpoint quite accurately some bias on the part of the instructor; if this occurs, it is helpful to thank the student openly and to remind the class how difficult nonjudgmentalism can be in practice.

9

Another area of potential problems involves the use of audio-visual materials in a sexuality class. While each instructor will undoubtedly develop an approach that feels comfortable and works well for his or her course design, there are a few issues that should be thought through carefully in advance. First, what is the proportion of time spent on audiovisual materials compared to lectures and discussions? In our experience, if more time is devoted to audiovisuals than to discussions, it is a sign that relatively little authentic learning is occurring. This is problematic for two reasons: students cannot adequately air their reactions to the movies or tapes they've watched without a reasonable time for discussion, and this type of planning may mean that the instructor is unwittingly avoiding the responsibilities and difficulties of running a spontaneous discussion session by using up more time watching films or tapes. Second, even relatively "innocuous" audiovisual materials may be offensive or unpleasant to some students. It is important that the instructor creates a climate for the use of films or tapes that does not embarrass or ridicule a person who has such a reaction. Furthermore, the instructor should be available, on an individual basis, to meet with any student in the class who has a need to discuss personal issues, including reactions encountered in response to a film shown in class.

One other area will be touched on in this essay. The very personal, private way in which most people regard their own sexuality must be respected by the instructor throughout the course. This doesn't mean that sex should be taught about in whispers or surrounded with long lists of negative admonitions, but it does mean that students should not be queried about their personal sexual proclivities and past sexual experiences as part of class discussions. Students may not fully realize the lack of confidentiality guaranteed in a classroom situation and may find themselves the subject of annoying or demeaning gossip after describing some personal experience in a classroom discussion. Furthermore, even when discussing one's own sexual experiences is totally voluntary, some students feel quite pressured to participate because of their desire to get a good grade, because of their sense of peer group pressure, or because of their desire to seem "with it" and knowledgeable. Finally, besides the embarrassment and anxiety that personal confessions can entail, there is a possibility that one student may be blackmailed or exploited by another because of the content of such a classroom interchange.

There is, to be sure, no single approach to teaching about sexuality that is always best. Every instructor develops a style to match his or her professional identity and personal philosophy; the style and the course design must also be comfortable, efficient, interesting, and informative in order to succeed. This Instructor's Manual and the second edition of the Masters, Johnson and Kolodny Human Sexuality text are designed for facilitating the teaching process with a high degree of adaptability to the varying needs of different instructors and courses. In the final analysis, while these publications can be of significant assistance in many ways, the true essence of teaching is still an art, the successful teacher an artist.

SELECTED FILMS

The following films are recommended for use in college sexuality courses but constitute only a small fraction of the large number that are available. For a more complete listing, consult R.S. Daniel's Annotated Guide to Audiovisuals listed in the Special Bibliographies section. Films about sexuality are also reviewed regularly in the SIECUS Report, Sexuality and Disability, The Journal of Sex Education and Therapy, and the Journal of Sex and Marital Therapy. Wherever possible, we have included dates and formats of the films. Addresses of distributors for the films are located elsewhere in this section.

ABORTION

Early Abortion. 8 minutes (Perennial).
Clearly describes vacuum aspiration abortions through diagrams and the filming of a real-life procedure. Supplemented by a group discussion about the effects of abortion.

The Politics of Abortion. 35 minutes (CBS).
This 1978 documentary by CBS examines various aspects of the abortion controversy. Leaders on both sides of the issue are interviewed, and the material is timely.

ABSTINENCE

Saying "No." 17 minutes (Perennial). 16 mm color or video.
Based on hundreds of interviews, this film uses a radio talk show format in which young women explain their personal reasons for sexual abstinence as a viable option.

First Things First. 1983. 30 minutes (Bill Wadsworth Productions). 16mm or video.
An adolescent couple decide that caring and being attentive to one another's feelings are more important than having sexual intercourse at this time in their lives.

ADOLESCENT PREGNANCY

Sweet Sixteen and Pregnant. 1982. 29 minutes (MTI Teleprograms). 16 mm or video.
Sally Kellerman narrates this documentary exploring the diverse

outcomes of five teenage pregnancies.

When Teens Get Pregnant. 19 minutes (Polymorph Films). 16 mm
    color.
Five teenage women at Brigham Women's Hospital speak about the
issues pregnant teens must cope with.

AGING AND SEXUALITY

Love in Later Life. 1983. 30 minutes (Multi- Focus). 16 mm or
    video.
A 69-year-old woman and 70-year-old man with a successful marriage
of 44 year's duration are shown in the nude, massaging one another,
and making love.

Rose by Any Other Name. 1979. 15 minutes (Multi-Focus).
A 79-year-old woman in a nursing home is discovered having sex with
another nursing home resident and this threatens the staff, the
administration, and her family. A fine springboard for discussing
stereotypes about the elderly and sexuality.

ANATOMY

Near the Big Chakra. 1972. 15 minutes (Multi-Focus).
Leisurely, close-up views of the genitals of thirty-eight women of
different ages that can help students become comfortable with the
notion of anatomic variability.

Plain and Fancy Penises. 80 color slides (Multi-Focus).
Close-up photos of penises in a variety of shapes and states
(flaccid, erect, circumcised, uncircumcised, etc.).

BIRTH

Birth of a Family. 24 minutes (Perennial).
Childbirth preparation classes with scenes from a delivery.

Gentle Birth. 15 minutes (Ploymorph Films).
A Lamaze-Leboyer delivery is shown, concisely depicting the
interaction of mother, father, and obstetrician.

CROSS-CULTURAL PERSPECTIVES ON SEXUALITY

Dadi and Her Family: A Rural Mother-in-Law in India. 45 minutes
    (Department of South Asian Studies, University of Wisconsin,
    Madison, WI 53706). 16 mm color.
Interviews and scenes of a family at the time of their youngest
son's marriage; the role of a daughter-in-law in the family system
of a changing Indian society.

EROTICA

World Erotica. 1971. 160 slides (Multi-Focus). Color and
    black and white.
A diverse collection of erotic art pieces from different eras and
cultures.

FANTASY

Orange. 1970. 3 minutes (Multi-Focus).
A short sensual film depicting some people feeling and peeling an
orange.

Raspberry. 20 minutes (Multi-Focus).
Wonderful film depicting female erotic fantasies; beautiful color.

GENDER ROLES

Men's Lives. 43 minutes (New Day Films).
Depicts many issues about masculinity in contemporary America with
great detail but no explicit sex.

Sex Role Development. 23 minutes (CRM McGraw-Hill).
Deals with ways of eliminating or lessening gender role
stereotyping.

Killing Us Softly: Advertising's Image of Women. 30 minutes
    (Cambridge Documentary Films). 16 mm color or video.
Jean Kilbourne lectures with slides about media's powerful impact as
a cultural conditioning agent.

HETEROSEXUALITY

A Ripple in Time. 1974. 24 minutes (Multi-Focus).
Delightful film of an older couple depicting sex as play. The
couple has obvious affection for one another. An excellent general
purpose film.

Insights. 20 minutes (EDCOA).
A couple discusses the film of heterosexual intercourse they made
with Dr. John Money. Rendered less threatening by splicing the
interview with the explicit sexual interaction.

Oral Sex. 11 minutes (EDCOA).
Explicit depictions of oral-genital sex along with some discussion
of religious concerns about this activity.

Reflections. 1976. 25 minutes (Multi-Focus).
A group of people discuss their experiences with swinging and then
become involved in group sex in a large mirrored room.

Watercress. 13 minutes (Multi-Focus).
An idyllic depiction of alternative sexual lifestyles in a country
setting.

HOMOSEXUALITY

A Very Natural Thing. 85 minutes (New Line Cinema).
Sensitive depiction of conflicts and relationships of homosexual men. Depicts gay bars, baths, liberation groups, and dealing with children.

Greetings from Washington, D.C. 28 minutes (Iris Films). 16 mm color or video.
A documentary recording of the 1978 march of 100,000 gay men and lesbian women in Washington, D.C. to call attention to the need for civil rights for homosexuals.

Holding. 1974. 14 minutes (Multi-Focus).
Lesbian film with depictions of close relationship and sexual interaction.

Michael: A Gay Son. 28 minutes (Filmakers Library, Inc.). 16 mm color.
Documentary style depicting the problems of gays in "coming out" to their families; based on an actual case study.

Nick and Jon. 1976. 20 minutes (Multi-Focus).
Very explicit homosexual interaction which features two attractive males who meet at a party. Dialogue includes many issues confronting homosexuals.

Sharing the Secret: Selected Gay Stories. 84 minutes (Ifex Films). 16 mm color.
A feature-length film from Canada interviewing five gay men and what it means to them to be gay in today's society.

Teenage Homosexuality. 11 minutes (Carousel Films). 16 mm color.
Originally a segment of CBS's program "30 Minutes," this film explores what it's like to be a gay adolescent from the perspectives of five Houston teenagers.

Vir Amat. 1971. 15 minutes (Multi-Focus).
Two attractive, professional males in an affectionate homosexual relationship. Explicit cosexual activity which is not too threatening is depicted.

Who Happen to Be Gay. 23 minutes (Direct Cinema Limited). 16 mm.
An ABC television documentary about three men and three women professionals who lead openly gay lives.

INCEST

Not in My Family: Parents Speak Out on Sexual Abuse of their Children. 1983. 34 minutes (Lawren Productions). 16 mm or video.
Five mothers describe what it has been like to be a mother in a home where the husband had an incestuous relationship with her daughter.

The Victim Nobody Believes. 23 minutes (MTI Teleprograms).
Three adult women who were victims of incest as children discuss their feelings and experiences in a revealing fashion. An excellent film.

INFERTILITY

One, Two, Three -- Zero Fertility. 28 minutes (Filmakers Library, Inc.). 16 mm color.
This describes various reasons for male and female infertility and what can be done to overcome them.

LOVE

The Love Tapes. 30 minutes (Filmakers Library, Inc.). Black and white videocassette.
Spontaneous reactions of diverse people of all ages, backgrounds, and sexual preferences to the opportunity to speak in privacy for three minutes each about love to video cameras set up in public and semi-public locations.

PHYSIOLOGY

Physiological Responses of the Sexually Stimulated Female in the Laboratory. 1973. 16 minutes (Multi-Focus).
Physiological and anatomical changes of the human female in response to sexual stimulation. Review of some of the Masters and Johnson findings with excellent photography.

Physiological Responses of the Sexually Stimulated Male in the Laboratory. 1974. 16 minutes (Multi-Focus).
Clearly demonstrates the principal physiologic events of male sexual arousal, including an interesting X-ray cinematography sequence showing ejaculation.

The Beginning of Life. 26 minutes (Pyramid Films).
This Japanese film depicts incredible photography of fertilization and growth of the fetus. The best film on this topic, it is highly recommended.

RAPE

Not Only Strangers. 1982. 23 minutes (Centron Films). 16 mm color.
A movie depicting a case of date rape and how the victim's two college roommates encourage her to report the rape to police. There is an excellent depiction of a female police sergeant discussing parameters of rape, with accurate information about circumstances surrounding rape, psychological conflicts.

Rape Series of four films: Rape Alert 17 minutes; Rape: Problems in Proof 30 minutes; Rape: Providing the Proof 30 minutes; and Rape: The Right to Resist 17 minutes (Aims International Meida).
A comprehensive treatment of the topic of rape including legal and preventative aspects.

Why Men Rape. 1980. 40 minutes (Learning Corporation of America).
    16mm color.
Interviews with convicted rapists in penitentiaries or psychiatric
hospitals yields an impression of rape from the rapist's viewpoint.
Includes a group of adolescents discussing the issues of rape and
sexuality.

SEX AND DISABILITY

Active Partners. 1976. 19 minutes (Multi-Focus). 16 mm
    color.
A day in the life of a male quadriplegic and his female partner
including their sexual activity.

Choices: In Sexuality with Physical Disability. Part 1:20 minutes,
    Part 2:40 minutes (Mercury Film Productions). 16 mm color or
    video.
The experiences and opinions of people who have physical
disabilities such as paraplegia, quadriplegia, ileostomies, cerebral
palsy. The first reel focuses on the emotional impact of
disability; the second focuses on specific sexual techniques,
problems, and solutions.

Sex and the Handicapped. 1973. 18 minutes (Multi-Focus). 16 mm
    color.
A demonstration of Sweden's use of live nude models in sex education
for the blind as well as the love-making of a young couple normally
confined to wheel-chairs.

Still A Woman, Still A Man. 17 minutes (Elliot Bay Associates),
    color slides and cassette.
People with a wide range of disabilities -- deafness, blindness,
spinal cord injury, multiple sclerosis, muscular dystrophy --
discuss their sexual and relationship concerns. No explicit sex
scenes.

Touching. 1972. 16 minutes (Multi-Focus).
A male paraplegic and his female partner share manual and oral
stimulation.

SEX EDUCATION

A Family Talks About Sex. 20 minutes (Wester Films, E.E. Brown
    Foundation).
Vignettes of a wide range of sexual issues between parents and
children. Includes discussion of children's natural curiosities,
masturbation, pregnancy, puberty, wet dreams, pornography,
premarital sex, contraception. Excellent and sensible role-
modeling.

SEX THERAPY

Becoming Orgasmic: A Sexual Growth Program for Women. Three films:
    Self-Discovery, 16 minutes; Pleasuring, 18 minutes; Sharing 18

minutes (Multi-Focus).

Women are helped to overcome anorgasmia through a series of self-exploration exercises. Sensitively presented.

SEXUAL DECISION MAKING

Making Decisions About Sex. 25 minutes (Churchill Films). 16 mm color.

The opinions and feelings of eight California teens ranging in age from 15 to 19 about the topic of having intercourse.

SEXUAL HEALTH

David -- Sexual Self-Help and Self-Pleasuring. 1982. 12 minutes (Multi-Focus). 16 mm color or video.

Shows a young man showering, performing breast, testicular and prostate self-examination, then masturbating to depict the interrelationship of sexual health and auto-eroticism.

Herpes Simplex II. 1982. 20 minutes (Milner-Fenwick). 16mm color or video.

Explores the emotional side of herpes using clips of a support group of herpes victims; medical aspects explored by means of narration and graphics.

Venereal Diseases. 17 minutes (John Wiley & Sons).

Concise coverage of practical information about syphilis and gonorrhea that includes brief interviews with patients at a V.D. clinic.

SEXUALITY IN HISTORICAL PERSPECTIVE

Women and Sexuality: A Century of Change. 1983. 36 minutes (Altana). 16 mm.

A well-researched and produced film comparing past views of women's sexuality and sex roles with those of today.

TRANSSEXUALISM

The Way of a Transsexual: Joanne's Story. 50 minutes (Confide-Personal Counseling Services).

A male-to-female transsexual tells of her own experiences in a touching and enlightening way.

17

FILM DISTRIBUTORS

Aims Instructional Media
626 Justin Avenue
Glendale, CA 91201

Altana
155 West 68th Street
New York, NY 10023

Elliot Bay Associates
2366 Eastlake Ave. E, Suite 234
Seattle, WA 98112

Cambridge Documentary Films
PO Box 385
Cambridge, MA 02139

Centron Films
1621 West 9th Street, Box 687
Lawrence, KS 66040

Churchill Films
662 North Robertson Blvd.
Los Angeles, CA 90069

Confide-Personal Counseling Services
Box 56
Tappan, NY 10983

CRM/McGraw Hill Films
110 15th Street
Del Mar, CA 92014

Direct Cinema Limited
Box 69589
Los Angeles, CA 90069

EDCOA Series
Multi-Focus
333 West 52nd Street
New York, NY 10019

Filmakers Library
133 East 58th Street
New York, NY 10022

Ifex Films
159 West 53rd Street
New York, NY 10019

Iris Films
PO Box 5353
Berkeley, CA 94705

Lawren Productions
PO Box 666
Mendocino, CA 95460

MTI Teleprograms
3710 Commercial Avenue
Northbrook, IL 60062

Milner-Fenwick
2125 Greenspring Drive
Timonium, MD 21093

Multi-Focus (formerly Focus International)
333 West 52nd Street
New York, NY 10019

New Day Films
PO Box 315
Franklin Lakes, NJ 07414

New Line Cinema
853 Broadway (16th floor)
New York, NY 10003

Perennial Education
477 Roger Williams
PO Box 855 Ravinia
Highland Park, IL 60035

Polymorph Films
118 South Street
Boston, MA 02111

Pyramid Films
PO Box 1048
Santa Monica, CA 90406

David Steven Enterprises
27 Harvey Drive
Summit, NJ 07901

Bill Wadsworth Productions
1913 West 37th
Austin, TX 78731

John Wiley & Sons
One Wiley Drive
Somerset, NJ 08873

JOURNALS

Alternative Lifestyles (Quarterly)
Human Sciences Press
72 Fifth Avenue
New York, NY 10011

Archives of Sexual Behavior (Bimonthly)
Plenum Publishing
233 Spring Street
New York, NY 10013

British Journal of Sexual Medicine (Monthly)
Medical News Tribune
1 Bedford Street
London WC2E9HD, England

Family Planning Perspectives (Bimonthly)
The Alan Guttmacher Institute
360 Park Avenue South
New York, NY 10010

Journal of Homosexuality (Quarterly)
Haworth Press
28 East 22nd Street
New York, NY 10010

Journal of Marital & Family Therapy (Bimonthly)
American Association for Marriage & Family Therapy
1717 K Street, NW, Suite 407
Washington, DC 20006

Journal of Marriage and the Family (Bimonthly)
National Council on Family Relations
1219 University Avenue, SE
Minneapolis, MN 55414

Journal of Sex and Marital Therapy (Quarterly)
Brunner/Mazel
19 Union Square West
New York, NY 10003

Journal of Sex Education and Therapy (Quarterly)
American Association of Sex Educators, Counselors and
Therapists
11 Dupont Circle NW, Suite 220
Washington, DC 20036

Journal of Sex Research (Bimonthly)
Society for the Scientific Study of Sex
PO Box 29795
Philadelphia, PA 19117

Journal of Social Work and Human Sexuality (Quarterly)
        Haworth Press
        28 East 22nd Street
        New York, NY 10010

Medical Aspects of Human Sexuality (Monthly)
        Hospital Publications
        360 Lexington Avenue
        New York, NY 10017

Sex Roles (Bimonthly)
        Plenum Publishing
        233 Spring Street
        New York, NY 10013

Sexuality and Disability (Quarterly)
        Human Sciences Press
        72 Fifth Avenue
        New York, NY 10011

SIECUS Report (Bimonthly)
        SIECUS
        80 Fifth Avenue, Suite 801
        New York, NY 10011

NEWSLETTERS

AASECT Newsletter (Quarterly)
        American Association of Sex Educators, Counselors, and
        Therapists
        11 Dupont Circle NW, Suite 220
        Washington, DC 20036

Sexuality Today (Weekly)
        Atcom, Inc.
        2315 Broadway
        New York, NY 10024

ORGANIZATIONS IN HUMAN SEXUALITY AND RELATED FIELDS

American Association for Marriage and Family Therapy (AAMFT)
1717 K Street, NW, Suite 407
Washington, DC 20006

American Association of Sex Educators, Counselors, & Therapists
    (AASECT)
11 Dupont Circle NW, Suite 220
Washington, DC 20036

21

International Academy of Sex Research
c/o Dr. Richard Green
Department of Psychiatry and Behavioral Sciences, Health Sciences
School of Medicine -- SUNY
Stonybrook, NY 11790

International Society of Psychoneuroendocrinology
c/o Dr. Richard Michael
Department of Psychiatry
Emory University School of Medicine
Atlanta, GA 30322

National Council on Family Relations
1219 University Avenue, SW
Minneapolis, MN 55411

Planned Parenthood
810 Seventh Avenue
New York, NY 10019

Sex Information and Education Council of U.S. (SIECUS)
80 Fifth Avenue, Suite 801
New York, NY 10011

Society for Sex Therapy and Research (SSTAR)
c/o Dr. R. Schiavi
Mount Sinai Medical Center
One Gustav Levy Place
New York, NY 10029

Society for the Scientific Study of Sex
PO Box 29795
Philadelphia, PA   19117

SPECIAL BIBLIOGRAPHIES

Because the literature of sexology is more widely dispersed than that of many other academic fields, this listing of bibliographies on specific sex-related topics is provided to expedite course preparations for college instructors. Some of the following bibliographies are annotated, giving a critical assessment of each cited work, while others are simply compilations of relevant journal articles and books. The most broadly encompassing work is the 212-page book by Brewer and Wright (1979), which lists 4,267 entries across the entire range of sexology.

American Library Association. Task Force on Gay Liberation. A Gay Bibliography. Philadelphia, 1975.

Astin, H.S., Allison, P., and Fisher, A. Sex Roles: A Research Bibliography. (DHEW No. [ADM] 75-166). Rockville, MD: National Institute of Mental Health, 1975.

Birren, J.E. and Moore, J.L. (eds.). Sexuality and Aging: A Selected Bibliography. Los Angeles: Ethel Percy Andrus Gerontology Center, University of Southern California, 1975.

Brewer, J.S. and Wright, R.W. Sex Research: Bibliographies from the Institute for Sex Research. Phoenix, AZ: Oryx Press, 1979.

Bullough, V.L., Legg, W.D., Elcano, B.W., and Kepner, J. An Annotated Bibliography of Homosexuality (two volumes). New York: Garland Publishing, 1976.

Byerly, G. and Rubin, R. Pornography: The Conflict Over Sexually Explicit Materials in the United States. New York: Garland Publishing, 1980.

Chappell, D., Geis, G., and Fogarty, F. "Forcible Rape: Bibliography." Journal of Criminal Law & Crimonology 65 (2): 248-263, 1974.

Daniel, R.S. Human Sexuality Methods and Materials for the Education, Family Life and Health Professions: An Annotated Guide to the Audiovisuals. Brea, CA: Heuristicus Publishing Company, 1979.

Griffith, E.R., Timms, R.J., and Tomko, M. (Eds.). Sexual Problems of Patients with Spinal Injuries: An Annotated Bibliography. Cincinnati, OH: Department of Physical Medicine and Rehabilitation, College of Medicine, University of Cincinnati, March, 1973.

Kemmer, E.J. Rape and Rape-Related Issues: An Annotated Bibliography. Garland Reference Library of Social Science, vol. 39. New York: Garland Publishing, 1977.

Kenton, C. Rape: January 1970 through June 1973. 64 Citations. Literature Search, no. 73-24. Bethesda, MD: National Library of Medicine, 1973.

Kirby, D., Alter, J., and Scales, P. An Analysis of U.S. Sex Education Programs and Evaluation Methods, Vol. IV, Bibliography. Atlanta, GA: U.S. Dept. of Health, Education, and Welfare (Public Health Service, Center for Disease Control), Report No. CDC-2021-79-DK-FR, 1979.

Maccoby, E.E., and Jacklin, C.N. "Annotated bibliography (of research in sex differences, 1966-1974)." in The Psychology of Sex Differences, pp. 395-627. Stanford, CA: Stanford University Press, 1974.

Money, J., and Athanasiou, R. "Pornography: review and bibliographic annotations." American Journal of Obstetrics and Gynecology 115 (1): 130-146, 1973.

Morin, S.F. Annotated Bibliography of Research on Lesbianism and Male Homosexuality, 1967-1974. (Journal Supplement Abstract Service, MS 1191.) Washington, DC: American Psychological Association, 1976.

Munroe, A.R. Research in Sexual Deviation and Sexual Offenses: A Bibliography. Ottawa: Canadian Criminology & Corrections Association, May, 1974.

National Center for the Prevention and Control of Rape. Printout of Literature Search on Rape. Rockville, MD: National Rape Information Clearinghouse, U.S. Dept. of Health, Education, and Welfare (Public Health Service, National Institute of Mental Health), 1978, Supplement 1979.

O'Farrell, Timothy J., Weyand, C., and Logan, D. (Eds.). Alcohol and Sexuality: An Annotated Bibliography on Alcohol Use, Alcoholism, and Human Sexual Behavior. Phoenix, AZ: Oryx Press, 1983.

Parker, W. Homosexuality: A Selective Bibliography of Over 3,000 Items. Supplement, 1970-1975. Metuchen, NJ: Scarecrow Press, 1977.

Perkins, B.B. Adolescent Birth Planning and Sexuality: Abstracts of the Literature. Consortium on Early Childbearing and Childrearing, Child Welfare League of America. Washington, DC, 1974.

Planned Parenthood of Minnesota. A Selected Bibliography on Sexuality, Sex Education and Family Planning. St. Paul, MN: 1976.

Rabin, B.J. Options' Resource Guide to Sexual Adjustment in Disability. Long Beach, CA: Association for Sexual Adjustment in Disability, 1977.

Scarlett, S., Thurry, C., and Zupan, I. Psychological, Sexual, Social and Vocational Aspects of Spinal Cord Injury: A Selected Bibliography. Minneapolis, MN: Minnesota Medical Rehabilitation Research and Training Center No. 2, July, 1976.

Sha'ked, A. Human Sexuality in Physical and Mental Illnesses and Disabilities: An Annotated Bibliography. Bloomington, IN: Indiana University Press, 1978.

Spiegel, J. Sex Role Concepts: How Women and Men See Themselves and Each Other. A Selected Annotated Bibliography. Washington, DC: Business and Professional Women's Foundation, 1969.

Stewart, K.R. (Ed.). Adolescent Sexuality and Teenage Pregnancy: A Selected, Annotated Bibliography with Summary Forewords. Chapel Hill, NC: Carolina Population Center, 1976.

Weinberg. M.S., and Bell, A.P. (Eds.) Homosexuality: An Annotated Bibliography. New York: Harper & Row, 1972.

Chapter 1

PERSPECTIVES ON SEXUALITY

OVERVIEW

The opening chapter introduces students to the multidimensional perspective appropriate for the study of human sexuality. These "dimensions" -- biological, psychosocial, behavioral, clinical and cultural are initially presented in the context of a case history, and are elaborated upon later in the chapter to alert students to the reasons why looking at sexuality from a single perspective is, at best, an incomplete form of analysis. Historical aspects of sexuality are briefly surveyed to emphasize that sexual attitudes and priorities vary widely from era to era and place to place. Some of the crucial factors that operated within American society to allow the so-called "sexual revolution" of the '60s to begin and flourish, along with the attitudes and trends that followed in the '70s and '80s are explored to point out that change is a given whereas the direction of that change is impossible to predict with accuracy. The work of the key sex research figures of the last century is discussed within the context of the historical perspective; analysis of the fundamental methods and limitations of their sex research is included to illustrate the development of methodology and the change in public response to such research over time.

While reading the chapter, the student is asked to consider these issues:

1. What is the distinction between sex and sexuality?

2. What are the various dimensions of sexuality and how is each defined? What are the dangers of assessing sexuality from a unidimensional perspective? Why must we guard against a simplistic interpretation of sexual behavior?

3. How have attitudes toward male and female sexuality changed over time?

4. How have the major sex researchers of the last hundred years influenced contemporary sexual attitudes?

5. What four factors contributed to the development of the "sexual revolution"? What other trends evolved that had direct impact on the way Americans, in particular, viewed sexuality?

26

LEARNING OBJECTIVES

At the conclusion of this chapter, the student should be able to:

1. Explain the major reasons for studying human sexuality.

2. Define "multidimensional perspective" as it applies to the study of human sexuality.

3. Differentiate between procreational, recreational, and relational sex.

4. Describe the role that biological factors play in influencing sexual desires, functioning, and satisfaction.

5. Identify the primary psychosocial factors that influence one's sexuality.

6. List several obstacles that can inhibit or lessen the pleasure or spontaneity of sexual encounters.

7. Compare and contrast the changing sexual mores and practices of different cultures throughout recorded history, and explain why it is difficult to predict the direction of future changes.

8. Identify the major contributors to contemporary views on human sexuality, briefly describe their research methodologies, and their culture's reactions to them.

9. Identify and describe four factors that contributed to the "sexual revolution" in America.

10. Identify three examples of "backlash" against the newer sexual mores of American culture and describe the reasons for them.

TEACHING STRATEGIES

Students may be both alarmed and intrigued when faced with the wide range of knowledge to which they will be exposed in a human sexuality course. Since this is the first truly multidisciplinary course many of the students have taken, some may be overwhelmed at the prospect of reading about biology, history, social science, ethics and religion in one chapter. The instructor can help reduce potential student anxiety by breaking the material into component parts, stressing the importance of first learning broad concepts and then specific facts, thus making the complex subject of sexuality less intimidating and more manageable.

If this chapter has been assigned to students in advance of the first class, it is helpful for the instructor to begin the initial session with a description of the course objectives and philosophy before discussing the subject matter per se. If an introductory lecture is given before Chapter 1 is assigned, a portion of the chapter material may be previewed to stress the importance of a multidimensional perspective and what that encompasses when applied to the study of human sexuality. A second lecture could then focus in more depth on the changes in attitude toward sexuality from the Kinsey era through the present.

One obvious starting point for teaching Chapter 1 is to deal with terminology. What are the distinctions between sex, sexuality, gender, and sexual orientation? These topics are not too personal and can be used to help students see that this course will encourage group discussion and understanding of material rather than being just a rote memory course. The emphasis in the text on sexuality as a "dimension of personality" is a convenient point of departure. How do various factors (biology, gender roles, sexual orientation, parental roles, church or media) influence one's sexuality? Slides from various media such as "Playboy" or "Cosmopolitan," or quotes from Harold Robbins, Alex Comfort, or "Dear Abby" can enliven such discussion.

A second topic for this lecture may be what students hope to gain from a course on human sexuality. Can information about sex be detrimental since it adds to the onslaught of media stories that contribute to new performance pressures? Will such information make sexual interaction mechanical? It is hoped that the class wil be led to acknowledge the importance of accurate information in sexual decision-making. Another aspect of this discussion can be the analogy to a public health model of prevention. That is, can information about sexuality and interpersonal relationships provide an emotional or psychological "innoculation" against later distress or disorder?

If the class is very large, discussion groups may be a needed adjunct. If the professor's style is more didactic, an appropriate topic for the initial lecture might involve the "tides of change" and how they have influenced sexuality. Dr. John Money of Johns Hopkins University has listed seven "tides" that have irrevocably influenced human sexuality: (1) the industrial revolution (its effect on changing gender roles, for example, since it is no longer necessary to capitalize on the brute strength of the male and the reproductive capacity of the female); (2) the advent of birth control pills (procreational and recreational sex can now be reliably separated); (3) the fact that the age of puberty is decreasing by about four months every ten years (yet despite this earlier sexual maturity, sex education remains focused on "sperm and eggs"); (4) the average lifespan is increasing (the average American woman now has about thirty years of postmenopausal life; geriatric sexuality is "alive and well" today); (5) the control of V.D. by antibiotics (opening the door to premarital and extramarital sex with less concern about consequences); (6) the plethora of communications about sex (creating new myths to replace the old); and (7) the greater cultural acceptance of divorce (making serial monogamy a norm). Each of these topics provides a wealth of possibilities for discussion, and the result would be a valuable overview of the course that does not duplicate students' readings.

STUDENT PROJECTS

1. Using library microfilm files, consult a sampling of six newspapers of January 5, 1948, to analyze the initial reception of Kinsey's research when Sexual Behavior in the Human Male was published.

2. You have to conduct an interview with sex researchers William Masters and Virginia Johnson. What questions will you ask them and why?

3. Discuss the "sexual revolution" with three different individuals -- someone who was a teenager in the '50s, in the '60s, and in the '70s. What similarities in values, attitudes, beliefs are there and what differences exist? How do your own experiences and opinions compare and contrast with theirs?

4. Visit a zoo to observe animal courtship or mating behavior. Compare it to human behavior patterns. How do our instincts influence our behavior?

PERSONAL REFLECTIONS

1. If you were suddenly sent by a time machine to live in Victorian England, how different do you think your sexual behavior would be? Do you think your sexual values would change in any way, or do you think that they would remain as they are now?

2. If your best friend has contracted genital herpes and has just told you about it, how do you think you would react? Would your relationship be affected by the news? What factors might your response be based on? Would it be possible for you to be rational and objective about this? In what ways might your responses give you insight into society's responses to the "sexual revolution?"

3. What are the things you would want your own son or daughter to know about you as a sexual being? When would you want them to find out? Would it be easy for you to discuss this aspect of your personality? Why? How have you been taught, socialized, conditioned to think about and discuss human sexuality? How might this impact on your child's experiences?

4. If you were a sex researcher, would observing people having sex affect your personal relationships? In what ways could you minimize this possibility?

CHAPTER 1 TEST QUESTIONS

Multiple Choice (* General Comprehension Questions)

1.* Human sexual behavior
   a. is unvarying from era to era.
   b. can be predicted utilizing cross-cultural research methods.
   c. is best studied from a multi-dimensional perspective.
   d. cannot be studied in a laboratory setting.

2.* Answering the question, "What is sexuality?"
   a. cannot be done.
   b. was not attempted until the Kinsey studies.
   c. is often oversimplified by the tendency to think in terms   of "normal 'vs' abnormal."
   d. should not include reference to past societal attitudes about sexual behavior.

3.* "Sexuality" refers to
   a. a dimension of personality.
   b. erotic response only.
   c. biological gender.
   d. cultural dimensions of reproduction.

4.* The development of sexology as a science
   a. has influenced contemporary attitudes toward sex and sexuality.
   b. began with the clinical work of Masters and Johnson.
   c. was a result of religious response to the proliferation of prostitution in the 1840's.
   d. has relied exclusively on new information about biological factors.

5.* The changes and trends in sexual behavior that are seen as significant today
   a. will have lasting impact on our sexual behavior over time.
   b. are in part the result of the practice of nonmarital cohabitation in our culture.
   c. have nothing to do with the legalization of abortion in 1973.
   d. were sparked primarily by the publication of Alex Comfort's The Joy of Sex.

6. "Procreational" sex refers to
   a. masturbation.
   b. sex for the purpose of having children.
   c. sex for the purpose of having fun.
   d. a temporary form of celibacy.

7. The biological side of sexuality involves all of the following except
   a. sexual functioning.
   b. sexual desire.
   c. sexual arousal.
   d. sexual values.

8. The behavioral dimension of sexuality allows us to learn all of the following except
    a. what people do sexually.
    b. how people conduct themselves sexually.
    c. why people act in certain ways sexually.
    d. the physical problems that can inhibit sexuality.

9. The growing acceptance of relational and recreational sex as opposed to reproductive sex is partly due to
    a. the impact of advanced education.
    b. availability of improved contraceptive technique.
    c. the start of a "men's lib" movement.
    d. gender role stereotypes prevailing in spite of some militant female groups.

10. In its early forms, Christian theology taught that "agape" was
    a. nonphysical love.
    b. a form of carnal love.
    c. a taboo against incest.
    d. a form of homosexual contact between adults and young boys.

11. "Courtly love" refers to
    a. the Chinese belief in using sex as a path toward immortality.
    b. a style of conduct discussed in the first chapter of the Kamasutra.
    c. an idealized code of sexual behavior in Europe during the 13th century.
    d. the Victorian brothels which boasted barristers as clients.

12. During the Victorian Era, all of the following occurred except
    a. piano legs were covered with crinolines.
    b. prostitution was legalized by an act of Parliament.
    c. it was indelicate to offer a "leg" of chicken to a lady.
    d. masturbation was hailed as a cure for insanity.

13. The founder of modern sexology is usually said to be
    a. William H. Masters.
    b. Sigmund Freud.
    c. Richard von Krafft-Ebing.
    d. Havelock Ellis.

14. Freud's concept of the Oedipus Complex refers to
    a. castration anxiety.
    b. sexual attraction of a young male child to his mother.
    c. penis envy.
    d. sexual attraction of a young girl to her mother.

15. The Kinsey Reports were
    a. universally applauded as statistically sound.
    b. given favorable press coverage by most U.S. newspapers.

c. criticized for dealing with sex as an impersonal act.
d. completely objective.

16. All of the following are true about nineteenth century America except
    a. 351 brothels were prosecuted in Massachusetts in the 1840s.
    b. The American Society for the Prevention of Licentiousness and Vice was formed.
    c. child prostitution was eradicated completely.
    d. a guidebook was published listing fashionable brothels in big cities.

17. Marie Stopes, an Englishwoman, is best noted for
    a. being a consultant to the American Society for Promoting the Observance of the Seventh Commandment.
    b. writing the law that raised the age of consent to 18.
    c. writing an explicit marriage manual that sold well on both sides of the Atlantic.
    d. marrying Havelock Ellis and inspiring much of his research.

18. A typical attitude of people in the 1950's toward sexuality was
    a. "If it's FUN you mustn't do it; if it's DUTY you must."
    b. women should be completely honest about themselves with their husbands.
    c. premarital sex was something teenagers should experiment with.
    d. husbands and wives should allow their children to see them making love.

19. All of the following contributed to the "sexual revolution" of the sixties except
    a. the availability of birth control pills.
    b. the publication of The Little Sermons on Sin.
    c. the reemergence of modern feminism.
    d. the protest movement among adolescents and young adults.

20. The criticism, "too mechanistic an approach" best describes the reaction of many reporters and health care professionals to the work of
    a. Sigmund Freud.
    b. Alex Comfort.
    c. William H. Masters and Virginia Johnson.
    d. Katharine Davis.

21. Human Sexual Inadequacy described
    a. the therapy approach of Helen Kaplan.
    b. the 1970's view of Freud's theory of penis envy.
    c. a two-week treatment program of sexual dysfunction that had a 20% failure rate.
    d. the anti-abortion stance of the Right-to-Life movement.

22. The "Squeal Rule"
    a. is part of the "squeeze technique" described by Masters and Johnson.
    b. requires that teenagers suffering from V.D. tell their school nurses.
    c. was part of the Moral Majority's attempt to block sex education in the public schools.
    d. refers to a 1983 attempt to implement a policy mandating that parents of teenagers who requested contraceptives be informed of their teens' requests.

23. "A woman who has the divine gift of lechery and loves her partner will masturbate him well..." is typical advice from
    a. the Kamasutra.
    b. The Joy of Sex.
    c. Ideal Marriage.
    d. How to Attain and Practice the Ideal Sex Life.

24. The sociological and cultural dimensions of human sexuality were the major concerns of
    a. Malinowski.
    b. Freud.
    c. Miller.
    d. St. Augustine.

25. A woman who greatly influenced the birth control movement in America during the post-World War I era was
    a. Marie Stopes.
    b. Katharine Davis.
    c. Margaret Sanger.
    d. Clelia Duel Mosher.

True/False

T   1. Gender identity refers to a person's private sense of being male or female.

F   2. In antiquity, Eastern thought placed a high value on celibacy.

F   3. Masters and Johnson founded the Institute for Sex Research at Indiana University.

F   4. Illness, injury, or drugs can alter or obliterate one's sexual response patterns.

F   5. Disorders of sexual behavior are more commonly due to biological problems than to psychosocial ones.

T   6. Some forms of male homosexual behavior were tolerated by the ancient Greeks.

T   7. Some historians believe that Victorian women were the forerunners of today's feminists.

T ✓ 8.   Sex acts and sexual behavior are not necessarily the same.

F   9.   Anna Freud was the founder of psychoanalysis.

T   10.   Child prostitution was prevalent until the late 1890's.

F   11.   Chastity belts were part of a literary convention and were never really used on women.

T   12.   Sexual problems may lead to difficulties in self-esteem or body image.

T   13.   The American Psychiatric Association no longer classifies homosexuality as a mental disorder.

T   14.   The growing awareness of the significance of all forms of sexual victimization is partly an outgrowth of the women's movement.

F   15.   Examining what people do sexually, and understanding how and why they do it, is part of the clinical perspective.

Fill in the Blanks

1.   The first book published in 1966 by Masters and Johnson was called (<u>Human Sexual Response</u>).

2.   A detailed Indian sex manual that survives today is called the (<u>Kamasutra</u>).

3.   (<u>Havelock Ellis</u>) was an English physician who thought many sexual problems had psychological causes and was modern in his attitudes about female sexuality.

4.   The (<u>Kinsey Reports</u>) of 1948 and 1953 were based on face-to-face interviews with 12,000 people from all walks of life.

5.   The "carnal love" of early Christian theology that was borrowed from the Greek was called (<u>eros</u>).

6.   (<u>Relational</u>) sex is meant for sharing with a cared-for person.

7.   A prominent taboo against (<u>incest</u>) had been established prior to 1000 B.C.

8.   Human sexuality has a (<u>multidimensional</u>) nature.

9.   Consideration of our early sexual attitudes is part of the (<u>psychosocial</u>) dimension of the study of human sexuality.

10.   No matter what the source of a sexual turn-on, one fact true for anyone is that you will experience specific (<u>biological</u>) responses.

11. During the thirteenth and fourteenth centuries in Europe, there was a certain (hypocrisy) between professed Church policies toward sexuality and actual practices.

12. A massive epidemic of (syphilis) in Europe during the sixteenth and seventeenth centuries might have contributed to the limitation of sexual freedom.

13. In 1892, Clelia Duel Mosher conducted a (female sex survey); its recent discovery provides added evidence that the Victorian period was not strictly antisexual.

14. "Make love not war" was a poular phrase during the (1960s).

15. (No single) dimension of human sexuality is universally dominant.

Discussion/Essay Questions

1. What are some of the ways our lives are touched by sexuality? Are there differences in "public" sexuality and "private" sexuality? If so, why?

2. Make a list of rules governing sexuality that seem to operate in contemporary American society. What would be the likely impact if one of these rules was changed to its exact opposite?

3. Has there been a true sexual revolution in America in the last twenty years? If so, for what reasons and by what criteria? If not, what trends would need to be more firmly established in order to be able to show that a revolution had occurred?

4. In what ways -- attitudinally and behaviorally -- might a person raised in a sexually permissive South Sea Island culture be different from a person raised in America?

5. Freud, Kinsey, and Masters and Johnson have been identified as key sexologists whose writings brought about major changes in thinking about sexuality. Compare their approaches, the eras in which they did the bulk of their research, and their methods.

6. Based on what you have learned so far in this chapter, make some educated guesses about the direction of change and growth in the field of human sexuality for the next fifty years.

7. If you could construct an ideal setting in which to learn about and teach human sexuality, what would it be? What are the most important elements in your imaginary milieu and why?

8. Do you feel our society is justified in promoting a "backlash" against the current trends that have evolved from the "sexual revolution?" If so, why; if not, why not?

Chapter 2

SEX RESEARCH: AN OVERVIEW

OVERVIEW

Sex research tends to be surrounded by an aura of mystery, dealing as it does with areas of study that are often considered controversial, private, even forbidden. Therefore, it is imperative that the student understands that research in human sexuality is, in fact, governed by the same criteria that govern other forms of scientific investigation: the need for ethical guidelines, well-planned and executed research designs, careful attention to detail, rigorous examination and evaluation of any obtained data. It is equally important for the student to recognize that facts gleaned from research studies should not necessarily be taken at face value. Therefore, this chapter describes several sex research methods along with their drawbacks and limitations, to help students learn to evaluate such studies and apply the findings to their own lives.

The first part of this chapter discusses sampling strategies and the populations sampled, methods of obtaining data and the reasons for choosing a given method, measurement or classification of data and data analysis. A detailed discussion of ethical concerns precedes analysis of sampling problems and research bias. The remainder of this chapter describes various methods used in sex research and for each method offers a summary and critique of representative studies. For example, survey research is represented by the Kinsey Reports, the Hunt Report, magazine surveys, the Hite Reports, the Blumstein and Schwartz survey as well as surveys of adolescent sexuality, homosexuality, and geriatric sexuality. Observational research is assessed utilizing the Masters and Johnson studies of sexual physiology as the basis for discussion. The chapter also analyzes the following methods: case study, clinical research, and experimental research. The chapter concludes by summarizing the research limitations and the problems of replication and researcher bias.

By developing an understanding of research methodology early in the course, the student is assisted in interpreting studies and data discussed throughout the rest of the text.

While reading the chapter, the student is asked to consider these issues:

1. In what ways does sex research follow the general scientific principles that govern research in other fields?

2. What are the ethical considerations that are critical to sex

research?

3. What are the factors that contribute to the design of a good scientific research study? Which of these factors are especially important in sex research?

4. What are the various formats of sex research studies? What are the advantages and disadvantages of each, from both a researcher's standpoint and a participant's standpoint?

5. How can the role of the researcher in the different methods of sex research affect the outcome of the study, and how can such influence be minimized?

LEARNING OBJECTIVES

At the conclusion of this chapter, the student should be able to:

1. Define sample, population, generalizing, homogeneity, random sample as these terms apply to sampling strategies.

2. Describe three ways in which statistics can be used to analyze research data.

3. Discuss the ethical concerns and ethical guidelines for sex researchers including informed consent, confidentiality, and honesty.

4. Describe potential forms of bias in sex research including sampling bias, volunteer bias, erroneous answers.

5. Describe the use of survey research as it applies to human sexuality. Give examples of such studies, including positive and negative aspects of the design of each one mentioned.

6. Describe the pros and cons of observational research in general and Masters' and Johnson's physiology research in particular.

7. Explain why the case study method can be especially problematic in the field of sex research.

8. Define outcome study, epidemiological study, placebo effect, Hawthorne effect.

9. List the problems and pitfalls encountered in conducting sex research and discuss how these limitations can be resolved.

TEACHING STRATEGIES

This chapter presents several challenges to the instructor because many students will resist having to learn about research methodology thinking the topic "too difficult" or "too scientific" for a course in human sexuality. Nothing could be further from the truth, and the instructor should be prepared to prove this to the students if necessary. The purpose of the chapter is not to make researchers or statisticians of the students; rather, to demystify the topic of sex research and give students a solid basis for assessing the strengths and weaknesses of various types of studies of human sexuality.

One obvious starting point for teaching the chapter is to deal with terminology. What is a population? a sample? What is homogeneity? generalizability? What are statistics and how are they used in sex research? By briefly covering the material in the opening section of the chapter without using too technical an approach, the teacher ensures that all the students understand basic concepts of research and data analysis. If there are time constraints, the instructor may want to integrate the material on sex research methodology into the introductory course lecture in more of a "survey" fashion. In this case, for example, the work of early sex researchers such as Krafft-Ebing, Freud, and Ellis can be contrasted with the methods of Kinsey, Masters and Johnson, Blumstein and Schwartz and other contemporary scientists. If time allows, however, it is useful to spend more time assessing each method of research described in the chapter. Students can usually be helped to see the differences between a well-designed study and a poorly conceived study by outlining two hypothetical sex research projects and how the investigators prepare for and implement their research. Depending on class size and student sophistication, the instructor may choose to divide the class into two or more groups, giving each group the task of designing a research study on the same topic. Comparing and contrasting results can yield interesting discussions about methodological issues, ethics, bias, and tends to be an excellent way of getting even the most resistant students involved in the subject matter. It's also helpful to students to realize that "perfect" studies rarely get carried out; most sex research has limitations imposed by constraints of time, money, and volunteer bias that are unavoidable in the real world. It is necessary to keep such limitations in mind when interpreting any data uncovered by a study.

STUDENT PROJECTS

1. Outline an appropriate (and feasible) research design for a study comparing the sexual attitudes of students attending Catholic, Protestant, and Jewish theological seminaries.

2. Assume that you are a member of a research team interested in studying childhood sexuality. In order to obtain approval from your university president to conduct this research, you must write a rationale explaining why the research is important.

3. You are the research assistant responsible for getting human subjects ready to participate in an observational study patterned along the lines of Masters and Johnson's original physiology work. What kinds of things will you tell your

participants about the study and the procedures and why? What will you omit, if anything, and why?

4. A sex researcher at a local university is being censured, and you are the head of the ethics review board. Write out the presentation you will make to your colleagues, specifying the areas of the individual's research that are in question, the reasons they are in question, and why the ethics board feels the need to publicly censure the researcher. Also, conclude with your positive suggestions for changing the research design to conform with ethical guidelines.

PERSONAL REFLECTIONS

1. A local medical school is recruiting volunteers for a sex research study. What would make you want to volunteer? What might prevent you from volunteering? Would the format of the study make a difference to you and why? What if a close friend of yours was one of the researchers? How would that affect your decision?

2. Imagine that your family's personal belief system has taught you that sexual behavior is something that should not be studied or observed by people other than the participants. Yet you have chosen to take this course and are now studying sex research. How could your belief system affect your reactions to the readings for this class? How could you deal with the problem of your family's bias and even your own?

3. How does reading about other people's sexual behavior in surveys such as the Hite reports or the more current Blumstein and Schwartz book make you feel about your own sexuality? Is it possible to read and assess such studies objectively? Does knowledge of sex research in any way change the way you behave sexually? Why?

4. If you were told you had unlimited financial and intellectual resources available, and were asked to construct the perfect research study of some aspect of human sexual behavior, what would your topic be and why?

CHAPTER 2 TEST QUESTIONS

Multiple Choice (* General Comprehension Questions)

1.* A research design includes all of the following except
   a.   selecting and formulating a question.
   b.   choosing appropriate sources of information.
   c.   deciding how to obtain data.
   d.   coercion of the subjects.

2.* Ethical considerations during a research project

a. are irrelevant to the outcome.
b. may influence various aspects of the research design.
c. involve a discussion with subjects on the benefits of participation but not the risks.
d. do not pertain to researchers involved in questionnaire studies.

3.* Sources of research bias may result from all of the following except
a. the placebo effect
b. intentional falsification of answers.
c. individual characteristics of the researcher.
d. the goal-gradient effect.

4.* Sex research studies are
a. almost always conducted on national probability samples.
b. never observational due to ethical constraints.
c. frequently conducted by questionnaire.
d. unlikely to be quantified.

5.* Any type of research must take into account
a. the economic status of the research subject.
b. the confidentiality of the research subject.
c. the political allegiance of the research subject.
d. the religion of the research subject.

6. Sampling bias refers to
a. the size of a research study.
b. the intent of a research study.
c. a systematic source of error reducing objectivity.
d. a popular method of sex research.

7. The most commonly employed approach to the study of human sexual behavior is
a. the participant-observer method.
b. the case study.
c. the outcome study.
d. the survey.

8. Case studies
a. are often done in a matter of hours.
b. usually require weeks or months of assessment.
c. are more widely used now than in the early days of sexology.
d. involve the use of instruments to record events in a lab setting.

9. All of the following were strengths of the Bell and Weinberg survey except
a. the sample was a truly representative one.
b. interviewers were meticulously trained.
c. 528 separate questions were asked.
d. a comparison groups was matched to the sample for age, race, gender, and education.

10. The 1983 book, <u>American Couples</u>, was notable because
    a. it dealt with childhood sexuality.
    b. it included extensive research about couples who live apart.
    c. it compared married couples, cohabiting heterosexual couples, gay male couples, and lesbian couples.
    d. it had a truly random sample as the basis for study.

11. Both of the Hite surveys
    a. presented data in quantitative terms.
    b. had extraordinarily high response rates to the questionnaires.
    c. posed questions in a completely neutral way.
    d. humanized issues of sexuality.

12. A major problem with the Kinsey Reports was
    a. the interview itself was not updated or expanded sufficiently to keep up with new developments.
    b. there was no mechanism to get the confidence of volunteer subjects.
    c. there were too few questions asked.
    d. college graduates were underrepresented in the sample.

13. In the initial stages of their physiology of sex studies, Masters and Johnson did all of the following <u>except</u>
    a. recruited their research sample from the local academic community.
    b. eliminated prostitutes from the sample population.
    c. assessed each potential subject's physiological stability, motivations for volunteering.
    d. took precautions to protect subjects' confidentiality and anonymity.

14. The change in people's behavior caused by knowing they are in an experiment is
    a. the placebo effect.
    b. the Electra complex.
    c. the Hawthorne effect.
    d. volunteer bias.

15. All of the following are limitations of the experimental method <u>except</u>
    a. lab experiments often involve artificial situations so findings may not apply to behaviors in real life.
    b. there is a problem with volunteer bias.
    c. researchers can't always be sure they have implemented proper controls over all the variables.
    d. the method permits conclusions about cause-effect relationships which can't usually be proven by other means.

16. The outcome study
    a. is a type of experimental research.
    b. is the result of a survey questionnaire.

41

c. is frequently done in conjunction with a control group.
d. is best exemplified by the early work of Freud.

17. Quantification is best defined as
    a. the distinction between research-based fact from a person's opinion.
    b. turning observations into numbers.
    c. the method used for recruiting subjects for a study.
    d. the first step in a field study.

18. All of the following are ways researchers protect a subject's confidentiality except
    a. assigning code numbers for identification.
    b. storing a masterlist with code numbers in a secure place.
    c. making sure more than one person has access to research data.
    d. destroying all identifiable research information once the study is completed.

19. Erroneous answers in sex research
    a. never happen on anonymous questionnaires.
    b. commonly occur because of faulty recall.
    c. can be eliminated completely in a personal interview situation.
    d. are almost never intentional.

20. Volunteer bias is most evident in
    a. experimental studies.
    b. observational studies.
    c. situations where college students form the bulk of the population being studied.
    d. sex research prior to 1940.

21. The work of Marvin Zelnick and John Kantner is notable because
    a. on three different occasions they succeeded in obtaining a true national probability sample.
    b. they were actually students of Sigmund Freud.
    c. they were the first to publish a major work on geriatric sexuality.
    d. they succeeded in carrying out a longitudinal study.

22. Replication of a study
    a. unerringly proves the original research findings to be correct.
    b. can, at the least, confirm the validity of a study.
    c. proves the absence of researcher bias in the original study.
    d. proves the original population sample was truly random and representative.

23. Human Sexual Inadequacy was
    a. the first published report of the original sexual physiology studies of Masters and Johnson.

b.   the first published report of homosexual behavior in the United States that was based on a representative sample.
c.   a report which described the results of sex therapy in 790 cases.
d.   a "how-to" book written for impotent men in the 1940's.

24. One problem with Robert Sorenson's research on adolescent sexuality was
a.   his low response rate.
b.   the fact that he did not use a random sample for his pool of research subjects.
c.   the fact that many parents wouldn't allow their teens to participate in this type of research.
d.   the fact that he did not approach teens in rural areas.

25. Magazine surveys of sexual behavior
a.   are free from volunteer bias.
b.   rarely distort the picture of sexual trends in the United States.
c.   sometimes draw over 100,000 responses, samples far larger than those obtained in other research studies.
d.   are particularly suited for people in low-income areas or people who are non-readers.

True/False

F   1.   A "population" is smaller than a "sample."

T   2.   Sex research that involves the use of experimental drugs is more safely done by studying animals, not humans.

T   3.   Even when a fact is based on a research study, it should not always be taken at face value.

F   4.   "Generalizing" refers to what happens in the experimental lab situation.

F   5.   Matters of practicality should not enter into a decision about choosing a method of gathering data.

T   6.   Statistics may be used to draw inferences.

F   7.   Confidentiality and informed consent are the same things.

F   8.   Freud was the first to develop a detailed code of ethical guidelines for sex research.

T   9.   Kinsey's research was criticized on the grounds of sampling bias.

F   10. Intentional falsification of answers may occur with questionnaires but not interviews.

T   11. The appropriateness of a research method is often

43

determined by the nature of the subject to be studied.

T   12. The Hunt report was actually commissioned by the Playboy Foundation to update Kinsey's data.

F   13. "Consumer Reports" has never conducted a survey on human sexual behavior.

T   14. George and Weiner recently conducted a longitudinal study of the effects of aging on sexuality.

T   15. The experimental method has been used to evaluate such topics as gender role effects on behavior and the premenstrual syndrome.

Fill in the Blanks

1.   The power of positive suggestion in a research project is called the (placebo) effect.

2.   The degree to which something measures what one is looking for is its (validity).

3.   Survey studies such as those done by Shere Hite are frequently influenced by (volunteer) bias.

4.   Research done in the natural environment of the subjects is called a(n) (field study).

5.   Studies that involve a type of treatment for a problem and assessment of the effects of the treatment are known as (clinical) research.

6.   The change in people's behavior caused by knowing they are in an experiment is the (Hawthorne) effect.

7.   A group of volunteers chosen from a population is called a (nonrandom) sample.

8.   (Generalization) is the duplication of findings of an earlier study.

9.   Explaining the purpose, procedures, potential risks and benefits of participation in a research project is a way of obtaining (informed consent).

10. (Surveys) are economical, flexible and usually free of significant risks to participants as methods of research.

11. The two surveys about human sexuality that have been the most widely discussed and criticized were done by (Kinsey) in the 1940's and 1950's.

12. In addition to gathering data about sexual behavior, Blumstein and Schwartz gathered information about nonsexual areas of relationships, notably, (work and money).

13. The Zelnick and Kantner studies included a series of reports on both sexual and (contraceptive) behavior of 15-19 year old unmarried females.

14. The (field study) is a research method used by anthropologists and sociologists as well as sex researchers.

15. (Epidemiological) studies focus on the pattern of distribution of a phenomenon, such as the spread of a sexually transmitted disease.

Discussion/Essay Questions

1. If a psychiatrist in private practice found that a dozen depressed homosexual men had cruel fathers, what would be wrong with his concluding that homosexuality is caused by cruel fathers?

2. What problems might be experienced in a research study of sexual fantasies of the general population? How would one collect a representative sample? What would be the relative advantages and disadvantages of using a self-administered written questionnaire versus a face-to-face interview to collect data for such a study?

3. Why is it important to understand research problems and procedures given the barrage of sexual information and misinformation thrown at us by the media?

4. Why are ethical guidelines so important in sex research?

5. Would you want to be a sex researcher? Why?

6. If you could interview Kinsey today, what would you ask him and what would you tell him about the status of sex research as it currently exists?

7. Do you think it is appropriate for popular magazines to conduct or underwrite sex research? Why?

8. What do you think is the very most important thing to have occurred as a result of all the sex research that has been done in the past four decades?

9. Of all the studies mentioned in this chapter, which one do you feel was the most significant? Why? If you could have, what changes would you have made in its implementation or design?

10. Can a person who is not a scientist be a sex researcher? Why?

Chapter 3

SEXUAL ANATOMY

OVERVIEW

Although many college students think that they are knowledgable about sexual anatomy, their misinformation and missing information is usually substantial. This chapter presents a concise summary of the relevant facts of sexual anatomy interwoven with practical discussions about the feelings people have about their sexual body parts. Students are introduced to the scientific terminology used to describe sexual anatomy and at the same time are informed about the normal variability in size and appearance of sexual anatomy from person to person, with in-depth discussion about common concerns about breast size and penis size. Similarly, the chapter stresses the fact that people "turn on" in response to many different sources of physical stimulation, not just in response to vaginal or penile stimulation. Throughout the chapter, practical information is provided on a number of topics such as clitoral circumcision, the status of the hymen as an indication of virginity, Kegel's exercises, the "tipped" uterus, the "G spot," breast augmentation and breast reduction surgery, male circumcision and surgical reconstruction of circumcised foreskin, the nature of semen, and the significance of enlargement of the male breasts, a condition known as gynecomastia. In addition, brief discussion of ovarian and testicular function provides students with a chance to integrate their understanding of sexual and reproductive processes.

While reading the chapter, the student is asked to consider these issues:

1. Why are many people poorly informed about sexual anatomy?

2. What are the parts of the male and female sexual anatomy and the function of each part?

3. What are some normal concerns and harmful misconceptions that people have regarding breast size and penis size?

4. How are ova produced by the ovaries, sperm by the testes?

5. What is the "G spot" and why is it controversial?

6. What are some other erogenous parts of the human anatomy besides the genitals, and what makes them erogenous?

LEARNING OBJECTIVES

At the conclusion of this chapter, the student should be able to:

1. Describe some common concerns people of all ages have about sexual anatomy.

2. Identify several sources of negative feelings and inaccurate information about sexual anatomy.

3. Identify and describe the parts of a female's sexual anatomy including the vulva, the mons, the labia, the clitoris, the perineum, the hymen, the vagina, the uterus, the fallopian tubes, the ovaries, the breasts.

4. Explain the function of the various parts of a female's sexual anatomy.

5. Identify and describe the parts of a male's sexual anatomy including the penis, the scrotum, the testes, the epididymis and vas deferens, the seminal vesicles, the prostate gland, Cowper's glands, the male breasts.

6. Explain the function of the various parts of a male's sexual anatomy.

7. Describe the process of egg and sperm formation.

8. Describe the "G spot" and the current controversy about it.

9. Discuss the role of plastic surgery as it applies to human sexual anatomy.

10. Identify and discuss potential erogenous zones for both males and females that are not in the genital area and what makes them erogenous.

TEACHING STRATEGIES

Because students who are not biologically oriented may have some initial hesitancy in approaching the topic of sexual anatomy, we suggest a lecture approach that can intrigue students with the incredible machinery of their bodies. Four techniques are recommended to make the study of anatomy more interesting and to prevent students from having to simply memorize definitions. (1) Discuss sexual and reproductive anatomy in conjunction with the appropriate physiology. In this approach, terms such as vas deferens become associated with sperm transport and fimbria with fingers that catch the ovulating egg. (2) Diagram the anatomy on the blackboard. Drawings help students develop a better schemata with which to code new anatomical terms; for example, a diagram that traces the journey of the egg from the follicle in the ovary through the Fallopian tube to the uterine-tubal juncture can turn the process into an adventure by mention of the various hazards that the egg encounters along the way. (3) Use photographic slides or movies to heighten students' interest. Watching a film of ovulation is almost always accompanied by exclamations of wonder and makes biological terms easier to remember. (4) Use models of pelvic and genital anatomy so that students can develop a better three-dimensional sense of anatomic relationships.

If the instructor's task in teaching about sexual anatomy is to transform the subject from a dry, museum-like array of body parts to a dynamic, engaging set of facts, it is also helpful to realize that many students lack familiarity with the broad range of anatomical variation and have some concerns about the normality of their own sexual apparatus. This can be alleviated by using a series of slides that show various appearances of the genitals and breasts of both sexes, which helps to desensitize students and assist them in recognizing individual differences. Discussion of erogenous zones naturally evolves from this, and the instructor can lead the class to acknowledge eventually that the entire body is potentially erogenous. Specific regions of the male and female body are rich in nerve endings, and each sex (and each person) likes different tactile pressures at different times. Thus, open communication and repeated sensual experience with the same individual are important. The irony of miscommunication can be demonstrated by mentioning how some men insert their fingers deep into their partners' vaginas thinking it is more stimulating for the women this way, when in fact, women have most of their nerve endings concentrated in the outer third of their vaginas. In parallel fashion, it can be demonstrated that many females are quite timid about stroking the partner's penis, unaware that many men find vigorous stroking highly arousing.

The topic of the "G spot" can be useful for many reasons. The controversy about this alleged erogenous zone mirrors much of the controversy in sex research today, and can be used as an example of the need for replication and verifiability in sex research studies. Additionally, the "G spot" became a media event, with books, articles and many television and radio talk shows focusing on it. As such, the instructor can delve into the interrelationship of media and sexuality in American culture today.

STUDENT PROJECTS

1. Look through several fashion magazines that are geared to both men and women. What images of sexuality are portrayed in each? How realistic do the models look to you? What can you conclude about the cultural messages we get through the media about our sexuality? How might they influence us?

2. Read one of the current popular romance novels. How is human sexual anatomy described and portrayed in such a book? Why do you think the romance novel is such a widely read genre, especially among women, in the 1980's?

3. Design a questionnaire to ascertain how people feel about their sexual anatomy. Administer the questionnaire to your class, allowing answers to be anonymous but designated as from a male or a female. Summarize the results of your findings and discuss their implications.

4. Interview a plastic surgeon to gather information about the reasons why women elect to have breast augmentations or reductions. For example, ask whether there are any noticeable differences in the motivations of single versus married women, heterosexual versus lesbian women. Find out if men are requesting any kinds of plastic surgery to enhance their sexual anatomy. What conclusions can you draw?

PERSONAL REFLECTIONS

1. Stand naked in front of a full-length mirror and take a careful look at your body. What do you like best about your sexual anatomy? What do you like least? Why? Have you ever been teased about your physical appearance? Could such an experience be affecting your self-perception today? Would you like to change such perceptions?

2. How do you usually dress? Do your clothes draw attention to or away from your sexual anatomy? Are you consciously aware of this? Why do you think you dress as you do?

3. Recall the first time you saw the adult genitalia of a member of the opposite sex. What was the situation? What was your reaction? What is your attitude today?

4. If you are female, do you wish your breasts were larger or smaller? If you are male, do you wish your penis were larger or smaller? How do you think your life would change if these wishes came true? What other ways can you think of to increase your confidence as a sexual being without changing the size of your breasts or genitals?

CHAPTER 3 TEST QUESTIONS

Multiple Choice (* General Comprehension Questions)

1.* Sex organs in the pelvic region are called
   a. gingiva.
   b. gentiles.
   c. genitals.
   d. glomerula.

2.* Which of the following is the most accurate statement about people's sexual anatomies?
   a. the notion that "biggest is best" is basically true.
   b. what is considered "sexual" in our culture involves a

49

fairly narrow range of body parts.
c. the largest sex organ for males and females is the skin.
d. when stimulated, only the sex organs located in the pelvic region can produce orgasms.

3.* Negative feelings about our own sexual anatomy may be the result of all of the following except
a. being discouraged from discussing sexual topics.
b. sexual images presented by the media that set up almost unattainable standards.
c. having or using inaccurate terminology for our sexual anatomy.
d. being encouraged to touch and explore our "private parts."

4.* Most people
a. don't share common concerns about sexual anatomy.
b. receive childhood messages about certain behaviors that are sex-negative in tone.
c. could care less about the status of their sexual anatomy.
d. have accurate information about both male and female sexual anatomy from early childhood on.

5.* Accurate information about sexual anatomy
a. only becomes important when you are about to marry.
b. cannot be gained until you take a human sexuality course.
c. is important to help distinguish between fact and myth.
d. does not usually lead to a better understanding of one's sex partner.

6. The male sex organs include all of the following except
a. the scrotum.
b. the testes.
c. the penis.
d. the labia.

7. The mons veneris refers to
a. folds of skin covering a large amount of fat tissue and thin layer of smooth muscle.
b. the area over the pubic bone which consists of a cushion of fatty tissue covered by skin and pubic hair.
c. inner lips that meet just above the clitoris.
d. glans that provide minimal lubrication during sexual arousal.

8. The clitoris
a. is always enlarged by masturbation.
b. is really a miniature penis.
c. has very few nerve endings.
d. varies in size and appearance from woman to woman.

9. The hymen
a. is not easily broken or stretched.
b. is always torn during intercourse.
c. when examined by a physician, is an accurate indicator of prior sexual behavior.

50

d.   can be partial or nonexistent is some females at birth.

10. All of the following are true about the human vagina <u>except</u>
    <u>a.</u> it can "clamp down" on the penis during intercourse and make physical separation impossible.
    b. it adjusts equally well to a large or small penis.
    c. it can enlarge and lose some elasticity after childbirth.
    d. it averages three inches in length.

11. The endometrium and myometrium are parts of the
    a. cervix.
    <u>b.</u> uterus.
    c. Fallopian tubes.
    d. ovaries.

12. The cervix
    a. protrudes into the anus.
    b. has many surface nerve endings.
    <u>c.</u> is the point at which sperm cells enter the uterus.
    <u>d.</u> when surgically removed causes a loss of sexual responsivity.

13. The "G spot"
    a. has been proven to exist as a distinct anatomic structure.
    b. is easy to locate in its sexually unstimulated state.
    <u>c.</u> was first suggested by a German physician in 1950.
    <u>d.</u> was found in 90% of a sample of subjects in a study conducted recently at the Masters and Johnson Institute.

14. Anatomically, the Fallopian tubes include
    a. the ovaries.
    b. the endocervical canal.
    <u>c.</u> the fimbria.
    d. the zona pellucida.

15. The practice of circumcision
    a. affects male sexual function in a positive way.
    b. increases the size of the adult penis.
    c. is defined as the surgical "splitting" and repositioning of the foreskin.
    <u>d.</u> is done routinely for religious and nonreligious reasons in the United States, less often in Canada and Europe.

16. All of the following are true of the testes <u>except</u>
    a. the left testis is usually lower than the right one.
    b. they are highly sensitive to touch or pressure.
    c. they produce sperm.
    <u>d.</u> they produce progesterone.

17. The prostate gland
    a. produces testosterone.
    b. is the size of an orange in a healthy male.
    <u>c.</u> produces seminal fluid.
    <u>d.</u> is located at the base of the coccyx.

18. All of the following are common myths about women's breasts except
    a. breast size determines the woman's level of sexual interest.
    b. women with large breasts experience little sexual sensation when their breasts are fondled.
    c. it is a sexual advantage to a woman to have large breasts.
    d. breast size is related to the ease with which a woman attains orgasm.

19. A man's concern about the size of his penis might indicate that
    a. the length of the penis determines a woman's satisfaction during intercourse.
    b. sexual technique and proficiency are directly related to penis size.
    c. the man is concerned with being "normal."
    d. the man is in immediate need of sex therapy.

20. All of the following are true about the sexual sensitivity of the breast, areola and nipple except
    a. it depends on breast size and shape.
    b. it depends on personal preference.
    c. it depends on learned habit.
    d. it depends on biology.

21. Mammary hyperplasia
    a. is the same as gynecomastia.
    b. can be treated surgically.
    c. occurs only in pregnant women.
    d. is reversed by the use of silicone gel implants.

22. Leydig cells
    a. are eliminated during circumcision.
    b. contain chromosomes and acrosomes.
    c. manufacture testosterone.
    d. are clustered around the "G spot."

23. All of the following is true about seminal fluid except
    a. 30% is produced by the prostate.
    b. 70% is produced by the seminal vessicles.
    c. one teaspoonful of semen occurs per ejaculate.
    d. the amount of fluid in the ejaculate increases by 30% or more after a vasectomy.

24. All of the following is true about gynecomastia except
    a. some men elect to enlarge their breasts by taking estrogen.
    b. it occurs in 40-60% of boys during puberty.
    c. it does not go away spontaneously and always requires surgical intervention.
    d. it can be caused by alcoholism.

25. All of the following are mentioned in the chapter as potentially erogenous areas except

a. the buttocks.
b. the anus.
c. the perineum.
<u>d.</u> the toenails.

True/False

F 1. The penis consists of the mons, labia, and perineum.

F. 2. A larger clitoris provides more intense sexual arousal.

T 3. The production of sperm is relatively continuous in the male unlike the female, where no new eggs are manufactured after birth.

F 4. Inverted nipples make it impossible for a woman to nurse a baby.

T 5. The "G spot" is said to exist on the front wall of the vagina midway between the pubic bone and the cervix.

T 6. The penis and clitoris are derived embryologically from the same tissues.

T 7. Clitoridectomy is still practiced today in some parts of the world.

F 8. Kegel exercises are done by a man to help him maintain his erections longer.

T 9. The consistency of cervical mucus varies during different phases of the menstrual cycle.

F 10. Numerically speaking, anal intercourse is more likely to occur among homosexual couples than heterosexual couples.

T 11. A micropenis may be due to a treatable testosterone deficiency.

F 12. Men who are preoccupied with penis size are less likely to develop sexual difficulties than men who are unconcerned with penis size.

F 13. The human ovum consists of a head, midpiece, and tail.

F 14. When a follicle moves to the surface of the ovary, ruptures, and releases an egg pregnancy cannot occur.

F 15. The testes are contained within the seminal vesicles.

Fill in the Blanks

1. The muscular organ having few sensory nerve endings and lined with a surface similar to the mouth's lining is the (<u>vagina</u>).

53

2. A female reproductive organ shaped like a pear is the (uterus).

3. There are 400,000 (primary oocytes or immature eggs) present at birth in a newborn girl.

4. The (Fallopian tubes) are also called "oviducts."

5. "An external organ that consists primarily of three parallel cylinders of spongy tissue bound in thick membrane sheaths" is a definition of (a penis).

6. Water, mucus, sugar, bases, and prostaglandins are the components of (seminal fluid).

7. The largest sex organ for both females and males is the (skin).

8. The process by which a primary oocyte divides into three polar bodies and a mature ovum is called (meiosis).

9. The part of the uterus that protrudes into the vagina is the (cervix).

10. The folds of skin that protect a woman's urinary opening and entrance to the vagina are the (labia).

11. The genitals are those sex organs of men or women that are found in the part of the body known as the (pelvis, pelvic region).

12. The female gonads are more commonly called (ovaries).

13. The region of a man's penis that has the highest concentration of nerve endings and is thus very sensitive to physical stimulation is the (glans).

14. The hormone that is most important in male sexual development is (testosterone).

15. Nine and one-half centimeters is the average length of the (nonerect) penis.

Discussion/Essay Questions

1. In what ways are females in our society often given negative messages about their sexual body parts?

2. What is the hymen and in what ways is it connected to virginity?

3. Describe the vagina, and note its anatomic relationship to the bladder, rectum, cervix, and clitoris.

4. Describe the anatomy of the penis.

5. Trace the journey of sperm from their point of origin to ejaculation.

6. What are the similarities and differences between the penis and clitoris?

7. Compare circumcision and clitoridectomy, stating pros and cons of both procedures.

8. Compare and contrast common concerns of both males and females regarding their sexual anatomies. What can and should be done to alleviate such concerns?

9. How would you teach your children about human sexual anatomy? When would you start? Why?

10. Compare and contrast male and female breasts. Discuss their functions, sexual responsivity, potential physical abnormalities.

Chapter 4

SEXUAL PHYSIOLOGY

OVERVIEW

Chapter 4 focuses on the physiological dimension of sexuality, stressing that whatever the source of sexual arousal, and however people interpret their sexual responses, the basic details of how the body responds to sexual stimulation are identical. How one's sexual anatomy functions is described in detail in terms of the four-stage cycle of human sexual response: <u>excitement</u>, <u>plateau</u>, <u>orgasm</u>, and <u>resolution</u>. Male and female responses are explained separately and comparatively; throughout the chapter common misconceptions are revealed and corrected. The subjective experiences of human sexual response are discussed, as are controversies and myths.

The hormonal regulation of sexual behavior is described, emphasizing the complicated relationship between hormones and sexual behavior. A discussion of the physiology of menstruation (follicular phase, ovulation, luteal phase), side effects of menstruation (dysmennorhea, premenstrual tension, PMS -- premenstrual syndrome), and attitudes toward sexual activity during menstruation concludes the chapter.

While reading the chapter, the student is asked to consider these issues:

1. What are the four basic stages of the sexual response cycle? How do they function? What are the physical and psychological similarities and differences in male and female responses? Is there such a thing as female ejaculation and what is the current status of research about this?

2. What are some common myths about sexual response and the potential effects of such myths on attitude and sexual functioning?

3. How do the sex hormones, testosterone, estrogen, and progesterone function in humans?

4. If sexual behavior is tightly controlled by hormones within most animal species, why is this <u>not</u> necessarily true for human sexual behavior?

5. What occurs during each of the three phases of the menstrual cycle: follicular phase, ovulation, and luteal phase? What

would happen if any or all of these phases was absent?

6. Discuss past and present cultural attitudes about menstruation. Discuss premenstrual tension, dysmenorrhea, and premenstrual syndrome in terms of their physical and emotional impacts.

LEARNING OBJECTIVES

At the conclusion of this chapter, the student should be able to:

1. Identify the sources of sexual arousal.

2. Explain the basic physiologic reactions during human sexual response.

3. List and contrast the physiologic changes that occur during the four phases of human sexual response.

4. Discuss the controversies that exist about the nature of female ejaculation and female orgasm.

5. Describe several common myths about sexual response.

6. List the sex hormones and discuss their effects on sexual function.

7. Identify and explain the three phases of the menstrual cycle.

8. Describe the most common problems experienced by women in relation to menstruation.

9. Examine your beliefs about sexual activity during menstruation and contrast them with other people's beliefs.

10. Analyze the strengths and weaknesses of recent research that has investigated the human menstrual cycle.

TEACHING STRATEGIES

This chapter can be divided into two lectures: (1) the sexual response cycle and myths related to sexual functioning, and (2) hormonal regulation of sexual function and behavior.

The details of the sexual response cycle are clearly described in the text and need not be repeated in lecture. One aspect of the sexual response cycle that requires emphasis, however, is the wide individual variation within and between the sexes. In one instance a man may move from excitement to orgasm with a short plateau phase, and on another occasion he may not ejaculate at all. A woman may, at one time, feel totally satisfied with several plateau peaks without orgasm and at another time feel terribly frustrated without orgasm. If a couple's sexual response if often divergent, they may complain of sexual dissatisfaction. "She needs too much foreplay," or "he is only interested in satisfying himself" are common complaints usually resulting from misinformation and an inability to experiment with the wide range of activities that allow two people to accommodate one another's sexual needs and desires. Ask the class how a couple could resolve such differences. Since the woman has the capacity to be multiorgasmic, can the man possibly "keep up" with her? How does the male's refractory period affect a couple's sexual play? Does the fact that a male is often erect before the female has lubricated mean that the female's excitement phase is longer?

Interwoven with the discussion of physiology in the text are the "new myths" regarding human sexual behavior. Many of these myths about males sexuality can be found in a Harold Robbins book or in "Penthouse Forum" which can be read to the class. These often describe in vivid detail a huge, pulsating, "rock-hard" erection which overtakes a helpless, passionate female. As excitement gradually builds to a crescendo, the female loses control in explosions of orgasm. The men exemplified in much of popular fiction rarely display the joys of closeness, intimacy, touching, and the playful teasing involved in the natural waxing and waning of sexual feelings -- with or without intercourse. At the other extreme are the very popular "romance" novels that portray a different style of sexual encounter. Contrast the various styles and differences in the myths that are thus created.

Another topic for discussion is that many individuals have no way of interpreting why, in certain situations, they find sexual excitement and/or orgasm to be of variable intensity. Ask your class to list a dozen factors that might contribute to this variability, making sure that they include both psychosocial and biological influences.

Discussion of the plateau stage of sexual arousal may elicit questions about the definition of premature ejaculation. How fast is premature? How often must premature ejacultaion occur to be considered a problem? Kinsey's notion that rapid ejaculation is biologically advantageous is in contrast to today's notions about sexual communication. In Kinsey's day, the male was taught to "do to" or "do for" the female who thus expected the "right" male would "make" her orgasmic. The contemporary alternative is that two people do "with" one another, each taking responsibility for communicating information about their sexual responses. Masters and Johnson discuss this idea at length in The Pleasure Bond (1975).

Another topic for discussion related to the plateau phase is clitoral retraction. The questions regarding clitoral stimulation raised by Masters and Johnson (1966) were "how and how much?" Observation of women masturbating suggested that many women apply more direct and rhythmic motion to the area where the clitoris retracts during the plateau stage. How can a man know when to change the pressure or motion? What body language cues might be important?

The text also mentions many myths and research theories related to orgasm that may be discussed in greater detail in the lecture. What do you think about the possibility of a female ejaculatory response? Why are one-third of women not orgasmic until marriage? Can masturbation influence this? What are subjective differences in female orgasm? What do you think knowing about a potential "G spot" orgasm may do for men and women's attitudes toward sexual response? Since the majority of men experience orgasm in coitus, can one assume that all women have the physiologic capacity for orgasm in intercourse? What are some of the new performance pressures placed on women? Each of these questions will elicit information that can clarify misconceptions regarding female sexuality.

The next lecture can shift to endocrine factors related to sexual behavior and reproduction. It is useful to have several blackboards to show the hormonal regulation from the varying perspectives of the uterus, gonads, pituitary, and hypothalmus. On the first board, draw a small follicle developing under the influence of pituitary hormones and then show the changes in the corpus luteum. On another board, show the perspective of the uterus in the build-up of the endometrium and in various hormonal influences eventually leading to pregnancy or menstruation. On the third board, draw a schemata of pituitary and hypothalmic hormones. If the class is sophisticated, neurotransmitters may even be discussed. After the completion of the three boards, the instructor can unite the dynamic process for the class. Such a presentation will help to simplify material that might have previously overwhelmed the students.

In discussing the menstrual cycle, remember that many males in your class will be completely uninformed about this subject; thus, discuss attitudes toward menstruation as well as the physiology. Delaney, Lupton, and Toth's book listed at the end of this chapter is a good source of material on the topic. Discussion of toxic shock syndrome, PMS and how it affects others besides the woman who is experiencing the symptoms, and premenstrual tension will probably be enlightening to the males in the class. It is important that the facts you offer be as up-to-date as possible so we suggest you consult the Index Medicus or the American College of Obstetricians and Gynecologists in Washington, D.C. to get the latest recommendations on etiology and treatment.

STUDENT PROJECTS

1.   Interview a local sex therapist or therapy team to find out what misconceptions about sexual physiology commonly create problems among sex therapy patients.

2.   Role-play with another student in your class the way you would explain menstruation to your twelve year old daughter, to your fourteen year old son.

3.   Interview several women of varying ages about their feelings about menstruation and the physical and psychological "symptoms" they experience during their menstrual cycles. On the basis of this, construct an alternative questionnaire to the "Menstrual Distress Questionnaire" cited in the text. See if you can develop one that is less biased, and determine if it is possible to design a "Menstrual Joy Questionnaire."

4. Talk to several people who are open about their sexual experiences. Talk to several people who have not had sexual intercourse but may have masturbated to orgasm. Talk to several people who have not experienced orgasm. Ask each to describe, in writing, what an orgasm feels like. Compare the responses of the imagined events with the responses of the sexually experienced people. What conclusions can you draw?

PERSONAL REFLECTIONS

1. Think about the pleasurable sensations you have experienced as a result of some form of sexual activity. Try to put these feelings into words. What problems arise when you use words to explain a physiological event? What other means of communication might you use to express those sensations? Do you think it is even necessary to discuss orgasms? Why?

2. Using your own values and beliefs as the basis for your answer, construct your ideal sexual interlude. Describe your partner, the setting, what should happen to each of you physically and emotionally. Has reality ever come close to or mirrored this fantasy? Do you think it can or should?

3. Prior to this class, which (if any) of the myths about human sexuality did you believe? Explore the ways in which this information has been passed on to you and by whom. Do you find it difficult to give up belief in such myths? Why? Should you give up believing the myths? Why?

4. For the male student: What were you taught about menstruation? When? By whom? Do you now find your information to have been accurate?
   For the female student: What were you taught about menstruation? When? By whom? Were you given any explicit messages about menstruation? Any implicit ones? If so, what were they? Have such messages affected your personal perceptions of your periods? Explain.

CHAPTER 4 TEST QUESTIONS

Multiple Choice (* General Comprehension Questions)

1.* Human sexual response is most accurately described as
   a. one's biological reflexes only.
   b. one's thoughts and feelings only.
   c. a mechanical kind of stimulus-response relationship.
   d. a multidimensional response.

2.* People study sexual physiology because
   a. it is an academic requirement established in 1978 by the American Medical Association.

          problems with his or her sexual functioning.
     c.   it may clarify many misconceptions about sex.
     d.   it helps them to fantasize during lovemaking.

3.* All of the following are true about sexual arousal except
     a.   sexual arousal is like an energy system.
     b.   sexual arousal can be unexpected and alarming.
     c.   sexual arousal cannot be a cerebral event.
     d.   the sources of sexual arousal are varied.

4.* The details of how the body responds to sexual arousal
     a.   are identical regardless of the source of stimulation.
     b.   vary tremendously depending on whether one is pre-
          pubertal, pubertal or menopausal.
     c.   are very simple and uncomplicated.
     d.   are different in males and females.

5.* Sexual physiology is
     a.   the study of the role of fantasy in sexual intercourse.
     b.   the study of the myths that inhibit human sexual function.
     c.   the study of the functions of our sexual anatomy.
     d.   the study of sexual disorders.

6.   All of the following are stages in the human sexual response
     cycle except
     a.   orgasm.
     b.   excitement.
     c.   repression.
     d.   resolution.

7.   Which of the following describes a basic physiologic reaction
     during sexual activity?
     a.   neuromuscular tension.
     b.   myopia.
     c.   migraine.
     d.   myasthenia gravis.

8.   All of the following are true about a male's erections during
     sleep except
     a.   they average about six per night.
     b.   they are controlled by specific content of dreams.
     c.   they last five to ten minutes.
     d.   they can occur in all age groups.

9.   The erection of a man's penis during sexual excitation
     a.   is constant as long as excitation continues.
     b.   results from spongy tissues of the penis rapidly filling
          with semen.
     c.   results from spongy tissues of the penis becoming engorged
          with blood.
     d.   is controlled by the os penis.

10. A woman's vaginal lubrication during a sexual encounter
     a.   starts approximately five minutes after the onset of

sexual stimulation.

    b.   is the result of a process called <u>transliteration</u>.

    c.   is always an indication that a woman is "ready" for intercourse.

    <u>d.</u>   varies in consistency, quantity, and odor from one person to the next and from time to time in the same woman.

11. During excitation

    a.   a person's sexual arousal always builds to a shattering peak.

    <u>b.</u>   mental distractions can affect the build-up of sexual tension.

    c.   the male's sexual response is instantaneous and constant.

    d.   the male's testes shrink slightly in size.

12. The <u>orgasmic platform</u> refers to

    a.   the angle of the penis in relation to the scrotum prior to ejaculation.

    <u>b.</u>   a vasocongestion causing the outer third of the vaginal tissues to swell.

    c.   a physical reaction found only in a woman who has experienced a pregnancy.

    d.   the darkening of the areolae of the male or female during the excitement phase of sexual contact.

13. Just prior to orgasm, all of the following may occur in a male <u>except</u>

    a.   the testes elevate and rotate forward.

    b.   small amounts of clear fluid may appear from the urethra.

    <u>c.</u>   there is a generalized decrease in neuromuscular tension.

    <u>d.</u>   breathing and blood pressure rates increase.

14. Orgasm refers to

    a.   the longest phase of the sexual response cycle.

    <u>b.</u>   a point during which time the body discharges accumulated sexual tension.

    c.   a pelvic event only.

    d.   a physical event during which both men and women ejaculate.

15. A primary misconception about orgasm is that

    a.   men's orgasms occur in two distinct stages.

    b.   all female orgasms follow the same reflex response patterns, regardless of the source of stimulation.

    <u>c.</u>   removal of a woman's uterus prevents orgasm.

    <u>d.</u>   myotonia occurs during the orgasmic phase in both sexes.

16. All of the following are common myths about sexual response <u>except</u>

    a.   males have a greater sexual capacity than females.

    b.   the male can always tell when and if his female partner has had an orgasm.

    c.   all orgasms are intense, explosive events.

    <u>d.</u>   the most important hormone in sexual functioning is

testosterone.

17. Vaginal lubrication is important because
    a. it prevents conception.
    b. it signals the onset of menstruation, proving a woman is not pregnant.
    c. it facilitates insertion of the penis into the vagina and prevents discomfort during intravaginal thrusting.
    d. it prevents the spread of syphillis.

18. Tenting refers to
    a. the use of a condom by a male during intercourse.
    b. the increase in breast size during the plateau phase of sexual activity.
    c. the expansion of the inner two-thirds of the vagina during the plateau phase of sexual activity.
    d. the clitoris pulling back against the pubic bone during the plateau phase of sexual activity.

19. "Sex flush" refers to
    a. the breaking of the hymen during one's first sexual experience.
    b. a spotty skin color change occuring during the late excitement or early plateau phase of sexual activity.
    c. the increased venous drainage in breasts of women who have nursed children.
    d. the liquid produced by Cowper's glands that may or may not carry live sperm.

20. Testosterone is
    a. only present in men.
    b. only marginally important in determining the human sex drive.
    c. sometimes called the male sex hormone.
    d. only manufactured in the adrenal glands.

21. All of the following are accurate statements about menstruation except
    a. the menstrual cycle consist of three phases: follicular, ovulatory, luteal.
    b. the average amount of menstrual flow is two to three cupsful per period.
    c. there is significant variation in the length of different women's menstrual cycles.
    d. PMS, dysmenorrhea, and premenstrual syndrome affect many women.

22. Female orgasmic response
    a. generally lasts for several minutes at a time.
    b. is not correlated with distinctive changes in brain wave patterns.
    c. is marked by rhythmic and simultaneous contractions of the anal sphincter, the uterus, and the outer third of the vagina.

d. is always accompanied by an ejaculate similar to semen.

23. Ejaculatory inevitability in the male
    a. has an exact counterpart in the female.
    b. can be stopped by thinking about something distracting.
    c. occurs as contractions begin that force semen into the bulb of the urethra.
    d. occurs several seconds after the appearance of semen at the tip of the man's penis.

24. All of the following are true about retrograde ejaculation except
    a. it has harmful physical effects.
    b. it results in infertility.
    c. the bladder does not close off properly during orgasm and semen spurts backwards into the bladder.
    d. it occurs in some men with multiple sclerosis.

25. Multiple orgasm in women
    a. occurs during most of their sexual activities.
    b. depends only on sexual interest.
    c. occurs more often during masturbation than during intercourse.
    d. parallels what happens to men during the refractory period.

True/False

F 1. There is a precise one-to-one relationship between sex hormones and human sexual behavior.

T 2. Premenstrual symptoms are often temporary.

F 3. Taboos about sexual intercourse during menstruation have been totally obliterated in our culture.

T 4. Being orgasmic can relieve a woman's dysmenorrhea.

F 5. Male orgasm and ejaculation are one and the same process.

F 6. People's sexual behavior and interest can be predicted by studying their hormone levels.

T 7. There is such a thing as a PMS legal defense.

F 8. Controlled, double-blind studies have shown that progesterone is the best drug for reducing premenstrual symptoms.

F 9. The pituitary gland acts like a thermostat in regulating hormonal function.

T 10. Freud postulated that women experience clitoral orgasms and vaginal orgasms.

T   11. Dr. Katharina Dalton found that female criminal acts, poor judgments, and suicides are more common in the premenstrual and menstrual phases.

F   12. PMS and dysmenorrhea are the same things.

T   13. Several researchers have confirmed that female sexual activity and sexual interest peak in the follicular phase, before ovulation.

T   14. Some men have the capacity for multiple orgasms before a true refractory period sets in.

T   15. Some researchers believe the condition of the PC muscle is an important determinant of the occurrence of orgasms in women.

Fill in the Blanks

1.   When the anatomic and physiologic changes that had occurred during the excitement and plateau phases reverse, the phase is called (resolution).

2.   (FSH) stimulates sperm production in the testes and prepares the ovaries for ovulation.

3.   The two basic physiologic reactions during human sexual response are vasocongestion and (myotonia).

4.   Ejaculation can't be stopped once the stage of (ejaculatory inevitability) has been reached.

5.   The first phase of the menstrual cycle is called the (follicular) phase.

6.   Irritability, lack of concentration, pain, and fatigue can be symptoms of (PMS or premenstrual syndrome).

7.   "Climax" and "coming" are two popular terms for (orgasm).

8.   The recovery time immediately after ejaculation is called a (refractory period).

9.   "Wet dreams" are also called (nocturnal emissions).

10. During the 1950's, a popular notion was that (mutual orgasm) was the ultimate peak in sexual pleasure.

11. Estrogens, testosterone, and (progesterone) are the most important sex hormones.

12. The (hypothalmus) has primary control over most endocrine pathways.

13. "Being on the rag" is a slang term for (menstruation).

14. When we study the functions and reflexes of sexual response, we are studying (<u>sexual physiology</u>).

15. A series of muscular contractions occuring initially at 0.8 second intervals describes (<u>orgasm</u>).

Discussion/Essay Questions

1. Explain the major differences in the sexual response cycles of males and females.

2. How and when does vaginal lubrication occur? Does the amount of vaginal lubrication correlate with a woman's level of sexual arousal?

3. Define each of the following terms and indicate in which stage of the sexual response cycle they occur: orgasmic platform, ejaculatory inevitability, refractory period, sex flush, myotonia.

4. Describe the two stages of orgasm in males.

5. How did the notion that certain types of female orgasm are "immature" originate? Is there any objective evidence that orgasms from clitoral stimulation are different from orgasms resulting from vaginal stimulation.

6. Which hormones influence sexual function and behavior? How do they work?

7. What is menstruation? Why does it occur?

8. Describe PMS, how it differs from dysmenhorrea, current research and controversies about PMS, and suggested treatment regimes.

Chapter 5

HUMAN REPRODUCTION

OVERVIEW

Chapter 5 deals with the dynamics of conception, pregnancy, labor, childbirth, and the early postpartum period. It focuses on both the physiological and psychological aspects of these events and addresses the positive as well as the negative sides of each. The reactions of both the prospective mother and father are discussed, and the importance of parent-child bonding once birth has occurred is also explored. Considerable attention is paid to normal fetal development but the effects of drugs, smoking, and alcohol on the unborn child during pregnancy as well as after its birth are also delineated as are current ways of detecting fetal abnormalities: amniocentesis, ultrasound, and chorionic villi sampling (CVS). The importance of choosing an obstetrician with whom one feels comfortable, the kinds of things to consider when making such a decision, the questions to ask, and the issues to decide are offered within the context of a discussion of some common attitudes toward the pregnant patient held by the medical establishment that might be improved through change. Problem pregnancies are discussed as are the problems that prevent conception. The impact of infertility on a couple and the latest advances in procedures currently used to aid infertile men, women, and couples are described in detail, including artificial insemination (AID,AIH), in vitro fertilization (IVF), surrogate parenting, and the ethical issues involved in such procedures.

While reading the chapter, the student is asked to consider these issues:

1. What are the male and female roles in fertilization and conception?

2. What are the physical and psychological highlights for mother and father of each of the three trimesters of pregnancy and of the postpartum period?

3. How are the three stages of labor distinguished? What is the father's role (or the labor coach's role) in each stage?

4. How do vaginal and nonvaginal methods of delivery compare? "Natural" and medicated deliveries? Home birth and hospital deliveries, including the relatively new option of "birthing rooms"?

5. How do the mother's use of drugs, cigarettes, and alcohol actually affect the unborn child during pregnancy, and potentially set the stage for major problems after delivery?

6. What are some of the causes of problem pregnancies? How does medical technology correct these problems?

7. What are some of the causes of male and female infertility? How does medical technology correct these problems? What is the impact of infertility on many couples?

8. What are some of the ethical issues in the most extreme of these solutions for infertility such as IVF and surrogate parenting?

LEARNING OBJECTIVES

At the conclusion of this chapter, the student should be able to:

1. Describe conception by explaining the sequence of events starting with ejaculation and ovulation and concluding with implantation.

2. Describe the changes in fetal development during each trimester of pregnancy.

3. Identify the physical, psychological, and social changes that typically occur in both the expectant mother and father during each trimester of pregnancy.

4. Explain the need for prenatal care and identify its effects on mother and fetus.

5. List and describe the stages of labor.

6. Discuss the pros and cons of hospital delivery, of home delivery.

7. Discuss the range of psychological reactions of both mother and father to childbirth, breast-feeding, and parenting.

8. Identify the major types of problem pregnancies, list the most common forms of birth defects, and describe the ways they can be detected and possibly prevented.

9. State the major causes of infertility in both men and women, and describe the current treatment options; explain the risks and drawbacks of these procedures, and discuss their chances of success.

TEACHING STRATEGIES

Learning about human reproduction requires the student to know and understand a huge amount of material. One of the topics that most interests students is what to expect during the processes of reproduction. They need guidance in sorting through the many books and opinions on the subject that often relay contradictory messages. Should a pregnant woman smoke or drink alcohol or coffee? Is it okay to take a sleeping pill or aspirin? Should intercourse be avoided during the third trimester? How much weight gain in the mother is optimal? Should a woman have prepared childbirth? How should the husband (partner, coach) be involved? Should the baby be taken to the nursery immediately following birth? Is anesthesia during labor and delivery good or bad? Should forceps be used? Should a woman have an episiotomy? Is induction of labor dangerous? Should a woman breast-feed or will this alienate the child's father? Perhaps the most important lesson for students to learn is that the answers to many of these questions are not firmly or immutably established.

In addition to these complicated questions, students are faced with many vocabulary words that may be new to them and will probably sound intimidating or frightening: toxemia, ectopic, placenta previa, amniocentesis, preeclampsia and so on. The instructor must patiently describe the processes that these terms name so that knowledge and understanding can banish the fear in students' minds. Most instructors will not want to spend too much time describing the "mechanics" of pregnancy and childbirth, choosing instead to deal with the other key aspects of the chapter.

One excellent way of making the subject "real" for students (many of whom probably have no intention of having children in the near future) is to conduct an interview in class with a couple experiencing the third trimester of pregnancy or with the parents of a newborn. Doing this gives students a more personal account of the unexpected joys and stresses couples may encounter and makes the textbook information come alive. It is important to solicit the father's perspective as well as the mother's during such an interview, and equally important that time be alloted for questions from students. Movies of childbirth and prepared childbirth classes can also be invaluable aids to learning.

When discussing the various styles of childbirth and the attendant medical decisions, the instructor should avoid making absolute pronouncements unsupported by data. For example, while it seems that many cesarean births are avoidable, many others are medically necessary. As another example, while forceps delivery is not always ideal, it can sometimes be life-saving. Try to stress the importance of individualizing decisions about pregnancy and childbirth based on a multiplicity of facts in each case and that no two pregnancy experiences are likely to be exactly the same.

A final topic that requires careful discussion is infertility. In the majority of cases, infertility can be reversed. But in cases where the male partner is sterile, doctor and parents may consider AI as an alternative. AI is a controversial topic that generates discussion in terms of psychological, biological and ethical components. Positive reasons for artificial insemination are not commonly explored. Some fertile couples decide to improve the genetic potential of their child-to-be by obtaining sperm from a gifted man. Explore the possible legal ramifications of using sperm donors and how they can be controlled. If, for example, a man's family has various chronic illnesses that the couple does not wish to pass on to their offspring, should the decision to use a donor with a healthy genetic heritage be considered immoral, humane, crazy, or extremely rational? The same kinds of issues apply to the current practice of IVF and surrogate parenting and should be discussed in class. Who is really the mother of the baby born to a surrogate and turned over at birth to the genetic father and his wife? Who are the likely candidates for IVF? Why are they willing to go through all that is involved? The instructor might want to show the PBS broadcast of the conception and birth of Elizabeth Jordan Carr as a lead-in to a discussion of the topic of IVF. Interviewing a lawyer who represents surrogate mothers or even interviewing a surrogate mother in class can be effective ways of bringing difficult issues to life. It is critical that the instructor remain objective and, hopefully, neutral should such proceedings occur in class.

STUDENT PROJECTS

1. Take a tour of the obstetrical floor of a local hospital. Talk with doctors, nurses, interns and residents, new parents about the experience of childbirth at that particular institution. Based on your initial impressions, what changes would you make in hospital policy and practice, if any.

2. Arrange to observe several prepared childbirth classes. If you have the time and inclination, find out if there are any expectant mothers who are without partners and need coaches. Arrange to be such a coach, and work with the mother through the actual delivery.

3. Interview an obstetrician or nurse-midwife to discuss their perceptions of the emotional side of the childbirth experience, including the father's role. Compare and contrast your findings with the perceptions of people who have had children. What conclusions can you draw?

4. Visit an infertility clinic to discuss the various services they provide. Ask, in advance, if it would be possible to see a live sperm specimen under a microscope. If they perform AID, ask about the procedures used to screen sperm donors, and how the donors are chosen for each couple.

5. Interview a social worker who specializes in adoptions at a local family and children's services agency. Discuss the criteria used to determine whether a couple may become adoptive parents. Ask about the agency's position about surrogate parenting and IVF as alternatives to adoption.

PERSONAL REFLECTIONS

1. Recall the stories you have heard others tell about the experiences of pregnancy, labor and delivery. How have these stories influenced your own attitude toward the prospect of pregnancy and childbirth? Are your opinions and beliefs similar to or different from those of men you know? Why?

2. Complete the following sentence: "Reading about things like AI, IVF, surrogate parenting makes me...."

3. Knowing what you do now about the complexities of human reproduction, the risks, and the potential complications, do you think your future decision to bear children (or not) might be affected? Why? (For students who are themselves parents, the following question applies: knowing what you do now about the complexities of human reproduction, the risks, and the potential complications, do you think you might have done things differently? Why?)

4. If you found out you were infertile, do you think you would pursue any or all the avenues described in the text to attempt to become fertile? Why?

CHAPTER 5 TEST QUESTIONS

Multiple Choice (* General Comprehension Questions)

1.* All of the following are accurate statements about human pregnancy except
    a. the events of pregnancy are described in terms of semesters.
    b. the unborn child is called an embryo during the first eight weeks after fertilization.
    c. the average pregnancy lasts 266 days.
    d. a placenta develops through which the baby receives oxygen and nourishment from the mother's bloodstream.

2.* During the process of fertilization
    a. the egg is a passive participant.
    b. the race to penetrate the egg is always won by the swiftest sperm.
    c. the egg produces a brief electrical block followed by the formation of an outer protein coat to avoid penetration by more than one sperm.
    d. it takes at least 200 million or more sperm in the Fallopian tubes to ensure fertilization of an egg.

3.* In order for human conception to occur
    a. a female must wait 72 hours after ovulation.
    b. a couple must have intercourse on a pre-set schedule.
    c. the female must use a spermicide prior to intercourse.
    d. the sperm must be deposited in the vagina close to the

time of ovulation.

4.* Parent-child bonding is
   a. the process in which a woman turns to her own mother for help after the birth of a baby.
   b. frowned upon during the mother and baby's hospital stay.
   c. a process which naturally excludes the father.
   d. a process in which a critical emotional link develops between parents and child largely via physical contact.

5.* The problem of infertility
   a. affects only one in seventy couples
   b. is caused in the majority of cases by blocked Fallopian tubes in women, low sperm count in men.
   c. is not currently being tackled by the medical profession.
   d. has no documented negative effects on the lives of most married couples.

6. All of the following describe parts of the fertilization process except
   a. the sperm must undergo decapitation.
   b. the sperm secretes a chemical to dissolve the zona pellucida.
   c. the egg embraces the sperm by extending its microvilli.
   d. the sperm contributes either an X or Y chromosome to the zygote.

7. Sex preselection
   a. cannot be accomplished.
   b. might lead to discrimination against male babies if past history gives us insight into human preferences.
   c. can be accomplished if the woman wears boots to bed or eats sweets depending on whether a boy or girl is desired.
   d. has been attempted and described by numerous researchers but the suggestions have yet to be supported by secure research data.

8. A zygote is
   a. always female.
   b. a single cell produced by fertilization.
   c. the same thing as a morula.
   d. a hollow inner portion of cells containing amniotic fluid.

9. Implantation of the blastocyst outside the uterus results in
   a. a utopian pregnancy.
   b. an edemous pregnancy.
   c. an eclectic pregnancy.
   d. an ectopic pregnancy.

10. Some of the symptoms of early pregnancy include
    a. infrequent urination.
    b. "morning sickness" at any time of the day.
    c. decreased amount of vaginal secretions.
    d. extraordinary surges of energy.

11. A <u>negative</u> pregnancy test
    a.   is a foolproof indication that one is not pregnant.
    b.   is only foolproof when a beta-subunit HCG radioimmunoassay is used.
    c.   is accurate if the results occur in conjunction with a missed period.
    <u>d.</u>   might indicate the need for a repetition of the test a week or two after the first negative test results.

12. The <u>couvade syndrome</u> refers to
    a.   the psychological problems caused by blocked Fallopian tubes.
    <u>b.</u>   physical symptoms of pregnancy experienced by husbands of pregnant women and not explained by other medical factors.
    c.   the need for privacy many women experience during labor.
    d.   a series of stresses related to the IVF procedures.

13. "Quickening" refers to
    a.   a pregnant woman's ability to have faster orgasms during intercourse.
    b.   the pregnant woman's unexplained need to tidy up her surroundings in the few days prior to labor and delivery.
    c.   what happens when the amniotic sac breaks.
    <u>d.</u>   the movement of the fetus that can be felt between the 16th and 17th week by the pregnant mother.

14. "Colostrum" refers to
    a.   the fluid that causes edema during pregnancy.
    b.   stretch marks on the abdomen of a pregnant woman.
    <u>c.</u>   a precursor of mother's milk.
    <u>d.</u>   the increased blood supply during pregnancy that can cause varicose veins.

15. "Braxton-Hicks contractions" are
    a.   similar to Kegel exercises in form and function.
    b.   also known as back labor.
    <u>c.</u>   painless short episodes of muscle tightening that aren't signs of labor.
    d.   occur as the head of a fetus is engaged.

16. Prenatal care
    a.   is the mother's responsibility only.
    <u>b.</u>   is a joint collaboration between the mother, her partner, and the physician or nurse she sees on a regular basis.
    c.   excludes the baby's father.
    d.   serves only a psychological function.

17. Poor maternal nutrition prior to and during pregnancy can cause
    a.   too-rapid fetal growth.
    b.   obese babies.
    c.   delayed deliveries.
    <u>d.</u>   higher infant death rates.

18. Teratogens refers to
    a. hormones produced in boys immediately after puberty.
    b. convulsions and coma that may occur in toxemia of pregnancy.
    c. the "bloody show" which indicates labor is about to begin.
    d. certain drugs that, when taken by a pregnant woman, can produce malformations in the unborn child.

19. The fetal alcohol syndrome may affect the fetus in all of the following ways except
    a. facial abnormalities.
    b. damage to the brain and nervous system.
    c. lowered blood prolactin levels.
    d. growth deficiencies.

20. Occiput, vertex, or cephalic presentations refer to
    a. kinds of episiotomies.
    b. types of cesarean sections.
    c. variations of breach births.
    d. how babies are born in 95 percent of vaginal deliveries.

21. "Natural childbirth"
    a. is not really natural if it occurs in a hospital.
    b. excludes the presence of physicians but allows the presence of a nurse-midwife.
    c. is the safest method of delivery in all cases.
    d. is designed to help break the woman's fear-tension-pain reaction chain.

22. BBT charts and the Rubin's test are used to
    a. detect possible causes of female infertility.
    b. detect low sperm counts.
    c. determine the condition of a fetus in utero.
    d. determine Rh incompatibility between mother and fetus.

23. AIH and AID refer to
    a. federal programs to help defray hospital costs for low-income expectant mothers.
    b. incurable, cancer-like diseases currently under study.
    c. surgical procedures to repair varicose veins in a man's scrotum, thus improving the sperm count.
    d. the two basic types of artificial insemination.

24. All of the following have had something to do with IVF except
    a. Patrick Steptoe and Robert Edwards.
    b. Elizabeth Jordan Carr.
    c. Louise Brown.
    d. Grantly Dick-Read.

25. All of the following are methods of detecting birth defects except
    a. the use of RhoGAM.
    b. ultrasound.
    c. amniocentesis.

d.   CVS.

True/False

T   1.   Scopolamine is an analgesic often used for pain reduction during labor and delivery.

T   2.   Couples not using contraception usually conceive within 5.3 months.

F   3.   The treatment of male infertility is more developed than is the treatment of female infertility.

T   4.   Chorionic villi sampling can be done in a woman's eighth week of pregnancy.

T   5.   The presence of an IUD seems to be associated with an increased chance of ectopic pregnancy.

T   6.   The appearance of fingernails, toenails, hair follicles, and eyelids is characteristic of the unborn child in its third month of development.

F   7.   The injection of vitamin K immediately after birth prevents transmission of infection from the mother's vaginal passage to the newborn's eyes.

T   8.   A recent Canadian study showed that the cumulative pregnancy rate in untreated couples with unexplained infertility was 65 percent.

F   9.   A fetus born at the end of the second trimester of its mother's pregnancy has an excellent chance of survival.

T   10.   If a mother is drug-addicted, her baby will be born addicted too.

F   11.   Luck has nothing to do with conceiving a baby.

T   12.   Tiredness is considered a symptom of pregnancy in the first trimester.

F   13.   A fetus is suspended in antibiotic fluid.

F   14.   The mother's rate of metabolism increases by 50 percent during pregnancy.

T   15.   The milk flow reflex in nursing mothers is controlled by oxytocin.

Fill in the Blanks

1.   A light, circular stroking of the woman's abdomen used during active labor to increase her comfort level is called (effleurage).

2. (Dilatation) reflects the degree of the opening of the cervix measured in centimeters during labor.

3. (Lochia) is the discharge that occurs during the first few postpartum weeks as the uterine lining reestablishes itself.

4. The thinning of the cervix during labor is called (effacement).

5. Another term for labor that is artificially started by a doctor or health-care professional is (induction or induced labor).

6. A pregnancy that occurs in the Fallopian tube, ovary, abdomen, or cervix is called (ectopic).

7. During the (first) trimester of pregnancy, the umbilical cord becomes a distinct structure.

8. During the (second) trimester of pregnancy, the fetal heartbeat can be detected.

9. Clomiphene and HMG are medications used to (help women who do not ovulate to ovulate).

10. The drug (Valium) can, if taken by a pregnant woman, cause her unborn child to develop a cleft palate.

11. A drug that caused numerous birth defects, notably, severe malformation of the arms and legs, and that is no longer prescribed for pregnant women is (thalidomide).

12. An abrupt drop in the mother's hormone levels, and a time of physical and psychological adjustment characterize the (postpartum) period.

13. The condition of (Rh incompatibility) is one in which antibodies from the mother's bloodstream destroy the red blood cells of her fetus.

14. The so-called "bag of waters" surrounding the fetus is technically known as the (amniotic sac).

15. The color of all infants eyes is (blue) since other colors only develop after a period of exposure to light.

Discussion/Essay Questions

1. What biological requirements must be met for conception to occur?

2. What are the signs and symptoms of early pregnancy?

3. What tests are currently available to detect the presence of fetal abnormalities? What are the pros and cons of each?

4. Describe fetal development during the three trimesters of pregnancy. What are some of the most dramatic developments and when do they occur?

5. Many individuals advocate breast-feeding, and there has been a dramatic increase in mothers who choose to nourish their children this way in recent years. What are the advantages and disadvantages of nursing compared to bottle-feeding?

6. How has the father's involvement in his partner's pregnancy and delivery changed over the past decades? Talk to your own parents about this and compare and contrast their experiences with those described in this chapter.

7. In what ways must a pregnant woman be an educated consumer of goods and services? Why?

8. Discuss the options available to people with infertility problems. Based on what you know, in what direction do you see future infertility programs developing? What would you hope to happen?

Chapter 6

BIRTH CONTROL

OVERVIEW

Chapter 6 discusses various methods of contraception, including the newest developments such as the cervical cap, the contraceptive sponge, the Norplant system for females and a male contraceptive called Gossypol, currently in use in China. Several perspectives are utilized in the delineation of each birth control option. Initially, students are asked why contraceptives are used and are then given background information to help them evaluate the effectiveness and safety of contraceptive methods. Each method of birth control is described, including a definition of the method, when it was first introduced, how it works, how it is used, its theoretical and actual effectiveness, its side effects and safety record, and its actual and potential effects on sexuality. Postconception methods of birth control, including the "morning after" pill, menstrual extraction, and abortion are also discussed. The psychology of contraceptive use and disuse and consideration of future trends in contraceptive technology for both males and females concludes this chapter.

While reading the chapter, the student is asked to consider these issues:

1. What birth control methods are currently available to females and males? What are the benefits and risks of each method? What possibilities does the future hold for contraceptive technology?

2. What are the methods of abortion? When is each method safe or unsafe and why? What are some of the differences between male and female reactions to abortion?

3. What sterilization procedures are available to males and females?

4. How would you assess the safety and effectiveness of a given contraceptive method?

5. What factors might affect a person's decision to use or not use a specific birth control method?

6. How do various types of contraception affect a person's sexual feelings and behavior?

LEARNING OBJECTIVES

At the conclusion of this chapter, the student should be able to:

1. List the factors that affect an individual's or couple's decisions about birth control.

2. Discuss the major reasons for using birth control.

3. Describe the factors which complicate our ability to evaluate the effectiveness and safety of birth control.

4. Differentiate between theoretical effectiveness and actual effectiveness of a particular birth control method.

5. Identify the commonly used methods of birth control; discuss the use, effectiveness, side effects, safety, and sexual effects of each method.

6. List the surgical procedures used to prevent pregnancy, describe each procedure, and discuss the safety and risks of each.

7. Explain the postconception methods of birth control and the reason each method may generate controversy.

8. Discuss why some people who don't want a pregnancy avoid the use of birth control or misuse the method of birth control they have selected.

9. Contrast the desire to avoid pregnancy with the desire to delay the timing of pregnancy in terms of choice and consistency of use of a birth control method.

10. Describe the future trends in male and female birth control and explain how these new directions are being pursued.

TEACHING STRATEGIES

One essential goal in teaching a human sexuality class is to help students learn to make sexual decisions they can live with comfortably. Conception and contraception are excellent topics for student exercises in such decision making. In their book, Sexual Style (1979), Meyners and Wooster list various exercises and also provide a discussion about how sexual decisions are made. Meyners and Wooster note that one such style is to base most of these decisions on outside authority such as the church, parents, or societal dictates. A second style is to leave the decision to fate, as in the attitude that "If I am meant to get pregnant, I will." The third and most common style today is the weighing of "costs vs. benefits." For example, the choice to have intercourse without contraception is made by weighing (at some level of awareness, though not necessarily a conscious awareness) the "cost" of a pregnancy against the "benefit" of spontaneity and avoidance the the hassles of obtaining adequate contraception. Discussing the three styles of decision making can help students to fully understand the statement from the text that "Not using birth control if you are sexually active is a specific kind of personal decision."

Another approach to sexual decisions is to begin the lecture by quoting various statistics either from the text or available from most family planning agencies about the prevalence of teenage pregnancy and unplanned pregnancy in general. Discussing why contraceptive usage is so low, and what programs might be devised to increase utilization often generates interesting personal comments about a student's own sexual decision making. If the class can be directed to suggest ideas for helping others become more cognizant of their actions and style of decision making, the result will be that they indirectly teach themselves these skills.

Chapter 6 also lends itself to discussions about research design. Why is it so difficult to know what side effects accompany the use of birth control pills? The instructor might describe a situation in which a group of women is given the pill and another group is given a placebo, then ask the following questions: How does the experimenter prevent potential pregnancies? If another form of contraception is used, how does that influence the results? If some women in both groups find that their sex drive is increased, decreased, or unchanged, how does one interpret the findings? What are the effects of studying the women's behavior and having the women keep daily records of changes? How does one quantify sex drive or moods?

After students read about the side effects and risks associated with the various forms of contraception, they may want to decide which, if any, would be best for them. The instructor can give examples of various styles of decision making, such as a woman who has never had a pregnancy and fears an IUD would possibly interfere with future plans for conception. She dislikes the messiness of foams and jellies and believes the sponge has not been sufficiently tested, so she decides to try birth control pills with a low dosage of estrogen. After waiting several months for her body to adjust, she reassesses her decision based on her body's reaction. She decides to be examined more frequently by her physician to compensate for the increased risks of various diseases. Ask several students to give similar fictitious examples and describe decision-making steps.

The topic of abortion should be approached cautiously because many students have strong opinions. If the discussion becomes too militant, it may become impossible to objectively discuss a variety of thoughts and feelings as there may be increased polarization instead of willingness to listen and learn. Since the ethical and religious aspects of the abortion issue are addressed elsewhere in the text, this may not be the time to do so unless students have been assigned the additional reading in advance of the discussion.

A final topic is the history of contraception. Point out to the class that the past few generations are the first in history to be able to engage in sexual intercourse with reliable control over pregnancy. Ask the class to speculate about what changes in reproductive and sexual behavior patterns might occur when one or more highly effective and reversible methods of male contraception become available.

STUDENT PROJECTS

1. Design an ad campaign to increase condom sales among adolescent males.

2. Design the "perfect contraceptive" for men, for women. Write a publicity article about each one suitable for publication in a major newspaper's science section.

3. Visit a local family planning clinic. What services do they offer? Do they have facilities for performing abortions? What legal restrictions do they operate within and who can get help from them? Interview one of their counselors. Ask about the kinds of misinformation they have to correct on a daily basis. Find out which birth control methods are most popular, and which generate the most customer dissatisfaction.

4. You have made the decision to get married or to live with someone. Outline the things you want to discuss about birth control issues, any anticipated problems you think you might have, and negotiating techniques if needed. How will you decide the issue of ultimate responsibility for birth control?

PERSONAL REFLECTIONS

1. It is a documented fact that birth control is "either not used, misused, or used sporadically by many people." Where do you fit into this picture? What have been the major influences that have shaped your attitudes about contraception?

2. Complete the following statement: "I really believe that discussions about birth control...."

3. Knowing what you now know about birth control methods, do you plan any changes in your typical sexual behavior patterns? Why?

CHAPTER 6 TEST QUESTIONS

Multiple Choice (* General Comprehension Questions)

1.* The primary objective of contraception is
   a. to space the children in one's family.
   b. to prevent unwanted pregnancy.
   c. to prevent venereal disease.
   d. to enhance one's sexual experiences.

2.* A person's decision about what method of birth control to use
     a.   depends primarily on the methods used by one's parents.
     b.   depends more on social values than life circumstances.
     c.   is most strongly influenced by financial considerations.
     d.   depends on any number of variable and varying factors.

3.* All of the following are true about current contraceptive
     practices except
     a.   4.9 million couples of reproductive age in the U.S. rely
          on vasectomy for contraception.
     b.   men shoulder the burden of contraceptive responsibility.
     c.   two-thirds of abortions in the U.S. in 1980 were obtained
          by women under the age of 25.
     d.   long-acting contraceptives are in use in other countries
          and are increasingly available in the U.S.

4.* It can be said that there are health risks associated with all
     of the following birth control methods except
     a.   the minipill.
     b.   the IUD.
     c.   the condom.
     d.   combination birth control pills.

5.* All of the following are accurate statements about evaluating
     contraceptive safety and effectiveness except
     a.   information from various sources may be biased.
     b.   scientific studies are uniformily equivalent in how their
          findings apply to you.
     c.   there is a difference between actual and theoretical
          effectiveness of any given method.
     d.   the longer a person uses a given method, the more
          effective it becomes.

6.   According to Forrest and Henshaw, the contraceptive method used
     most frequently by sexually active U.S. women aged 15-44 is
     a.   rhythm.
     b.   the IUD.
     c.   sterilization.
     d.   the pill.

7.   The two types of oral contraceptives currently in use are
     a.   the combination pill and the minipill.
     b.   the combination pill and the placebo.
     c.   the minipill and the NORPLANT system.
     d.   the minipill and MPA.

8.   Birth control pills prevent pregnancy by
     a.   increasing the woman's normal cyclic output of FSH and LH.
     b.   drowning the partner's sperm in chemical acid released by
          the pill.
     c.   thinning the woman's cervical mucus.
     d.   inhibiting the development of the lining of the woman's
          uterus.

9. The most effective <u>nonsurgical</u> method of contraception is
    a. the cervical cap.
    b. plugging the place at which the Fallopian tubes open into
        the uterus.
    <u>c.</u> the birth control pill.
    <u>d.</u> the IUD.

10. Some health risks to women using birth control pills include
    a. hair loss.
    <u>b.</u> disorders of the circulatory system.
    c. loss of appetite leading to anorexia nervosa.
    d. lack of vaginal lubrication thereby increasing the risk of
        contracting a sexually transmitted disease.

11. Which of the following is <u>not</u> a beneficial side effect of the
    birth control pill?
    a. it may prevent endometrial cancer.
    b. it may improve acne.
    <u>c.</u> it may protect against heart disease.
    <u>d.</u> it can reduce PMS.

12. Which of the following describes a woman who should avoid using
    the IUD as her main birth control method?
    a. a mentally retarded woman.
    b. a woman who wants a promptly reversible method of
        contraception.
    c. a woman who wants a reliable contraceptive method that
        requires no active participation on her part.
    <u>d.</u> a woman who has had a prior ectopic pregnancy.

13. The IUD prevents pregnancy by
    a. allowing sperm to travel down the tail of the IUD after
        intercourse has taken place.
    b. surrounding a fertilized egg and pushing it out of the
        uterus.
    <u>c.</u> by interfering with the implantation of the fertilized egg
        in the lining of the uterus.
    d. preventing the development of the zona pellucida.

14. Among the potentially serious problems caused by IUDs may be
    a. the loss of menstrual periods.
    b. perforation of the cervix.
    c. higher risk of sexually transmitted disease.
    <u>d.</u> higher risk of pelvic infection.

15. All of the following are true about the use of a diaphragm
    <u>except</u>
    a. a woman's motivation and memory are important factors.
    b. it can be inserted up to two hours before intercourse and
        should remain in place at least six hours afterwards.
    <u>c.</u> the blocking effect of the diaphragm against sperm is very
        effective by itself.
    d. the size and fit of the diaphragm should be rechecked
        periodically, especially after a major weight loss and/or

pregnancy.

16. The use of the diaphragm may include all of the following side
    effects except
    a.   danger to later fertility.
    b.   possible allergic reactions to the rubber in the
         diaphragm.
    c.   inconvenience in terms of sexual spontaneity and arousal.
    d.   possible overgrowth in the vagina and cervix of bacteria
         linked to toxic shock syndrome if the diaphragm is worn
         for more than 12 hours at a time.

17. The main problem associated with condom usage is
    a.   defective condoms.
    b.   inconsistent use.
    c.   burning or irritation to the genitals.
    d.   expense.

18. Some advantages of condom use include all of the following
    except
    a.   enhanced erectile capability in men who are often
         impotent.
    b.   little or no postcoital "drippiness" for the man's sexual
         partner.
    c.   protection against many sexually transmitted diseases.
    d.   help for men who have difficulty controlling ejaculation.

19. Some common problems with spermicide may include all of the
    following except
    a.   burning or irritation of the vagina.
    b.   failures due to the use of outdated products.
    c.   burning or irritation of the penis.
    d.   increased incidence of pelvic inflammatory disease.

20. Some of the major advantages of the contraceptive sponge
    include all of the following except
    a.   ease of insertion.
    b.   no reported incidence of pelvic irritation or toxic shock
         syndrome.
    c.   length of time that it retains its contraceptive
         protection against multiple acts of intercourse.
    d.   the fact that it is unobtrusive, tasteless and odorless.

21. Which of the following is not an operation performed to achieve
    female sterilization?
    a.   laparoscopy.
    b.   culdoscopy.
    c.   culpotomy.
    d.   vasectomy.

22. The "morning after" pill
    a.   is suitable for routine contraceptive use.
    b.   has no side effects.
    c.   can be used on a long-term basis with no lasting effect on

the mother or fetus if pregnancy occurs.
d. is a useful option in special situations such as rape or condom leakage.

23. Vasectomy
    a. is the simplest and safest form of surgical contraception.
    b. stops sperm production six to eight weeks post-surgery.
    c. changes the amount of the ejaculate.
    d. may increase the man's risk of heart disease and cancer.

24. All of the following are accurate statements about abortion except
    a. abortion can be spontaneous or induced.
    b. during the fourth and fifth months of pregnancy the safest method for abortion is dilatation and evacuation.
    c. modern abortion techniques are still riskier to the mother than a full term pregnancy would be.
    d. the male's reaction to the abortion experience is often neglected.

25. According to the text, not using contraception even though pregnancy is not desired may indicate all of the following except
    a. inadequate knowledge.
    b. personal embarrassment about sexuality in general or about a particular method.
    c. hostility, power struggles, differences in reproductive goals.
    d. suicidal tendencies.

True/False

T   1. There is currently a pocket-sized electronic device that flashes a red light when a woman is fertile.

F   2. The contraceptive sponge is only effective for one act of intercourse.

T   3. The major problem with the NORPLANT system is abnormal menstrual bleeding which usually abates after about one year of use.

F   4. Depo-Provera and MPA are different forms of long-acting birth control for men.

T   5. Gossypol is a promising male contraceptive currently in use in China.

T   6. Men tend to react to abortion first in an abstract, intellectual way and later tend to have to deal with feelings of guilt, anger, or hurt.

F   7. Asking "how well will a birth control method prevent unintended pregnancy?" refers to questioning its safety.

T 8. Among healthy women with no serious pre-existing medical problems, the risk of dying from a legal abortion in the U.S. is less than one per 100,000 procedures.

T 9. Most women taking birth control pills report no significant changes in sexual interest, behavior, or enjoyment.

F 10. Operations to reverse sterilization procedures are easy, safe, and effective.

T 11. Coitus interruptus or withdrawal is a chancy, often frustrating form of birth control.

T 12. An IUD can cause pain during intercourse.

F 13. Because breast-feeding inhibits ovulation in some women, it is a very reliable method of birth control.

T 14. It takes six to eight weeks after a vasectomy is performed before the ejaculate is sterile.

T 15. Personal motivation and contraceptive practice are closely interrelated.

Fill in the Blanks

1. Birth control pills are also known as (oral) contraceptives.

2. (Condoms, prophylactics) are also known as "rubbers."

3. DES, diethylstilbestrol, is occasionally used as a (morning after) pill to prevent implantation of the fertilized ovum.

4. Vaginal chemical contraceptives are more commonly known as (spermicides).

5. Centuries ago when an Arab camel driver would put a large pebble into a camel's uterus for contraceptive purposes, he was using a forerunner of the (IUD or intrauterine device).

6. The improper or inconsistent use of a contraceptive is also called (user failure).

7. The most common bothersome side effects of (the pill) mimic those encountered in pregnancy.

8. The most serious risk of using an IUD is (perforation of the uterus).

9. If used in combination with (a vaginal spermicide), the effectiveness of the condom as a birth control method is almost as good as the pill.

10. Identifying the "safe days" in one's menstrual cycle based on the length of previous cycles is part of the (calendar) method of birth control.

11. The (ovulation or Billings) method depends on changes in cervical mucus to indicate the probable days of fertility during the menstrual cycle.

12. A simple surgical procedure that cuts and ties each vas deferens is a (vasectomy).

13. An unusual postconception method of birth control pioneered by the women's self-help movement is (menstrual extraction).

14. The most common abortion method done during the first trimester of a pregnancy is called (vacuum aspiration or suction).

15. If a medical problem disrupts a pregnancy, (spontaneous) abortion can occur.

Discussion/Essay Questions

1. Sexually active adolescent males are often unwilling to use condoms because they believe it would lessen their sexual pleasure. If you were leading a discussion group of 9th grade boys on the subject of contraception, what could you tell them to possibly change their minds?

2. If you were providing counseling to a woman who was uncertain about whether or not to have an abortion, what points would you make on both the pro and con sides of the issue?

3. Compare and contrast the various rhythm methods of birth control with the more modern, chemically controlled methods such as the pill or postconception methods. What emotional decisions contribute to the choice of one method over another?

4. In what ways is the choice of a birth control method a lifestyle decision?

5. Design a study to measure changes in a woman's sexual excitement and responsivity before and after voluntary sterilization.

6. If excellent male contraceptive methods were available, do you think most women would turn over the responsibility for conntraception to the men? Explain.

Chapter 7

DEVELOPMENTAL SEXUALITY: A BIOLOGICAL VIEW

OVERVIEW

Looking at the factors that influence sexual development throughout the life cycle provides an important foundation for understanding human sexuality. In this chapter, biological influences on sexual development in prenatal life, childhood, and puberty are delineated. The discussion of prenatal sexual differentiation stresses the importance of genetic and hormonal control mechanisms by describing both normal development and several examples of abnormal sex differentiation such as Klinefelter's syndrome, Turner's syndrome, the adrenogenital syndrome, and the syndrome of testicular feminization. These discussions are used to suggest to the student the possibility that prenatal hormone programming may influence subsequent sex behavior patterns, although the Research Spotlight, "The Nature-Nurture Argument," stresses the difficulty in drawing absolute conclusions based on the data that are currently available. After briefly describing the fact that a relatively full range of sexual reflexes are present in infancy and childhood, the chapter then shifts its focus to the biological changes that occur during puberty. The mechanisms that control puberty and the sexual changes that typically occur with puberty are explained, including specific attention to wet dreams and attitudes about vaginal secretions. The chapter concludes with a discussion of late puberty and the relationship between pubertal hormones and sexual behavior, and contrasts this with what occurs in the case of precocious puberty.

While reading the chapter, the student is asked to consider these issues:

1. What components are needed for prenatal male and female sexual differentiation to occur?

2. What are some disorders of prenatal sexual development, such as sex chromosome problems, male or female pseudohermaphroditism, and the effects of hormones taken by pregnant women?

3. How is infant and childhood sexuality manifested biologically in males and females?

4. What are the biological processes of puberty for males and females as noted in hormonal changes, physical growth and development, and sexual maturation?

5. What is the nature-nurture argument and how does it pertain to

the study of human sexuality?

6. What are the differences between precocious puberty and late puberty in terms of biological mechanisms and sexual behavior?

LEARNING OBJECTIVES

At the conclusion of this chapter, the student should be able to:

1. Identify the genetic and hormonal mechanisms that control prenatal sexual differentiation.

2. Describe the development of the external genitalia from the embryonic tissues in male and female fetuses.

3. Explain the process of male and female brain differentiation and identify the differences.

4. Identify the causes of abnormal prenatal development and explain each cause including chromosomal, genetic, and hormonal or drug exposures.

5. Discuss the biologic developmental sexuality of infancy and childhood.

6. Contrast the range of physical sexual responsiveness in boys and girls.

7. Describe the hormonal control of puberty and the physical changes that occur in both males and females during adolescence.

8. Discuss the relationship between pubertal hormones and sexual behavior in early, normal, and late puberty.

9. List the factors which influence the age of menarche.

10. Describe the nature-nurture controversy as it applies to human sexual behavior.

TEACHING STRATEGIES

One way to begin the class discussion is by asking, "What determines sex?" The ensuing discussion will help students understand the need for learning the concepts and terminology presented in this chapter. If students answer that sex is determined by chromosomes, ask how chromosomes program what we observe to be "man" or "woman." In answering your question, students will see that chromosomes are only one link in a chain of determinants of sex and sexuality. Briefly repeat and discuss the seven determinants mentioned in the text: (1) presence or absence of the Y chromosome in the fertilizing sperm, (2) HY antigen,

(3) fetal gonad development, (4) Mullerian inhibiting substance, (5) fetal androgen production, (6) fetal hormonal influences on the central nervous system, (7) differentiation of the external genitalia. The relative importance of each sequential determinant will become more clear by studying abnormal conditions involving errors in the program. Clinical conditions presented in this chapter, such as Klinefelter's syndrome and the adrenogenital syndrome, represent a unique opportunity for a more complete understanding of the total picture of biologic development.

An interesting example of the relevance of clinical syndromes to help students understand the factors involved in normal development is the study of excess fetal adrenogenitalization. We know from amniocentesis that all humans are exposed to different amounts of fetal androgen between the 16th and 26th weeks of pregnancy. It is well established that fetal androgen in lower mammals influences the brain pathways that mediate sex-different behavior. Conditions like the adrenogenital syndrome may teach us more about the contribution of fetal adrenogenitalization in humans. Perhaps differences within and between the sexes are influenced by early hormone exposure.

Some students may become upset by the mere thought that sex differences may have a biologic basis. Point out that if hormones do exert an influence, they do not restrict sexual behavior. No human behavior is intrinsically sex-restrictive (with the obvious potential exceptions of nursing and menstruating). Explain, instead, that certain types of behavior may be more difficult for one sex than the other, and suggest that biologic influences may be contributing factors leading to that differential ease or difficulty.

Subsequent discussions can focus on hormonal influences that activate eroticism. Pubertal hormones act like the dimmer switch of a light, slowly activating sexual interest and experimentation as well as initiating the various changes in the body outlined in the text. It is important that students learn that although hormones activate, they do not have a clear-cut one-to-one correlation with sexual interest.

The information on early and late puberty may generate much discussion. You may find that many of your students were "late bloomers" and may want to discuss it at length. Don't let the class get too side-tracked by sociological discourse since this is, after all, a chapter on the biological view of developmental sexuality.

STUDENT PROJECTS

1. Interview two sets of parents, a couple whose child is a toddler and a couple whose child is an adolescent. Compare and contrast their concerns about the ways in which sexual behavior and interest manifest themselves in each age category. Finally, discuss the topic with your own parents and ask them how they handled their concerns about your sexual behavior. If your are a parent yourself, include your own experiences in your results.

2. Locate a physician (ideally, a pediatrician) who has had experience dealing with cases of abnormal sexual differentiation or precocious puberty. What stresses, if any, does having a child with such problems place on the family and how does the physician counsel everyone to best cope with the situation? How does the physician counsel the patient?

3. Think back to your own high school days. You probably knew at least one "late bloomer" and one person who was physically mature at an earlier age than most of you. Contact both people and ask them how they experienced the biological side of puberty. Did their physical status affect their social status? Has it had any long-term effect on their lives?

PERSONAL REFLECTIONS

1. Can you remember noticing physical sensations of genital arousal as a young adolescent? Were you ever embarrassed or upset by physical feelings such as erections or vaginal lubrication? Did you label these feelings as "sexual" at the time or were you unaware of what they meant or where they came from?

2. If you had a child and observed that child masturbating and clearly enjoying what he or she was doing, how would you react? Why do you think you'd react that way?

3. Pretend you are the subject of a scientific study. Outline all the ways in which the nature-nurture controversy could apply to you, your behavior, and your life from your earliest memories to the present. Ultimately, for you, which has been more influential -- nature or nurture?

4. As an adolescent, were you well-informed about the biological aspects of sexuality? If you weren't, would it have made a difference in how you lived your life if you had been? If you were, what role did that knowledge play in your sexual development, if any? Knowing what you know now, would you do things any differently or would your concerns be different if you could re-live those years?

CHAPTER 7 TEST QUESTIONS

Multiple Choice (* General Comprehension Questions)

1.* The time before birth when the sexual development of a fetus is controlled strictly by biological forces is the
a. perinatal period.
b. primordial period.
c. prenatal period.
d. prostaglandin period.

2.* At the moment of conception, the combination of genetic material from each parent starts a process called
   a. ovulation.
   b. testicular feminization.
   c. adrenogenitalization.
   d. sexual differentiation.

3.* The human egg always has the
   a. X sex chromosome.
   b. Y sex chromosome.
   c. midpiece and tail.
   d. XY chromosome pattern.

4.* The hormone differences between young girls and boys
   a. indicate the presence of genetic abnormality.
   b. generally develop after the age of four.
   c. are very minor prior to puberty.
   d. don't exist.

5.* A period of change from biological immaturity to maturity describes
   a. premature puberty.
   b. delayed puberty.
   c. puberty.
   d. pseudohermaphroditism.

6. When an embryo's gonads are formed during the 5th and 6th weeks of pregnancy, they can differentiate into the testes or ovaries, depending upon coming events. The gonads are said to be
   a. bipolar.
   b. bisexual.
   c. bipotential.
   d. biped.

7. In order for gonads to develop into testes, there must be a controlling substance present called the
   a. H-Y antigen.
   b. H-Y antibiotic.
   c. H-X antigen.
   d. H-Y antibody.

8. During embryonic/fetal development, the external genitals look the same in both sexes during the
   a. 3rd week.
   b. 7th week.
   c. 16th week.
   d. 20th week.

9. All of the following may lead to abnormal prenatal sexual development except
   a. sex chromosome disorders.
   b. exposure of the fetus to drugs taken by the mother.
   c. genetic conditions.

d. exposure of the fetus to a fetal monitor.

10. Klinefelter's syndrome
    a. is marked by an extra Y chromosome in a genetic male.
    b. occurs only once in every 50 live male births.
    c. leads to infertility.
    d. is detected immediately at birth.

11. Turner's syndrome is characterized by
    a. short height.
    b. a 45 Y karotype.
    c. too frequent menstruation.
    d. abnormal genitals.

12. A person born with both testicular and ovarian tissue is called
    a. a pseudohermaphrodite.
    b. a transvestite.
    c. a true hermaphrodite.
    d. a homosexual.

13. When the testes do not descend into the scrotum of a newborn
    male baby, the testes are said to be
    a. cryptic.
    b. carcinogenic.
    c. cryogenic.
    d. cryptorchid.

14. The adrenogenital syndrome is associated with
    a. excessive amounts of progesterone produced during fetal
       development.
    b. internal sex structures that are completely male.
    c. female pseudohermaphroditism.
    d. babies who look like girls but have internal sex
       structures that are both male and female.

15. All of the following are true about the testicular feminization
    syndrome except
    a. it is an inherited condition.
    b. excessive, abnormal levels of testosterone are produced.
    c. it is not usually diagnosed until the age of 16 or later.
    d. the vagina is short and ends in a blind pouch.

16. Prenatal hormone exposure
    a. is done routinely as a part of prenatal medical care.
    b. has been scientifically studied and is no longer a matter
       of controversy.
    c. may influence a child's later patterns of behavior.
    d. may affect later behavior but cannot affect sexual
       anatomy.

17. The relationship of learning and biology as it applies to how
    one's sexuality may develop
    a. is an irrelevant issue as the relationship cannot be
       clearly determined.

b. is best explained as an interaction that is constantly occurring as one grows and changes.
c. need not be discussed since biology is so much more important than learning from birth on.
d. need not be discussed since the range of sexual behaviors that can be learned is so limited.

18. The adolescent growth spurt occurs
a. two years earlier in boys than in girls.
b. as a result of proper nutrition alone.
c. at the same time in all parts of the body.
d. because rising sex hormone levels in puberty temporarily cause bone growth.

19. All of the following are true about the hormonal control of puberty except
a. a girl's estrogen levels gradually increase eight to ten times above those found in childhood.
b. a boy's testosterone levels increase ten to twenty times.
c. adrenal hormone output triggers the growth of pubic and axillary hair.
d. a girl's testosterone levels increase five to ten times.

20. The first physical sign of puberty in girls is usually
a. onset of menarche.
b. appearance of pubic hair.
c. appearance of vaginal lubrication.
d. beginning of breast development.

21. The earliest physical change during puberty in boys is
a. growth of the testes.
b. growth of pubic hair.
c. growth of the penis.
d. growth of facial hair.

22. All of the following are true of female breast growth during puberty except
a. it is controlled by heredity.
b. it is controlled by estrogen levels.
c. it begins with the enlargement of the areola and nipple, followed by breast bud development.
d. it can begin as early as age eight or as late as age thirteen.

23. All of the following are accurate statments about menarche except
a. menstruation began at an average age of sixteen a century ago.
b. the age at menarche has now leveled off, but decreased steadily on a decade-by-decade basis.
c. the age at menarche is not affected by socioeconomic factors.
d. the age at menarche is influenced by climate, heredity, and nutrition.

94

24. All of the following are accurate statements about sexual maturation in boys except
    a. ejaculation is not possible before puberty.
    b. increasing levels of progesterone stimulate growth of the prostate and epididymis.
    c. LH stimulation and testosterone production stimulate testicular growth.
    d. genitals reach adult size and shape at an average age of 14.9.

25. "Late" puberty
    a. usually results in more frequent and intense teenage sexual activity.
    b. is a sociological concept rather than a biological reality.
    c. is the mirror-image of "early" puberty in terms of the behaviors it engenders.
    d. usually results in less frequent masturbation in both boys and girls compared to their normally-maturing peers.

True/False

T   1. Female sexual differentiation occurs automatically and does not require hormone stimulation.

F   2. All the sexual reflexes are present in infancy and childhood.

T   3. The genetic code for a female is 46 XX.

T   4. During prenatal development, the testes of a male fetus normally migrate into the scrotum passing through the inguinal canal.

F   5. The sexual problems of a man with Klinefelter's syndrome can be alleviated with injections of cortisone.

T   6. Studies have been done which suggest that prenatal hormone exposure may predispose toward certain aspects of sex-linked behavior.

T   7. Once a baby is born, learning is usually more important than biology in shaping his or her sexuality.

F   8. All boys can ejaculate prior to puberty.

T   9. There has recently been an epidemic of precocious puberty among children in Puerto Rico, perhaps due to ingestion of chicken that contains estrogen.

F   10. During puberty, estrogen levels in girls increase 80 times above the childhood levels.

T   11. A girl's first menstrual cycle can be an ovulatory one.

F   12.   Nocturnal emissions are always caused by erotic dreams.

T   13.   Turner's syndrome is marked by a missing sex chromosome.

F   14.   The average age of the start of male genital development is 10.1 years.

T   15.   Girls who are younger at menarche tend to have intercourse and give birth at earlier ages than girls with later menarche.

Fill in the Blanks

1.   If the (H–Y) antigen is not present prenatally, primitive gonads will always develop into ovaries.

2.   Testosterone is an example of an (androgen), a hormone that causes masculinization.

3.   A genetic male with a 47 XXY chromosome pattern, who has low sexual desire and is impotent, suffers from (Klinefelter's) syndrome.

4.   A person born with both testicular and ovarian tissue is called a (true hermaphrodite).

5.   In childhood, the (gonads) are relatively nonfunctional.

6.   Another term for the onset of menstruation is (menarche).

7.   The transient breast enlargement seen in boys during puberty is called (gynecomastia).

8.   Girls are usually (taller) than boys of the same age from about age 11 to age 14.

9.   The earliest stage of breast growth in which there is only a small mound of tissue is called (the breast bud).

10.   In males, the deepening of the voice during puberty is due to testosterone stimulation of the (larynx or voice box).

11.   The degree of facial and body hairiness in both sexes is controlled by hormones and by (genetic factors).

12.   A person born with gonads that match his or her sex chromosomes but genital appearance that resembles the opposite sex is called a (pseudohermaphrodite).

13.   (Nature vs. nurture) is a way of describing the controversy about the relative importance of biological forces and learning and the environment in controlling human development.

14.   The maturing process of (puberty) lasts anywhere from one and

one half to six years.

15. The (adolescent growth spurt) does not always start at the same time in all parts of the body.

Discussion/Essay Questions

1. What is the difference between H-Y antigen and Mullerian duct inhibiting substance?

2. Describe one resulting disorder of each of the three causes of abnormal prenatal sexual development: chromosome disorders, genetic conditions, and exposure of the fetus to drugs taken by its mother.

3. Are children born as sexual beings, or are their documented physical reactions (erection, orgasm, lubrication) only reflex responses? Why?

4. Describe two different psychological reactions to the first wet dream: one by a boy with no knowledge about wet dreams who comes from a family that has taught him masturbation is sinful; another by a boy whose parents have taught him many facts about pubertal development and seem to be open-minded about adolescent sexuality.

5. Describe your conception of an "ideal" puberty for a boy and for a girl. How does your ideal compare to the reality of your own experiences during puberty?

Chapter 8

CHILDHOOD AND ADOLESCENT SEXUALITY

OVERVIEW

In this chapter, psychosocial and social factors that influence sexual development throughout childhood and adolescence are discussed. Gender identity and gender role are presented as a contrast to Chapter 7's discussion of the biological determinants of sex chromosomes, sex hormones and sexual anatomy. Learning theory, cognitive-developmental theory, biosocial interaction theory, Freud's theories are briefly explained as a precursor to a more complete discussion of childhood and adolescent sexuality and to illustrate the complexity of trying to define the components of childhood and adolescent sexual behavior. Sources of early sexual learning and stimulation are described, as are the different perceptions children of varying ages have of sexual matters. Parental values and attitudes and their impact on a child's own emerging sexuality are explored, as is the topic of childhood sex play, its low rate of recall, and when sexual contact between siblings constitutes mere game-playing and when it might be construed as coercive, dangerous, and incestuous.

The biological changes of adolescence are accompanied by a number of social, psychological and behavioral changes, many of which are discussed here: sexual fantasies, issues of independence, masturbation, petting, intercourse, homosexual experience, unintended teenage pregnancy, decision making regarding birth control. The controversial "squeal rule" is examined in the Personal Perspective box and there is discussion of the "unhappy nonvirgins" who now constitute approximately 30 % of adolescents who have had coital experience. Boxed Items include discussions of controversies about sex education in general, and practical pointers about how parents can educate their children about sex.

While reading the chapter, the student is asked to consider these issues:

1.   How does gender identity differ from gender role?

2.   Why is it useful to study the various theories of psychosexual development? Which seem to be most reliable, and which seem outdated?

3.   How does childhood sexuality develop from birth on? What are some highlights that almost all children experience? What are some of the most common parental reactions? How do parents contribute to a child's sexual development?

4.   How can you define childhood sex-play? When might it cease

being play and start being coercive or incestuous? What steps should parents take to guard against the sexual exploitation of one child by another?

5. How does adolescent sexuality differ from childhood sexuality? What are some highlights that almost all teens experience? What are some of the most common parental reactions? What impact could the "squeal rule" have on adolescent sexual behavior, and on communication about sexual matters between parents and teens?

6. What are some of the reasons for the rash of unintended teenage pregnancies? What are some typical adolescent attitudes towards contraception?

7. Can we assume that all sexually active teens are satisfied with their sexual experiences? Who are the "unhappy nonvirgins" and what is their problem?

8. What are some controversies about sex education? How can parents be effective sex educators?

LEARNING OBJECTIVES

At the conclusion of this chapter, the student should be able to:

1. Differentiate between gender identity and gender role.

2. Identify at least three theoretical viewpoints about gender development and describe each.

3. Describe the typical patterns of sexuality during each of the following developmental periods: infancy, early childhood, school age, and adolescence.

4. Describe the role of parents and significant others in the development of childhood and adolescent sexuality.

5. Explain some reasons for and consequences of unintended teenage pregnancy, and the ways many teens feel about their sexual experiences.

6. Explain the controversy inherent in the "squeal rule."

7. Explain some of the controversies inherent in sex education, and some ways in which parents can learn to be effective sex educators.

TEACHING STRATEGIES

An extremely important and beneficial role of the instructor is to influence the ways students think about and organize the information they learn. In a course such as this, the tendency of students and professors alike may be to split issues into concrete, distinct categories such as nature and nurture as indicated in questions like, "Is homosexuality biologically or environmentally mediated?" or "Are sex differences learned or inherent?" Clarification is advisable to avoid such either-or pronouncements. The instructor can focus on the "biological interactionist" approach to help students broaden their thinking about the development of sexual behavior, regardless of whether that behavior is typical or atypical. A useful concept in the biosocial context is "threshold." The threshold for the acquisition and expression of various sex-different behaviors may be influenced by various genetic or biochemical factors. A convenient analogy for this is a person's native language, as John Money has pointed out. An intact temporal lobe of the brain is essential for the acquisition of language, but in no way does it dictate which language is to be spoken. Interaction with other people is critical in determining the spoken language. Similarly, gender scripts are postnatally assimilated.

The discussion of childhood sexuality is comprehensive, including discussions of bonding with a parental figure and of genital rehearsals. Bonding begins in early development with the experience of the tactile senses and a need for close contact with the caretaker. Students may need clarification of how this bonding relates to sexuality. One theory is that attachment to and eventual separation from a parent (or surrogate parent) are stages that most mammals, including humans, require. Interference with such development may affect the capacity of the animal or human to bond during adulthood. Discussion of the findings of Harlow, whose rhesus monkeys were deprived of early tactile stimulation, or research by Spitz or Bowlby on early deprivation can provide a sociobiologic approach to the development of human affectional systems. Though such data remain speculative, they are rich in clinical implications that can help students understand and cope with difficulties they may themselves be experiencing in establishing adult pair-bonds.

It is important to discuss the practical implications of the information on childhood genital rehearsals. How would students advise parents to respond to a two year old who masturbated several times a week? Or to a four year old asking how sperm get into a vagina? Or to six-year-old boys playing doctor? Or to one sibling forcing another to play "show me yours and I'll show you mine"? Students can be made aware of their own biases through such discussions.

Adolescent sexuality can be a separate discussion topic. Students rarely consider all the potential stresses, "steps," "passages" and "crises" that adolescents typically face and the ways in which they involve sexuality. A useful exercise is to have students list the stresses related to sexuality for teenage males, females, and couples. In order to keep the discussion from becoming too personal, the instructor may want to use examples from fiction or biography (for example, Holden Caulfield in Catcher in the Rye or the terror Havelock Ellis experienced regarding wet dreams). The instructor has the potential to prevent the emotional stress of many students by providing the "anticipatory guidance" or "emotional innoculation" that accurate information imparts. Therefore, another useful exercise is to ask students to construct such a prevention program. What would they include, and how could such a program be evaluated?

Unintended teenage pregnancy, birth control choices, and the controversy over the "squeal rule" and sex education in general can be very volatile topics since they tend to hit so close to home for many of the students taking a course on human sexuality. We suggest a neutral stance for the instructor, and if necessary, the option of a debate if feelings in a class run to extremes. Students must be made aware of the importance of the decisions they make about their sexual behavior, the impact such decisions have on their own lives as well as those of their partners and any potential offspring, and how communication between people is critical in assuring that decisions are not haphazard but truly informed. If the class indicates a need to explore the area of communication with parents, role playing uncomfortable situations can be a helpful springboard.

STUDENT PROJECTS

1. Interview any adult with whom you have had a long-standing and comfortable relationship. Discuss who the principal sex educator was in that person's life and contrast their experience with yours. Compare notes on the "squeal rule." In the best of all possible worlds, how would that adult suggest sex education be handled? Contrast this with your ideas on the same subject. How have attitudes about sex education and sex educators changed since the adult was an adolescent? What conclusions can you draw?

2. Interview a child psychiatrist to explore the topic of sexual difficulties of school-age children. To what extent are such problems likely to be harbingers of adult difficulties? How common are they? Are there any cases in which sexual difficulties reflect family dysfunction?

3. Talk with a thirteen year old just starting junior high school and a seventeen or eighteen-year-old junior or senior in high school. What do they each perceive as the major sexual and social hurdles, problems, challenges? What suggestions would the seventeen year old have for the thirteen year old? Finally, how do their perspectives contrast with yours now that you are in a college environment?

4. Interview a lawyer who handles cases of sexual abuse, harrassment and coercion. What is the lawyer's opinion of how cases of childhood sexual coercion should be handled? What is the lawyer's opinion of the "squeal rule"? Is it legally defensible?

PERSONAL REFLECTIONS

1. Think back to your own adolescence and answer the following questions as honestly as you can:
    a. Did your sexual values derive more from parental influence or peer influence? How did you fit into your peer group? Did you experience a "tyranny of values"?
    b. What is your earliest recollection of sexual activity with a partner? Was it with a male or a female? Can you remember how you felt emotionally? Physically? Was it a positive or negative experience?
    c. Did you feel free to discuss sexual matters with either or both of your parents? Do you think you will be comfortable as a parent discussing sex with your own teenage children? Do you want to be the prime source of their sexual information?

2. Can you remember any of your pre-adolescent sexual rehearsals? If so, what do you recall and do you think your parents knew what was going on? If you cannot recall anything, why do you think this is the case?

3. Who do you think is ultimately responsible for birth control? Have you made any decisions about birth control and what contributed to your decision-making process?

4. You are a legislator responsible for writing into law a doctrine that would assure all adolescents were adequately educated and protected regarding sexual issues. Write the doctrine.

5. Have you ever seen a very young child masturbating? Have you ever viewed the genitals of a very small child? What were your reactions? Why do you think you responded as you did?

CHAPTER 8 TEST QUESTIONS

Multiple Choice (* General Comprehension Questions)

1.* Gender identity refers to
    a. an individual's behavior and communication to others.
    b. an individual's privately experienced feelings of being male or female.
    c. a part of one's psychological development that begins after puberty.
    d. the biology of sexual development.

2.* Throughout childhood and adolescence, sexual development
    a. is only influenced by biologic determinants.
    b. is dormant.
    c. is bisexual.
    d. is influenced by a combination of biological, psychological and social factors.

102

3.* The formation of gender identity
   a. occurs at the moment of conception.
   b. begins with the release of LH and FSH.
   c. occurs early in childhood.
   d. begins at puberty.

4.* Childhood has been called "the last frontier in sex research" for all of the following reasons except
   a. researchers have interviewed more people in the less-populated areas of the U.S. than in heavily populated areas.
   b. communities may accuse researchers of undermining the moral fabric of society.
   c. there is very little reliable data about sexual behavior during childhood.
   d. faulty recall, exaggeration, and omissions are common responses to questionnaires.

5.* The biosocial interaction theory is the most comprehensive way of looking at all phases of sexual development because
   a. sexual development is rigidly controlled by "nature."
   b. sexual development is rigidly controlled by "nurture."
   c. the control of genetic forces are sufficient to overcome the impact of postnatal learning.
   d. biological processes do not unfold in a cultural vacuum, and learning doesn't occur without the biological apparatus of the brain itself.

6. Differential socialization refers to
   a. the different ways blacks and whites have been treated in American society during the past fifty years.
   b. how adolescents behave in the presence of their parents versus how they behave in the presence of their peers.
   c. the way in which parents treat boys and girls from birth on because of different expectations of them.
   d. the critical periods in the overall process of sexual development.

7. The "biosocial interaction theory" of gender development
   a. was proposed by Freud.
   b. says a core gender identity is in place by the age of three.
   c. proposes that sexual development is rigidly controlled by "nature."
   d. proposes that gender development parallels the intellectual development of the child.

8. The "cognitive-developmental theory" of gender development
   a. was developed by John Money.
   b. was developed by Freud.
   c. says castration anxiey is needed to develop mature sexual attitudes.
   d. proposes that children mimic adult behavior not to gain rewards but to achieve self-identity.

103

9. Freud's concept of a period of sexual latency
   a. is accepted as accurate by modern sexologists.
   b. refers to the active sex drive of a human being.
   c. refers to a time when one's sexual interests and behaviors are diverted to nonsexual behaviors and interests.
   d. is said to begin before the resolution of the Oedipus complex.

10. Sexual play during infancy
    a. does not exist because of an infant's poorly-developed eye-hand coordination.
    b. occurs more frequently in infants raised in nurseries than in infants raised in family environments.
    c. is an abnormal developmental pattern.
    d. is possible since sexual reflexes of vaginal lubrication and erection are in operation within 24 hours after birth.

11. All of the following are accurate about parental reactions to the discovery of sex play except
    a. girls are told not to do it; boys may get mixed messages.
    b. many adult sexual difficulties can be traced to negative parental reactions to sex play.
    c. all societies exhibit parental disapproval of childhood sex play.
    d. parents may encourage children to be aware of their bodies but not their genitals.

12. The six- or seven-year-old child typically
    a. has not yet acquired a clear understanding of basic anatomic differences between the sexes.
    b. loves to "show off" his or her body, loves to run around nude.
    c. participates in sexual experimentation activities such as "hospital" or "house" with children of the same or opposite sex.
    d. pays no attention to parental attitudes and practices regarding nudity in the home.

13. Homosexual play among children
    a. usually leads to adult homosexuality.
    b. is a normal part of growing up.
    c. should be punished with aversion therapy.
    d. indicates the need for psychological counseling.

14. Austrian sex researcher Ernest Borneman suggests that
    a. adolescence is accompanied by total recall of all childhood sexual experiences.
    b. operant conditioning is the most powerful motivator of childhood sexual behavior.
    c. Bandura's model of social learning is the best explanation of adolescent psychosexual development.
    d. puberty is characteristically accompanied by amnesia -- blocked memories -- of prior sexual experiences.

15. Parents can minimize the risk of incest victimization between siblings by all of the following except
    a. discourage siblings who are more than two years apart from bathing together.
    b. avoid having an older sibling share a bedroom with one who is much younger.
    c. encourage open sexual experimentation so that the children won't be tantalized by the "forbidden."
    d. obtain psychological counseling if a coercive situation seems to be developing.

16. During adolescence
    a. sexual fantasies and dreams become much less frequent.
    b. premarital sex is usually encouraged by parents.
    c. some teens see sex as a way of proving their ability to make independent decisions.
    d. more girls than boys masturbate to orgasm.

17. According to recent research data, the age of first sexual intercourse has
    a. increased for girls during the past few decades.
    b. shown less change over time for adolescent males than females.
    c. a direct correlation with teenage promiscuity.
    d. shown black teenage males tend to be less sexually active at a specific age than white teenage males.

18. Recent studies about homosexual experience during adolescence indicate
    a. transient patterns of homosexual activity translate into "being homosexual."
    b. 60 % of teenage girls studied had at least one same-sex encounter.
    c. a moderate decline in adolescent homosexual experience.
    d. teenagers who are homosexual have few problems when deciding to "come out."

19. All of the following are true about "unhappy nonvirgins" except
    a. an estimated 30% of adolescents who have had coital experience are included in this group.
    b. these are teens who had unrealistically high expectations about what sex "should" be.
    c. many revert to abstinence as a means of coping.
    d. such teens rarely experience sexual dysfunction.

20. All of the following are true about unintended teenage pregnancy except
    a. one adolescent pregnancy begins every 35 seconds.
    b. there are few health risks associated with teenage pregnancy.
    c. America's teenage birth rate is 17 times higher than Japan's.
    d. 30,000 pregnancies occur annually among girls under 15 years of age.

105

21. All of the following are documented consequences of unintended teenage pregnancy except
   a. teenage mothers are overrepresented in poverty statistics.
   b. babies born to teens are nearly twice as likely to die in infancy than babies born to women in their twenties.
   c. teenage mothers are more likely to vigorously pursue a higher education.
   d. complications of pregnancy during adolescence include toxemia, hemorrhage, miscarriage.

22. Teenage fathers
   a. tend to stay with and support the girls they impregnate.
   b. stay in school longer than boys who do not father children when teenagers.
   c. work harder and so have higher incomes than their peers who postpone fatherhood.
   d. are considerably less affected by the impact of teenage pregnancy than are the teenage mothers.

23. The effort to reduce the rate of unintended teenage pregnancy can be most positively affected by all of the following except
   a. educating males about contraceptive options at an early age.
   b. exposing teens to sex education courses.
   c. demanding the teens be celibate until they can support themselves economically.
   d. helping teens recognize how birth control practices relate to their own lives.

24. Opposition to sex education in schools
   a. exists in a more vociferous form than ever.
   b. is based on the doctrine of separation of church and state.
   c. is illustrated in the statistic that 95% of parents ban their children from attending such courses.
   d. has been based on the contention that the quality of materials and teaching in public school sex education was uneven to poor.

25. When educating their own children about sex, parents should
   a. lecture.
   b. include discussions about values, emotions, decision-making and biology.
   c. never tell too much at once.
   d. use slang terms for sexual body parts to make the child feel that you're "one of them."

True/False

F 1. Gender role and gender identity describe the same thing.

F 2. Current sex research has proven Freud's theories correct.

T. 3. A person's sexual development is influenced by biological, social, and psychological factors.

F   4.   The "last frontier in sex research" refers to adolescent sexuality.

F   5.   The only function of sexual fantasies during adolescence is to induce orgasm.

F   6.   According to recent statistics, necking and petting are behaviors than teens rarely engage in anymore.

T   7.   B. F. Skinner developed the theory of operant conditioning.

F.   8.   According to Freud, the phallic stage occurs from birth to age three.

T.   9.   Electric shocks might be one form of aversion therapy.

T.   10. 400,000 American teenagers have abortions each year.

F.   11. America's teenage birthrate is the lowest in the western hemisphere.

F   12. A 1981 study of 1,200 teens visiting family planning clinics found that the average time before coming in for birth control was one month.

T   13. Finkelhor's data on sex between siblings found that 73% of the experiences reported occurred when at least one sibling was over age eight.

T   14. Children who attend nursery school or day-care centers before reaching school age are apt to confront many situations with sexual overtones.

T   15. How parents respond to observing a child's sexual reflexes during infancy may be part of the child's earliest sexual learning.

Fill in the Blanks

1.   By the age of (two) years most children have begun to walk, talk, and establish a sense of being a boy or girl.

2.   Teenage (attitudes) toward sex have changed more rapidly than actual behavior.

3.   Freud believed that in the first year of life the mouth is the primary focus of sexual energy and gratification. He called this time the (oral stage).

4.   A fantasy wish of a boy to possess his mother sexually was called the (Oedipus complex) by Freud.

5. Solitary sexual behavior is usually called (masturbation).

6. "Physical contacts between females and males in an attempt to produce erotic arousal without intercourse" is how Kinsey defined (petting).

7. A sexual experience with someone of the same sex is called (homosexual).

8. In Pavlov's experiment with dogs, the musical sound produced salivation, a (conditioned response), even if food wasn't present.

9. (Social learning) theory says people model their behavior according to their observations of the behavior of others.

10. The biosocial viewpoint stresses there are certain (critical) periods in the overall process of sexual development.

11. A conflict between positive and negative consequences in a given situation is called a(n) (approach-avoidance) conflict.

12. A child who is deprived of warm, close (bonding) during infancy may experience later difficulties forming intimate relationships.

13. A typical four year old's notions about sex may be described as (vague, magical).

14. A recent study of over 800 children in Australia, North America, Britain, and Sweden found no evidence of a phase of development where sexual interest is suspended, thus refuting Freud's (latency period) theory.

15. According to Finkelhor's study, the commonest type of sexual activity between siblings was (genital touching).

Discussion/Essay Questions

1. You are a pediatrician who has just received a phone call from a distraught mother who has discovered her six-year-old daughter playing doctor with a six-year-old boy from the neighborhood. What kinds of advice and information will you be giving her during your phone conversation?

2. Adolescents are subjected to a variety of different pressures for and against becoming sexually active. Describe these various influences and indicate which you feel are the most powerful and why.

3. Discuss what factors in our society have contributed to the push for passage of a "squeal rule." What alternatives might exist that could accomplish the same kind of communication without the inherent negative stigma of the "squeal rule"?

Write a proposal for that alternative.

4. Write out a curriculum proposal for a sex education course spanning grades one through twelve that includes parent involvement. Make sure to include a unit on sexual coercion and a rationale for each topic you include. Pretend you will have to defend this proposal before your local school board.

Chapter 9

ADULT SEXUALITY

OVERVIEW

Adult sexuality is discussed from a developmental perspective utilizing the notion that adulthood is a time of transition (just as childhood and adolescence are times of biological, psychosocial, and psychological changes). Similarities and differences between early, middle, and late adulthood are explored with emphasis on issues that tend to complicate this broad phase of human sexual response such as cohabitation, marriage, divorce, the disappearance of the double-standard regarding premarital sexual experience, midlife crises, menopause, male climacteric, ageism and other cultural stereotypes that impact on the elderly. This chapter is a logical extension of the material covered in chapters 7 and 8.

While reading the chapter, the student is asked to consider these issues:

1. How do the various stages of adult sexuality compare and what are the major psychosocial and psychological choices inherent in each?

2. How do cultural stereotypes, bias, ageism affect adult sexual behavior? What can we do to prevent or ease the negative effects of such things?

3. Why is the notion that being young and single automatically leads to sexual happiness not necessarily true?

4. What does the increase in the number of cohabiting couples tell us about modern sexual behavior?

5. What is the status of divorce today, and what is its impact on the people who experience it?

6. What are some of the problems of mid-life crises, in addition to the empty-nest syndrome and sexual burnout?

7. How do the problems of heterosexual and homosexual men and women compare during mid-adulthood?

8. What are the biological, psychological aspects of menopause?

9. How do male and female aging compare, and how is sexual response affected?

110

LEARNING OBJECTIVES

At the conclusion of this chapter, the student should be able to:

1. Describe the typical patterns of sexuality during the following developmental periods:
   a. early adulthood (ages 20-39)
   b. middle adulthood (ages 40-59)
   c. late adulthood (ages 60+)

2. Define cohabitation, mid-life crisis, menopause, male climacteric, empty-nest syndrome, sexual burnout and explain why each is significant in the context of a particular period of adult sexuality.

3. Describe some of the ways in which marriage can complicate sexual relationships.

4. Describe some of the ways in which divorce can be positive and negative.

5. Explain the biological changes during menopause and their potential effects on sexual functioning.

6. Explain the biological changes during late adulthood and their potential effects on sexual functioning.

7. Explain how elderly people can adapt their sexual behavior to the physical changes of aging.

8. Discuss the psychosocial considerations of male and female aging.

TEACHING STRATEGIES

It is important for the instructor to stress the developmental perspective when discussing adult sexuality. If the bulk of a class is youthful, it is likely that they will have difficulty seeing sexuality in terms of a long-term, continually evolving process. Younger students are just as prone to have anti-aging biases as older adults are to harbor biased attitudes towards adolescents and young adults. Therefore, to guard against blind spots inhibiting the students from accurately assimilating the material, instructors might use the "passages" approach. For example, students seldom anticipate that after years of marriage, partners may seem less sexually attractive to one another. Having students consider some of the ways boredom could be constructively or destructively handled in the context of a long-standing marriage (since this is probably the major sexual difficulty experienced by couples during adulthood) could be a useful starting point. This might be followed by asking what other passages related to adult sexuality the class could anticipate? Ultimately, the goal is to have each student appreciate

111

the fact that each stage of adulthood involves its own pressures, crises, and satisfactions.

Mid-life crisis is a very important topic for the sexuality class. It is not infrequent that adults go through periods which may include affairs, disillusionment with marriage, loss of sexual desire for their partner, desire for sex with numerous partners, and so on. Once again, using the anticipatory guidance approach, the instructor migh ask, "How common are such experiences? How long do they last? What are constructive and destructive ways of coping?" Many of the parents of students may be struggling with these kinds of issues, so it is important that the instructor be sensitive to the feelings of the students whose families may be in states of dysfunction.

Geriatric sexuality is an area replete with misconceptions, and a breeding ground for sexual difficulties. Have the students devise ways to prevent these difficulties. For example, could Madison Avenue techniques be used to change attitudes about the "dirty old man"? What information might students share with their parents about sex after fifty? In discussing this topic -- which can be tricky since students may find it so hard to relate to -- emphasize the fact that the elderly are stigmatized in many ways in our society, and that the common stereotypes about aging contribute to the sense of "depersonalization" many older adults seem to feel.

It can be very exciting for students to meet older adults who have marriages that are vibrant and vital. If the instructor can arrange for such a couple to come and talk with students, it can be a growth-enhancing experience for all concerned.

STUDENT PROJECTS

1. Visit a nursing home for the elderly and obtain permission to speak with some of the men and women about their daily routines, their sources of entertainment, and so on. What conclusions can you draw about the possibility for sexual encounters and privacy? What changes would you suggest? How did you feel when you left?

2. Interview a divorce lawyer to elicit a profile of the "typical" divorced adult of the eighties. Are sexual issues usually prominent in the decisions to divorce? Is there such a thing as a "typical" divorce case?

3. Interview some young adults who frequent singles bars. What can you learn about sexual behavior among the younger, non-married adults?

4. Speak with three couples in various stages of adulthood who have been together, either married or cohabiting, for more than one year. Compare and contrast their experiences, their perceptions of how sexual behavior fits into their lives.

5. Interview a sex therapist or marriage counselor to discuss the ways in which a midlife crisis can affect a person's sexuality.

PERSONAL REFLECTIONS

1. Thinking about your own parents' or grandparents' marriages, are you able to see any evidence of mid-life crises or problems associated with later adulthood? Do you think these relatives would ever be comfortable discussing such things with you? Do you think it is any of your business? Have you been affected in any way?

2. What are the things you personally are looking forward to in terms of each stage of adult sexuality? Knowing what you do now, do you think you will be able to avoid falling into the traps of negative self-fulfilling prophecies?

3. When you are in mid-life or later adulthood, what things do you hope to be able to tell your own children about yourself and how the sexual part of your personality was integrated into other aspects of your life? Or do you think such discussion might be better left unsaid? Would you classify yourself as a seeker, a traditionalist, or an experimenter? Why?

CHAPTER 9 TEST QUESTIONS

Multiple Choice (* General Comprehension Questions)

1.* The phase of adult sexuality
   a. spans ages twenty through menopause or male climacteric.
   b. is marked by rigid, unchanging sexual behavior patterns.
   c. is a time of transition and development.
   d. is the most trouble-free time of adult life.

2.* Adulthood is a series of passages through fairly predictable crises contributing to one's growth according to
   a. Erik Erikson.
   b. Carl Jung.
   c. Daniel Levinson.
   d. Gail Sheehy.

3.* All of the following describe common patterns of sexual behavior during young adulthood except
   a. the experimenter.
   b. the cohabitants.
   c. the seeker.
   d. the traditionalist.

4.* Cohabitation
   a. is only found among married couples.
   b. is on the decline in today's sexual behavior patterns.
   c. is being institutionalized as part of the family system.
   d. is usually the last stage of marriage prior to divorce.

5.* Aging
   a. by itself is responsible for diminished sexual interest.

b. has no impact on biological or pscyhological aspects of human sexuality.
c. can alter, but not necessarily obliterate, human sexual function.
d. dictates when a person must stop having sexual relations.

6. Both aging adults and young adults often have a major problem with
a. lack of privacy for sex.
b. sexual burnout.
c. lubrication and/or erection.
d. casual sex.

7. The backlash against the "anything goes" attitude of the sexual revolution of the 1960's and 1970's is shown in all of the following except
a. having sex with a large number of partners being frowned upon.
b. increasing disillusionment with casual sex and one-night stands.
c. complaints of overwhelming sexual urges dominating a person's life.
d. increased awareness of the possibility of exposure to a sexually transmitted disease.

8. All of the following are true statements about sexual freedom except
a. sexual freedom can lead to disappointment.
b. sexual freedom is unequivocably positive.
c. sexual freedom can lead to pressure and conflict.
d. sexual freedom can lead to satisfaction.

9. During young adult married life
a. there is no way to balance one's sexual needs and one's other needs and responsibilities.
b sex is likely to become much more exciting and gratifying.
c. the frequency of sexual activity generally declines.
d. the fear of contracting AIDS is greatest.

10. According to Blumstein and Schwartz, all of the following are true about cohabitants except
a. their sex lives suffered if there were problems in nonsexual areas of their lives.
b. women usually initiate sex more often than their married counterparts.
c. only about one-third of cohabitants have sex with people outside of their relationship.
d. the longer they stayed together, the frequency of their sexual relations declined.

11. If the mean frequency of intercourse is 14.8 per month, the couple is most likely in what year of marriage?
a. 5
b. 1

c.   25
d.   10

12. The majority of divorces involve spouses who
     a.   are in early adulthood.
     b.   have not yet reached middle age.
     c.   have experienced menopause or male climacteric.
     d.   are physically abusive to one another.

13. Some of the difficulties divorced people face include all of
     the following except
     a.   delight with a new-found sexual freedom.
     b.   self-consciousness about sex with a veritable stranger.
     c.   concerns about adequacy of one's sexual performance.
     d.   lack of ease with rituals of dating.

14. During second marriages, it is usually the case that
     a.   people learn from prior mistakes.
     b.   sexual problems dissipate if they had existed in the prior
          marriage.
     c.   the problems tend to be much less complicated than those
          encountered in first marriages.
     d.   many of the same problems that plagued a first marriage
          reappear in a second one.

15. A midlife crisis
     a.   is usually a brief, easily handled single episode.
     b.   often coincides with the menopausal years and is thus
          particularly trying for some women.
     c.   rarely involves sexual issues.
     d.   only involves sexual issues.

16. When children leave home, the end result for a marriage is
     often
     a.   negative as the wife loses interest in the husband,
          focusing instead on getting those children situated.
     b.   an empty-nest situation that affects the mother but not
          the father.
     c.   an empty-nest syndrome that affects the father but not the
          mother.
     d.   positive if it gives the couple a chance to focus on their
          own interactions and creates opportunities for freer, more
          relaxed sex.

17. Sexual burnout
     a.   is the same as occupational burnout.
     b.   is a malady only of the very young adults sowing their
          "sexual wild oats."
     c.   stems from tedium and satiation with the same sexual
          routines.
     d.   is the same as the sexual disinterest that accompanies
          depression.

18. The 1982 study by Rubin found that women in mid-life

115

a. experience major problems with their sexuality.
b. participate in sex primarily to please their partners.
c. are better able to relate sex to their own wishes and needs, and take the sexual initiative more often than before.
d. enjoy putting a great deal of sexual pressure on their husbands to "get back at them" for the reverse situation earlier in their marriages.

19. During menopause
a. symptoms are universal -- all women experience the same things.
b. most women seek treatment for symptom relief.
c. E.R.T. is the most common symptom.
d. hot flashes are the most common symptom and usually disappear spontaneously.

20. Osteoporosis
a. is the major symptom of the male climacteric.
b. is due to the thinning of the vaginal walls.
c. can be treated in part by estrogen replacement therapy.
d. is the thinning of the breasts and vulva during menopause.

21. The years following the menopause
a. are marked by an increased rate of depression or major psychiatric disorders.
b. are influenced by a multitude of environmental and personality factors.
c. are the most sexually barren of a woman's life.
d. are marked by complete loss of vaginal sensation.

22. The normal pattern of reproductive aging in men
a. mirrors that of women almost exactly.
b. rarely involves a drop in sex hormone levels.
c. does not start until the male climacteric begins.
d. has the effect of making erections last longer than in younger adulthood.

23. Ageism refers to all of the following except
a. cultural negativism toward geriatric sex and romance.
b. stereotypical opinions that older people are old-fashioned in morality.
c. the feeling that younger gays take advantage of older homosexuals.
d. the gray panther movement.

24. Studies of sexual behavior in late adulthood have found that
a. patterns of sexual activity become very unstable.
b. male's declining interest seems to be the major limiting factor to continued sexual activity.
c. there is little or no correlation between the quality of sexual activity in early and late adulthood.
d. the relationship between the partners at the time of menopause and/or male climacteric is the major determinant

116

of their sexual behavior in later years.

25. Sexual activity in older adults
    a. is almost universally confined to coital behavior.
    b. rarely includes oral stimulation.
    c. is likely to include masturbation if the person masturbated when younger.
    d. is impossible if the male cannot obtain or maintain an erection.

True/False

F   1. The "traditionalist" describes a person who judges sexual experiences in terms of frequency, performance proficiency, and variety.

T   2. The percentage of female college students having premarital intercourse has increased from about 30% in 1965 to about 65% in 1980.

F   3. Commercialization of sex has helped the modern young adult develop realistic expectations of what sex should be.

T   4. It is not clear how frequently sexual dissatisfaction is a primary cause of divorce.

T   5. One study has found that lack of sexual desire was more prevalent among divorced men than among those who were married.

F   6. Divorced people who remarry have an increased sense of well-being compared to those who remain single.

T   7. In many cases, divorce is the soundest option available to a couple.

T   8. From a sexual perspective, the male is particularly vulnerable to the midlife crisis.

T   9. During mid-adulthood, many women are just as likely as men to seek out extramarital sexual opportunities.

F   10. People suffering from sexual burnout have symptoms of sleep and appetite disturbance.

T   11. By their late fifties, men tend to begin to show more concern for emotional sensitivity and interpersonal relations.

F   12. It is still quite rare to see a middle-aged woman dating a younger man.

F   13. There has been a sudden upsurge in the divorce rate for people in mid-adulthood.

117

T 14. Lesbians often have an easier time making the transition into mid-adulthood than do homosexual men because lesbians tend to be involved in long-term, one-to-one relationships.

T 15. A reduction in muscular tension in the aging female may in part account for the reduced intensity of orgasm sometimes experienced by elderly females.

Fill in the Blanks

1. The authors of this book maintain that the period of adult sexuality is a time of (transition, development).

2. In young adulthood, the (seeker) is one who strives to find the ideal relationship.

3. The fact that young adults are more sexually active today than in generations past is in part due to the disappearance of the (double-standard).

4. According to many current studies, the prevailing trend in sexual relationships is sex in the context of (caring relationships, long-term commitments, cohabitation).

5. According to U.S. Census Bureau statistics, about (one out of five) couples who marry now will divorce before their fifth anniversary.

6. A woman's midlife crisis is often plagued by the (empty nest) syndrome.

7. It is not until mid-life that many women experience the sexual pleasure of (orgasm) for the first time due to their on-going process of sexual self-discovery.

8. Depression is often accompanied by sexual (disinterest).

9. Rubin's 1982 study found that for mid-life women, the most characteristic pattern was one of (improving) sexuality.

10. Many men in their late fifties and beyond become increasingly interested in sharing tenderness and affection as they become less preoccupied with (career concerns).

11. There is a gradual decline in female fertility from the age of (30) on.

12. Another term for the climacteric is the (perimenopausal years).

13. Malfunctions in the temperature control mechanisms in a woman's hypothalmus are thought to be the cause of (hot flashes).

14. A somewhat controversial, albeit useful, therapy for the symptoms of menopause is (<u>estrogen</u> <u>replacement</u> <u>therapy</u> <u>or</u> <u>E.R.T.</u>).

15. The aging male may experience less intense ejaculations due to a reduction in the amount of (<u>semen</u>).

Discussion/Essay Questions

1. Compare the psychosocial perspective on sexuality of the 21 year old with that of the 65 year old. Do they share anything in common?

2. In what ways might a mid-life crisis affect the sexuality of a 40-year-old man who has been married since college and has just been divorced?

3. What are the things a 21-year-old woman and her 50-year-old menopausal mother might discuss about their sexuality? What might each teach the other?

4. Is it possible for men and women to understand one another's sexuality? How might such communication be facilitated?

5. Develop a program to help adult men and women who have never taken a course in human sexuality (and never will do so) become more finely attuned to their own sexual needs and desires.

Chapter 10

GENDER ROLES

OVERVIEW

The developmental theme of the preceding chapters is continued here with an in-depth look at patterns of gender role socialization. Students are introduced to the concepts of gender role stereotyping and ways of defining masculinity and femininity. This serves as a point of departure for an examination of influences on gender role socialization from prenatal attribution to factors operating in infancy, early childhood, the elementary school years, adolescence, and adulthood. Once the survey of "traditional" gender role socialization is complete, the focus shifts to the concept of androgyny and then to a discussion of the psychology of sex differences. The gender-related dilemmas of transsexuals are discussed, and the chapter concludes with an exploration of the interaction between gender roles and sexual behavior, including a perceptive and important discussion of the meaning of sexual equality.

While reading the chapter, the student is asked to consider these issues:

1. How can common stereotypes about masculine and feminine sexuality affect behavior?

2. How is gender role often socialized in our culture during birth and infancy, early childhood, elementary school years, and adolescence?

3. How are gender roles enacted during the adult years in marriage, in business, in family life?

4. What is androgyny and what are some of the controversies about it?

5. What are the psychological and physical components of both male and female transsexualism?

6. How is it possible to raise a male and a female child in a nonsexist environment?

LEARNING OBJECTIVES

At the conclusion of this chapter, the student should be able to:

1. List the traits that are most often used to characterize the typical man and woman in our culture, and discuss the potential harm that such stereotypes can inflict.

2. Identify the major patterns of gender role socialization at each developmental level.

3. Define androgyny, and describe the reasons that there is no firm agreement among researchers about what constitutes an androgynous person.

4. Discuss the determination of psychological differences that exist between the sexes, and explain the use of an alternative (i.e., "brain-based") approach to investigate differences between the sexes.

5. Describe how gender role expectation in adult life affects marriage, work, politics, and play.

6. List the biological and psychological factors that have been suggested as causes of transsexualism.

7. Contrast the gender role expectations between American and Mangaian cultures and analyze their impact on sexual attitudes, behavior, and stereotypes.

8. Describe the double standard as it used to exist in terms of sexual behavior in our society, and the reasons why the authors assert the double standard is changing.

9. Predict some of the expectations for gender role in our society two decades from now.

10. Describe some of the ways that parents can initiate nonsexist child-rearing practices with their own children.

TEACHING STRATEGIES

Gender roles -- everything a person does that reflects his or her perception of self as male or female -- is established from infancy through adulthood by means of interaction with societal messages. Why are behavioral scientists so interested in the development of gender role differences? The fundamental reason is that such differences reveal important information about postnatal factors contributing to individual differences and personality. The text reviews developmental influences on socialization including parents, toys, books, media, peer pressures, school. There is also a comprehensive review of the scientific investigations into the behavioral effects of channeling children into masculine or feminine roles.

Even in today's era of increasing liberation, strict gender role socialization occurs and can be a major factor leading to dysfunctional relationships between previously committed individuals. Pressures to act in a traditionally or stereotypically masculine or feminine manner can inhibit people from pursuing their own interests, from self-actualizing. Thus, such a discussion of gender roles may provide valuable anticipatory guidance for the student. One interesting way in which this material can be taught is by utilizing Erving Goffman's Gender Advertisements (New York: Harper Colophon Books, 1979). His insightful analysis of how contemporary American gender roles are portrayed in the "small-scale spatial metaphors" of ordinary magazine advertisements can help students to quickly and accurately grasp the ubiquitous nature of gender role stereotypes. The instructor can ask students to consider how repeated exposure to such "programming" about gender roles reinforces and perpetuates the stereotypes.

The topic of androgyny is a particularly interesting one, especially to students who are living in a world in which many of the old stereotypes -- the macho, insensitive, aggressive man and the emotional, dependent, unassertive woman -- are slowly dissolving. Encourage the students to define permissible niches of androgynous behavior since it is very likely that many of the individuals in your classes are attempting to define for themselves a comfortable balance of masculine and feminine traits. Ask questions such as, "If a woman takes charge during a time of major crisis, will the man in her life be threatened?"; "If a man breaks down and cries, will the woman lose respect?"; "Does a man feel threatened when a date beats him at a competitive sport?" "What would happen to a relationship if the woman earned considerably more than her partner and held a more prestigious position?" Discussions of this sort encourage students to explore their deepest beliefs, values, and attitudes and may help them to learn things about themselves that they didn't realize existed.

Another aspect of androgynous behavior relates to the care-taking of infants and division of household responsibilities. Even though most male college students say they plan to share such responsibilities on a 50/50 basis, the fact is that few men actually do. Society makes such equal sharing even more difficult since it is rare that men take time from their careers to engage in child rearing. This aspect of the double standard still stands. Therefore, the discrepancy between attitudes and behaviors can cause distress and be a very real impediment to the development of an optimal interaction between any one man and woman. Ask the students to search for examples of this from their own experiences. You might provide the scenario of the couple who decides to move to another locale in order to further the man's career. In so doing, the woman's own career suffers but she decides it is okay since she will devote her time to caring for their young child (a socially acceptable alternative). However, she develops major feelings of resentment and anger about these enforced "choices" and blames her husband for causing her to miss out on her own opportunities. He then develops strong feelings of guilt about this. Have the students try to determine who is at fault in such a situation. The husband? The wife? Society? No one? Getting students to understand the uselessness of blame, and that for every person who is "done to," there is a person who has allowed someone to do something to him or her, can be a valuable lesson and can be a

122

powerful exhibit of why gender role stereotypes are so hard to cope with.

Try to take the classroom discussion beyond the point of bemoaning current conventions by examining potential alternatives. You might ask the class to help you compile a list of a dozen parental behavior patterns that contribute to gender role stereotyping and then have them propose several options for each trait that would build flexibility into the way a child could be brought up. Remember, however, that some students may feel strongly opposed to changes in gender roles, and they will need to be protected from feeling unduly threatened by such a discussion. The instructor can accomplish this by explaining that these processes may be viewed as styles and choices that don't have to be followed rigidly or even consistently. Emphasize that there are no single right or wrong answers to the question, "How should I bring up my child?"

Transsexualism is a fascinating area of discussion that can be elaborated upon in class. The instructor can discuss various theories and data presented initially in the text regarding the development of gender roles and apply this to the relatively unusual condition of transsexualism. For example, there are data suggesting that the hypothalamic-pituitary responsiveness of some transsexuals is more similar to the sex opposite to their genetic sex. Other transsexuals have common pathologic features in their childhood development. Once again, it is difficult to ascertain the relative influences of nature and nurture, but empirically it is essential for a full understanding of gender development. The instructor should be alert to students who might wish to label transsexuals as "freaks," and should try to help students develop an understanding of the transsexual as a human being with special, difficult problems. Help students learn to avoid the tendency to negatively label people with such unusual conditions.

STUDENT PROJECTS

1. Visit a local day-care center or a nursery school. Observe the children at play for an hour, noting how frequently they engage in gender stereotyped play and nonstereotyped play. See if you can interview the parents of the child who shows the most stereotyped behavior, and the parents of the child who seems most nonstereotyped. What differences, if any, can you find in the way they have brought up their children?

2. Perform a content analysis of the portrayal of gender role stereotypes on Saturday morning children's television. Tabulate programs and commercials separately in terms of content. On the basis of your findings, what conclusions can you draw about the impact of such messages on gender role behavior on young boys and girls?

3. Do the same analysis asked of you in question 2, above, but instead watch the same number of hours of M.T.V. on cable television. What conclusions can you draw about gender role

stereotypes presented to the teenage audience by this network and their major sponsors?

4. Examine several types of popular magazines geared to the adult audience. Try to obtain a wide range -- "Field and Stream," "Vogue," "Women's Day," "Ebony," "Playboy," and so on. How do such magazines perpetuate gender role stereotypes, in what ways, and what percentage of their ads do so? Do you think such ads impact on adult gender role stereotyping?

PERSONAL REFLECTIONS

1. How were your parents' lives influenced by gender role stereotypes? Do you think they were aware of them? Did they fight them or give in to them? Given the seeming acceptance of androgyny today, do you see your parents' behaviors changing in this direction?

2. Do you know anyone you consider to be androgynous? What sort of life does that person lead? Is there any problem with conformity to sex-linked stereotypes?

3. How would you react if you found out that a good friend of yours was a transsexual and had undergone surgery two years before you met?

4. In the best of all possible worlds, should there be gender role equality and sexual equality between males and females?

CHAPTER 10 TEST QUESTIONS

Multiple Choice (* General Comprehension Questions)

1.* Stereotypes about sexuality are
   a. based on solid evidence and critical judgment.
   b. useful since they create concise definitions of "masculinity" and "femininity."
   c. now giving way to more dynamic scientific views.
   d. accurate approximately 95% of the time.

2.* "Masculinity" and "femininity" refer to all of the following except
   a. the degree to which a person's behavior and/or appearance match cultural expectations about such things.
   b. traits measured by psychological tests.
   c. separate characteristics that coexist to some degree in every individual.
   d. lists of characteristics that accurately describe one's personality, sexual preferences, lifestyle.

3.* Gender differences in socializing children occur
   a. because girls' higher metabolic rates of activity prepare

124

them for more verbal activities.
   b. because most parents intentionally and consciously behave
      differently depending on the child's sex.
   c. for reasons that are not fully understood at present.
   d. because infant boys are talked to and looked at more than
      girls and this continues as the children grow.

4.* All of the following have been found to be important sources
    for children to learn gender roles except
   a. picture books.
   b. watching male and female animals at play.
   c. television.
   d. games and toys.

5.* Adhering to gender appropriate roles is
   a. most important during preschool years when children are
      first learning gender differences.
   b. most important during elementary years when children
      choose like-sexed playmates.
   c. more important during adolescence when what was earlier
      seen as play is now perceived as the real thing.
   d. not possible at all unless a child has two parents as role
      models.

6. An adolescent boy may be expected to follow all of the
   following roles in relation to gender roles except
   a. learn household management skills.
   b. become interested in girls and sex.
   c. succeed at athletics.
   d. not show signs of "feminine" interests or traits.

7. The adolescent boy mentioned in question 6 may not behave
   according to such stereotypes. This is most likely because
   a. he grew up in an orphanage.
   b. he is transsexual.
   c. he is homosexual.
   d. his family has a more progressive attitude to gender roles
      and how children should be socialized.

8. All of the following are true of many adolescent females except
   a. they become underachievers or hide their intelligence in
      school.
   b. they experience a fear of social rejection and loss of
      femininity if too successful.
   c. they never experience ambivalence about the relationship
      between femininity and sexuality.
   d. they are often pressured into opting for marriage and
      motherhood in lieu of higher education and career.

9. Recently, it has been suggested that the different prenatal
   hormone exposures of males and females may possibly account for
   a. behavioral differences in infancy.
   b. the desire for transsexual surgery.
   c. a person's predisposition to become a cross-dresser.

d.   pheromones that trigger sex-stereotyped responses in parents to the infants.

10. A proponent of the nonsexist childrearing approach is
    a.   Freud.
    b.   Heimlich.
    c.   Pogrebin.
    d.   Jung.

11. The toddler's understanding of gender roles
    a.   is nonexistent.
    b.   is minimal.
    c.   is complete.
    d.   is greater than his or her ability to verbally express it.

12. According to recent data reported by Collins in 1984, parents of boys are likely to become concerned if their sons
    a.   play with war toys.
    b.   play with frilly, "feminine" dolls.
    c.   play with "E.T." dolls.
    d.   play with girls.

13. Research by McGhee and Frueh led to the conclusion that
    a.   kids who watched more than 25 hours of television per week had more stereotyped gender role perceptions than those who watched less than 10 hours per week.
    b.   television watching had no impact on gender role perceptions; the peer culture was the prime influence.
    c.   if parents interfered with a child's television watching habits, the impact of the gender role stereotyping was dramatically increased.
    d.   kids who watched less than ten hours per week had more stereotyped gender role perceptions than those who watched 25 or more hours per week.

14. Our culture's gender role stereotypes usually come into full bloom during
    a.   early childhood.
    b.   late childhood.
    c.   adolescence.
    d.   adulthood.

15. All of the following are indications that changes regarding sex role stereotypes are occuring except
    a.   men are willingly participating in ordinary household tasks.
    b.   dual-career families are becoming more common.
    c.   men are refusing to take responsibility for family planning decisions.
    d.   men may agree to be househusbands so their wives can pursue outside careers.

16. Nonsexist childrearing is more possible if
    a.   parents ignore their childrens' school experiences.

b. parents do not allow their children to watch any television at all.
c. both parents share equally in basic childcare and recreational activities.
d. discipline is verbal only and never physical.

17. Androgyny is best defined as
    a. the presence of stereotypical feminine and masculine characteristics in one person.
    b. the presence of feminine and masculine reproductive organs in one person.
    c. the presence of stereotypical feminine characteristics in homosexual males.
    d. the absence of stereotypical male characteristics in heterosexual males.

18. An indication that sexism is widespread in our society is
    a. the number of lesbian couples that exist in major cities.
    b. the number of women subjected to sexual harassment on the job.
    c. the number of people who choose transsexual surgery to "escape" the pressures of sexism.
    d. the increasing number of transvestites in our society.

19. Becoming androgynous implies
    a. losing the qualities associated with one's gender.
    b. taking on the qualities associated with the opposite sex.
    c. developing the opposite-sex qualities that already exist within us and manifesting them in ways determined by our own-sex qualities.
    d. developing the opposite-sex qualities that already exist within us and manifesting them in ways determined by culturally acceptable opposite-sex qualities.

20. Recent studies of androgyny found that
    a. it helps a person to be more versatile.
    b. it helps a person to be more adaptable.
    c. it is associated with more personal satisfaction and less work stress.
    d. androgynous females may have fewer psychological problems than masculine- or feminine-stereotyped people.

21. Transsexual individuals may experience all of the following except
    a. a sense of incongruity between their anatomical sex and their gender identity.
    b. a feeling of being trapped inside the wrong body.
    c. a sense of being out-of-phase with one's sexual anatomy.
    d. a desire to cross-dress as the primary means of obtaining sexual arousal.

22. Ideally, the transsexual who wishes to undergo surgical sex re-assignment must do all of the following except
    a. live in a cross-gender role for one to two years prior to

final surgery.
b. take no additional hormones or medication of any kind.
c. choose a new name to match the gender conversion.
d. be evaluated periodically by a pscyhiatrist or a psychologist.

23. "Sex and equality" is a concept which asserts that
    a. sex is something a man does for a woman.
    b. emotional needs are best viewed as "masculine" and "feminine."
    c. the relationship between the sexes is best expressed as "two on a seesaw."
    d. a person can't be sexually emancipated without first becoming personally emancipated.

24. The sexual double standard describes
    a. the behavior of sexually liberated women only.
    b. a situation in which the man is expected to set limits in sexual interaction.
    c. a situation in which the female is expected to be the sexual expert.
    d. a gender stereotype slowly being replaced by concepts of equality and mutual interaction.

25. Sexual emancipation requires
    a. power as its pivotal motivator.
    b. passive acceptance of one partner by the other.
    c. willingness to negotiate a solution if the partners' sexual needs conflict at times.
    d. a focus on individual needs, not a focus on partnership.

True/False

T 1. Sex discrimination will not disappear overnight.

T 2. If a person's behavior matches cultural expectations, social equilibrium tends to be preserved.

F 3. In most societies, female children are preferred over males.

T 4. Christine Jorgenson is a transsexual.

T 5. Due to biological factors, it is possible that boys may actually be prepared for earlier independence than girls.

F 6. Girls are more social than boys.

F 7. Androgynous college students are more likely to be gay than those who behave according to more rigid gender role stereotypes.

F 8. It is easier to perform female to male transsexual conversion surgery than male to female.

128

T   9.   It is possible, though challenging, to raise a child in a nonsexist atmosphere.

T   10.   The "double standard" can create a number of sexual problems.

T   11.   In Mangaia, the cultural message is that sexual pleasure is for everyone.

F   12.   Androgyny is totally positive.

T   13.   Married women have higher rates of mental and physical problems than single women.

F   14.   Gender roles are entirely shaped during childhood and adolescence.

T   15.   Gender role distinctions are gradually blurring in today's society.

Fill in the Blanks

1.   If a person's behavior (conforms) to a culturally established norm, the person is said to be healthy or well adjusted.

2.   Behavioral scientists now view masculinity and femininity as separate characteristics that (coexist) to some degree in each person.

3.   (Differential socialization) seems to occur even in parents who consciously try to avoid gender stereotyping.

4.   During the elementary school years, boys are expected to exhibit masculinity mainly through (sports activities or competitive physical activities).

5.   A teenage boy who shows so-called "feminine" interests may be regarded as a potential (homosexual) if the community he lives in believes in rigid gender roles.

6.   After puberty, girls were often found to become (underachievers) to hide their intelligence.

7.   Studies have shown that high-achieving women have (lower) rates of marriage than other women.

8.   The "double standard" labels a woman who has more than one sex partner as (promiscuous).

9.   During the adult years, (occupational achievement) has become the yardstick of masculinity for middle- and upper- class America.

10. The fact that more women than ever are entering "male" occupations hopefully indicates that (sex discrimination) is on the wane.

11. Jan Morris and Rene Richards are (transsexuals).

12. In Mangaia, girls are expected to learn to be (orgasmic) at a young age.

13. Rather than having a "double standard" regarding sexuality, it might be better to see men and women as (equal participants) in sexual relationships.

14. Studies in the psychology of sex differences show that men and women are (more similar than different).

15. Childrens' chief role models are (their parents).

Discussion/Essay Questions

1. How do parents' attitudes toward their child's sex influence that child's development?

2. How would you empirically establish whether transsexual surgery should be continued or discontinued? How would you assess the effects of the operation?

3. What effects can gender role have on a sexual relationship? Distinguish between gender role stereotypes and expectations and actual behavior.

4. If most people in our society suddenly became androgynous, how would this be likely to change relationships between the sexes?

5. You are on a panel of medical and psychological personnel who are trying to assess whether or not Mr. X should be a candidate for transsexual surgery. Outline every possible question you will want explored and give a rationale for those questions.

6. Outline a program to help adolescents overcome the negative aspects of gender role and sex role stereotypes. What are your ultimate goals of the program? What would be the long-range effects? How might society be changed as a result?

Chapter 11

LOVING AND BEING LOVED

OVERVIEW

In an age in which sex is frequently regarded more as a matter of technical proficiency and numbers of conquests than it as as a matter of warmth and emotions, it's important to look at the phenomenon of love and how it does (or doesn't) relate to sexuality. This chapter begins by tackling the gargantuan task of defining love, and then presents a summary of the all-too-sparse research on love by examining the works of Erich Fromm, Peele and Brodsky, Dorothy Tennov, and John Alan Lee. In addition, a new conceptual framework is proposed to help the students consider love in terms of a "romantic love cycle." This is followed by a detailed discussion of love and sex that examines the meaning of intimacy, the pros and cons of sex without love, the possibility of love without sex, and the important areas of personal values and sexual decisions. The chapter concludes with a look at love and marriage.

While reading the chapter, the student is asked to consider these issues:

1. What are the elements of interpersonal love that encourage both partners to grow, and the elements that make love a form of dependency or addiction?

2. How are intimacy and desire related to love?

3. What is the romantic love cycle?

4. How do companionate love and infatuation differ from romantic love?

5. How are love and sex interrelated, and what are the cultural links between love, sex, and marriage?

6. How can a person effectively maintain a loving relationship?

LEARNING OBJECTIVES

At the conclusion of this chapter, the student should be able to:

1. Define love and distinguish it from sexual desire.

2. Describe what happens to love relationships when respect and caring are missing elements.

3. Distinguish between love as a healthy relationship with growth potential, and love as a form of dependency or addiction.

4. Discuss the psychological theories about the nature of romantic love, and outline a conceptual model of the romantic love cycle.

5. Identify the six primary types of romantic love, according to Lee.

6. Explain the basis of companionate love.

7. State the two types of evidence that support the view that there is a biological component of love.

8. Contrast relational sex with impersonal sex.

9. Identify the sources of potential conflict among personal values involved in sexual decision making.

10. Discuss the relationship of love and marriage, and explain the mate selection process in our culture.

TEACHING STRATEGIES

"Love" and "preparation for relationships" are often the most relevant and critical topics for college students, many of whom feel they are the first ever to experience the agonies and ecstasies of love. The challenge is to extrapolate information from the relatively small amount of scientific data on the topic so that the students can apply it in a practical and personal way. The text reviews most of the major sources of data, and a fascinating lecture could be based on any of the books mentioned, notably <u>Love</u> and <u>Addiction</u> by Brodsky and Peele, <u>Love</u> and <u>Limerence</u> by Tennov, <u>The Natural History of Love</u> by Hunt, or <u>The Psychology of Romantic Love</u> by Branden.

A possible lecture could begin by addressing the question, "Why is U.S. culture so obsessed with love?" Point out how this is propagated by popular music, advertising, motion pictures, television, romantic novels, and so on. Discussion can also focus on the role of rapid social change, the dissolution of the extended family, the decline of religious affiliation, industrial urbanization, secularization, and mobility, all of which contribute to making love the American panacea to loneliness and career discontent and a way of providing meaning to life.

The text addresses the question, "What is love?" and "How does one know love?" The range of replies can be augmented with quotes from literature, poetry, philosophy, and psychology. A Shakespearean sonnet or poems by e.e. cummings, Elizabeth Barret Browning, or Erica Jong can be used effectively to capture students' interest. Next, it is useful to ask, "What is the role of science in love?" Have the students consider whether or not it is possible to accumulate a systematic body of knowledge on the topic. See if the class feels that education about love might be another aspect of anticipatory guidance and could serve both to prevent distress and to improve the quality of relationships. If, as expected, students reply that yes, this would be so, the remainder of the presentation could examine how such systematic knowledge might be applied.

Have the students cite some misconceptions about love. Sources such as "Dear Abby" columns typically portray the idea that people intuitively know when they are in love, as if brought together for eternity by some gripping force. Discussion of these kinds of misconceptions and presentation of more realistic expectations is important. Limerence and companionate love will probably be new concepts for most students. Compare and contrast limerence to infatuation. Emphasizing that a person can experience many types of love at different times will help students more accurately label their emotional states.

Many students may be struggling with the related concept of intimacy. For example, explore questions such as how men can show intimacy with other men without being accused of homosexuality. Examine the ways in which intimacy may differ between acquaintances, friends, family members, lovers. If the only permissible channel for intimacy is with a mate, a dependency may develop that puts unnecessary pressure on the relationship. Students should be encouraged to examine the benefits of establishing levels of intimacy with various people.

Another important discussion topic is finding and attracting a partner. Numerous publications currently give advice on establishing social and dating skills. Give students some examples of specific factors contributing to weak or problematic social skills. The instructor could act as a role model, or the class could role play both appropriate and inappropriate ways of starting a conversation, keeping it flowing, establishing eye contact, making self-disclosures, and so on. How can a person find a date, give and receive appropriate body language, initiate contact, make a date fun, initiate or avoid sex, end and evaluate a date? Volunteers from a class might be encouraged to act out suggested scenarios depicting the correct or incorrect ways to employ the various social skills.

"Love and intimacy disorders" is a topic that can be broached from the standpoint of marital counseling literature, which has described various types of neurotic relationships in which the couple live in torment or affect one another destructively. Information about these types of relationships can help students recognize and prevent such pairings in the future. For example, a woman may put her partner on a pedestal and idolize him. Many men enjoy being worshiped and are comfortable in that role. Eventually, however, the man must come down from the pedestal resulting in trauma for the relationship. Another example is a relationship based on "saving" the partner from addiction or suffering. When the partner is rescued, the basis for the relationship is undermined. Other examples from the clinical literature are available to help students learn more about themselves and their relationships. Two particularly useful books are Therapy for Couples by Billie S. Ables and Jeffrey M. Bradshaw (San Francisco: Jossey-Bass Publishers, 1977), and Helping Couples Change by Richard B. Stuart (New York:

133

Guilford Press, 1980) which contain a great deal of information that could be utilized to create an interesting lecture segment.

STUDENT PROJECTS

1. Interview at least one friend who is currently in love and at least one who isn't. Ask each to list what they consider to be the most important components of a loving relationship. Compare and contrast their responses.

2. Design a curriculum to be taught to ninth grade students as a form of "love education." Should sexuality be included in this curriculum? What impact would actually implementing a "love education" course possibly have?

3. Interview a marriage counselor to discuss the commonest reasons marital harmony dissolves. Are people's expectations of marriage usually unrealistic? Is a troubled marriage usually one spouse's fault? What are the major ingredients that maintain marital stability over time?

PERSONAL REFLECTIONS

1. What are some important lessons you have learned from love experiences that you wish you had known about before you first fell in love? Could you have been taught about love and loving, or does it require first-hand experience? Is it at all disappointing to learn that many people react similarly to being infatuated, falling in love, and falling out of love, or is this a consolation?

2. Describe one type of romantic partner you are attracted to. Give details concerning physical appearance, personality, intelligence, social skills and so on. Try to determine why such characteristics attract you.

3. If your parents were to arrange your marriage, what type of person would they pick to be your mate? Would they be most likely to agree or disagree with your ideal choice? Why?

4. Suppose the person you are in love with and are about to marry is seriously burned in a fire. His or her face is badly scarred. How might this disfiguration affect your feelings toward the person? Would your friends' and relatives' responses to this person's appearance affect you? Would love really be "blind"?

CHAPTER 11 TEST QUESTIONS

Multiple Choice (* General Comprehension Questions)

1.* Robert Heinlein's description of a "condition in which the happiness of another person is essential to your own" refers to
   a. addictive love.
   b. homosexual love.
   c. person-to-person love.
   d. infatuation.

2.* In order for love to be more than just a form of desire, which of the following is essential?
   a. caring about the loved person
   b. wanting the other person's wealth
   c. needing to control the loved person
   d. a need to combat loneliness

3.* In The Art of Loving, Erich Fromm included all of the following in his description of a meaningful type of love except
   a. self-realization.
   b. respect.
   c. preservation of one's individuality.
   d. depending on the other person.

4.* The difference between "love" and "desire" is best expressed by saying that
   a. love is more single-minded than sexual desire.
   b. sexual desire is more powerful than love.
   c. caring and respect are more important in love than in sexual desire.
   d. sexual desire is completely intertwined with spiritual concerns.

5.* Love readiness includes the
   a. attitude that love is encumbering.
   b. attitude that love is a distraction.
   c. attitude that love is rewarding and ennobling.
   d. desire for casual sexual relationships.

6. When respect and caring are not present in a love relationship, Peele and Brodsky believe that
   a. what results is a healthy relationship with growth potential.
   b. it is easier to focus on raw passion.
   c. the resulting love is really a dependency relationship.
   d. it cannot possibly flourish into anything more than a platonic relationship.

7. Dorothy Tennov uses the term "limerence" to refer to
   a. any sexual joke that begins like, "There once was a man from Las Vegas...."
   b. a set of physical exercises designed to enhance one's sexuality.
   c. a sexual attraction of one male homosexual to another.
   d. a powerful form of romantic love in which one is "love-struck."

135

8. John Alan Lee's use of the term "mania" refers to a
   a. game used by sex therapists to desensitize sexually inhibited clients.
   b. kind of love in which there is a great deal of gamesmanship.
   c. kind of love based on intense physical attractions with emphasis on the sexual component.
   d. turbulent love, much like a roller coaster, apt to come to an abrupt end.

9. Being in love
   a. can occur whether or not love is returned.
   b. is a permanent state once attained.
   c. never changes into companionate love from romantic love.
   d. always leads to sexual action.

10. Infatuation is also known as all of the following except
    a. puppy love.
    b. pseudo-love.
    c. adolescent love.
    d. ludic love.

11. People who are infatuated with one another
    a. are acutely aware of one another's faults.
    b. can be assured that they will feel equally intense about one another.
    c. can trust their emotions as accurate reflections of what is happening in the relationship.
    d. should realize that their relationship may be short-lived and based on wishful thinking.

12. The distinction between infatuation and love is best made
    a. by an objective observer.
    b. at the moment of greatest intensity in the relationship.
    c. in retrospect.
    d. by a marriage counselor or some other trained health-care professional.

13. Eros describes
    a. casual love.
    b. love based on physical attraction.
    c. stormy love.
    d. love that emerges from friendship.

14. The most satisfying love relationships, according to Lee, occur between
    a. people who share the same approach to loving.
    b. people who have opposing approaches to loving though they share the same definition of love.
    c. people who share the same approach to love though they have different definitions of love.
    d. people who have been married and divorced at least once.

15. The romantic love cycle describes all of the following except

a. love readiness.
b. love in transition.
c. resolution and truce.
d. computer dating.

16. Love readiness
    a. can be accurately measured by electroencephalogram.
    b. can be determined by measuring prostatic acid phosphatase.
    c. can be determined by measuring LH and FSH output.
    d. has yet to be measured.

17. According to a recent study involving college-age couples matched by computer, it was found that romantic chemistry usually involves
    a. intelligence.
    b. whether the person of the opposite sex is good looking.
    c. personality.
    d. social charm.

18. The dimensions of "intimacy" involve all of the following except
    a. the conviction that the happines of the other person is a principal concern.
    b. trust between partners.
    c. the willingness to be emotionally open with one another.
    d. an understanding of the boundaries of the closeness.

19. The process of sexual decision making
    a. is unrelated to how one is socialized.
    b. can be an outgrowth of how one judges the importance of personally held values.
    c. should by guided principally by one's religious beliefs.
    d. should not be expected to create any tension or conflict within oneself.

20. The most accurate description of the relationship between love and marriage is
    a. the two are synonymous.
    b. all modern cultures emphasize love before marriage.
    c. few marriages maintain a perpetually loving relationship.
    d. good marriages should never be susceptible to the disappearance of love.

21. Researchers who have examined the question of what causes the feeling of love between two people have found that
    a. men really do prefer "hard-to-get" women.
    b. men end more romances than women do.
    c. physical attractiveness seems to be an important element.
    d. college-age women fall in love more quickly than do college-age men.

22. "Love at first sight"
    a. exists only for adolescents.
    b. is mythological and cannot be proved.

c.   exists only for adults.
d.   can be real, but may be a rationalization of one's feelings of sexual arousal.

23. The truce stage may lead to all of the following except
     a.   love in transition.
     b.   companionate love relationship.
     c.   further conflicts.
     d.   love readiness.

24. Companionate love
     a.   is a sorry substitute for romantic love.
     b.   can include a satisfying, exciting sexual side.
     c.   is generally an abrasive relationship.
     d.   is the most passionate form of love.

25. The recent research on the biological components of love have found all of the following except
     a.   there are some specific differences in the reactions of the autonomic nervous system to various types of emotions.
     b.   "love" may be accompanied by a unique set of physiological responses.
     c.   LH, FSH, and other hormones are triggers of the love experience.
     d.   neurotransmitters such as dopamine and norepinephrine surge during romantic love experiences.

True/False

T   1.   According to evolutionary biologists, reproductive success may be partially linked to love.

T   2.   Divorce rates are low in cultures where marriages are arranged.

F   3.   Ideally, love should be a dependency relationship.

T   4.   It is often very difficult to draw a line between loving and liking.

T   5.   The intensity of romantic love may distort someone's objectivity.

F   6.   A person's "love-style" is unchangeable and is the same in all relationships.

T   7.   Some people never experience love readiness.

F   8.   Marital satisfaction usually increases the longer people have been married.

F   9.   In reality, instantaneous love never occurs.

F   10. According to researchers, about 85% of the people who fall out of love end their love relationships by mutual consent.

T   11. Companionate love is characteristic of marriage and long-term committed relationships.

T   12. Sexual arousal can be easily interpreted as love.

F   13. Storge is the author of an essay entitled "The Future of Marriage."

F   14. There can be no true intimacy without any sexual contact.

F   15. Impersonal sex is inherently bad.

Fill in the Blanks

1. In any type of love, the element of (caring) is essential.

2. (Sexual desire), rather than love, is narrowly focused and easily discharged.

3. (Romantic) love is when we immerse ourselves almost completely in another person.

4. (Agape) is based on a traditional "Christian" view of love that remains an ideal more than a reality.

5. (Love readiness) seems to increase the probability that two people will fall in love.

6. The excitement of getting to know someone intimately and the excitement of (sex) are two aspects of falling in love.

7. A person who is head-over-heels in love is said to be caught in the grip of (limerence).

8. When lovers begin to test one another, they may be in the (transition) phase of love.

9. A close, trusting relationship between two people who are willing to be emotionally open describes (intimacy).

10. Friendly, nonsexual love is also known as (platonic) love.

11. (Erich Fromm) wrote The Art of Loving.

12. (Equity theory) claims that men and women are happiest when they marry a person with similar attributes.

13. "Pseudo-love" is another way of describing (infatuation).

14. A love that is based on reality and is very durable is called (companionate).

15. Marriage, unlike love, can be defined in (<u>legal</u>) terms.

<u>Discussion/Essay</u> <u>Questions</u>

1. In what ways might our society provide people with better preparation for loving and being loved?

2. Explain the key elements of the romantic love cycle.

3. Describe the kinds of intimacy one might experience from birth through late adulthood. How do the kinds of intimacy change?

4. What is love? Whose opinions most closely reflect your own and why?

5. Discuss the interrelationship between sex, love, and marriage. What personal decisions must be made with each step?

6. Compare infatuation, limerence, and love.

Chapter 12

INTIMACY AND COMMUNICATION SKILLS

OVERVIEW

The need for intimacy in human relationships is universal, but the ability of people to achieve and maintain intimacy is often problematic. Thus, the focus of this chapter is understanding the nature of intimacy, the many forms it may take, how to get it and maintain it, and problems and pitfalls associated with it. As part of the discussion of intimacy, a significant amount of Chapter 12 is concerned with communication skills since these are essential to the development and maintenance of intimacy. An examination of the reasons many of us have difficulty talking about sex in spite of the fact that it isn't inherently different from other kinds of intimate communications concludes with suggestions for overcoming such difficulty and enhancing sexual intimacy. A Boxed Item deals with the pervasive problem of loneliness in our society.

While reading the chapter, the student is asked to consider these issues:

1. Why can self-knowledge and self-acceptance foster the development of intimate relationships?

2. Why can too much self-disclosure impede and hinder intimacy?

3. Are there ways in which males and females differ in their needs for intimacy and the kinds of intimate relationships they develop?

4. How can shyness, aggressiveness, self-centeredness, selfishness, lack of empathy, unrealistic intimacy expectations, and fear of intimacy set limits on formation of intimate relationships?

5. What is pseudo-intimacy and why is it problematic? What is loneliness and why is it problematic?

6. What are some of the requirements for communication to be effective?

7. Why are non-verbal messages powerful forms of communication and what are some typical forms of nonverbal messages, especially as they relate to sexual intimacy?

8. What are the differences between "I", "you", and "we" sentences and how can they be utilized to advantage or disadvantage in

intimate relationships?

9. What is the role of affection and of anger in intimate relationships?

10. What are the tools of effective listening?

LEARNING OBJECTIVES

At the conclusion of this chapter, the student should be able to:

1. Define intimacy and discuss the variety and complexity of intimate relationships.

2. Outline the basic components of intimacy and discuss their interrelatedness.

3. Analyze the sex differences in intimacy and evaluate research evidence regarding sex differences in self-disclosure.

4. Identify the different types of intimacy problems.

5. Distinguish between genuine intimacy and pseudo-intimacy.

6. Explain the communication process and identify the sources of communication trouble.

7. Contrast the ways of communicating in an intimate relationship with those used with other persons.

8. List the techniques for effective listening.

9. Describe the ways to enhance communication between sexual partners.

10. Explain how to deal with feelings of loneliness.

TEACHING STRATEGIES

The students may find this chapter to be a breath of fresh air after all the technical, rather difficult information presented in preceding chapters. Many of them will be struggling with issues of intimacy within friendships or love relationships so the information is usually readily absorbed and students often want to personalize their discussions. Depending on the size and cohesiveness of the class, the instructor can allow such personal, in-depth discussions as a starting point or can handle the topics in a more formal manner. A good way to do this is to ask the students to write out dialogues that they consider to represent an intimate relationship, a pseudo-intimate relationship, a situation in which one party is an effective listener, and a situation in which neither party communicates effectively. Have volunteers read their dialogues to the class and see if other class members can determine what is happening in each case. The instructor may choose to have the dialogue presented as if it were a grand rounds in a hospital and the students were the interns and residents diagnosing a difficult case and suggesting effective therapy.

Another way of exploring the topic of communication is to have the class assess the instructor as a communicator. What kind of teaching style is used? How do the students usually feel when they enter class, during class, after class? What is the comfort level of students in the class? How do students try to influence the instructor and vice-versa by means of non-verbal and verbal communication strategies? What kinds of intimacy are fostered in the classroom setting? Is a human sexuality class a forum for different kinds of intimate relationships to develop than another kind of class? If so, why; if not, why not? If the instructor is willing to stand up to such scrutiny, and if the students aren't afraid to engage in such an assessment, such an exercise can be extremely effective to elucidate the complexity of the ways in which intimacy and communication are intertwined.

The topic of loneliness, examined in the text as a Boxed Item, is germane to many students who are away from home for the first time, in an impersonal environment, unsure of their social and intellectual status. Thus, the instructor must guard against the tendency to turn the class discussions into therapy sessions for a few needy students, however well-intentioned such efforts might be. Instead, treating the material in this chapter in terms of skill-building is more useful to more students. How can you conquer loneliness? Who do you know that deals with lonely feelings without being overwhelmed by them? The instructor might use an example of a soap-opera character who is a caricature of the lonely, ineffective communicator and have students re-write a script for that character changing the image to intimate, effective communicator.

The barriers to sexual intimacy can be discussed in terms of prior chapter's material. For example, how were the students socialized to think about and talk about sex? How has this affected them? Do gender roles contribute to this? How about sex-role stereotyping or other outside influences such as religious teaching? This chapter gives the instructor the chance to tie together many themes of prior chapters.

STUDENT PROJECTS

1. You are submitting an outline to a publisher for your first romance novel. One of your characters is a woman who has spent her entire adult life (she is 26) longing for love and never finding it. Another of your characters (a 30-year-old man) is adept at establishing and maintaining intimate relationships. Describe each of your characters in detail, so your editor will know everything about them and what makes them tick.

2. You are responsible for next year's freshman orientation at your school. What kinds of things should freshmen be advised about to help them avoid feeling lonely and isolated? How can

the upperclassmen help the incoming students cope?

3. Ask your parents or any adults with whom you have shared an extended relationship to tell you how the nature of intimacy in their lives has shifted over the years. Compare and contrast their experiences with your own up to now. Can older and younger people have similar experiences in spite of age differences?

4. Get together with five other people from your human sexuality class. Devise a rating scale for traits mentioned in the chapter regarding communication skills, personality traits, and so on, and then, independently of one another, rate your instructor. Do you come up with the same results? What does this tell you about the subjectivity involved in assessing such things? What other conclusions can you draw?

PERSONAL REFLECTIONS

1. Based on what you have read in Chapter 12, how would you assess your communication skills? If you had to summarize the nature and number of intimate relationships you have had and currently have, how would you describe them?

2. Have you ever been a pseudo-communicator?

3. Are you an effective listener? Who is the person (or persons) you are most likely to resist listening to? Why?

4. What has been your loneliest moment or period in your life? Were you able to overcome it? Why?

5. Tape record your end of a phone call with a friend. What kind of sentences did you use most often? Were you surprised? Was your friend aware of this?

CHAPTER 12 TEST QUESTIONS

Multiple Choice (* General Comprehension Questions)

1.* Intimacy
   a. is not desirable until one completes puberty.
   b. is most desirable during middle adulthood.
   c. is desirable but often difficult to maintain.
   d. can be easily achieved if one follows a specific pattern as outlined by Erich Fromm.

2.* The Latin word for intimacy, "intimus," means
   a. one must share.
   b. deepest.
   c. caring.
   d. trusting.

3.* Which of the following is the best definition of intimacy?
   a. it is the equivalent of romance.
   b. it most strongly resembles platonic affection.
   c. it is a permanent condition that proves people's love for
       one another.
   d. it is marked by a mutual sense of acceptance, commitment,
       tenderness, trust.

4.* Intimacy with self
   a. means a person is too selfish to be on intimate terms with
       anyone else.
   b. is important if one is to develop intimate relationships
       with other people.
   c. is a polite way of defining masturbation and other auto-
       erotic activities.
   d. is a definition of hypnosis done in the context of a
       therapeutic relationship.

5.* Communication within an intimate relationship
   a. operates on the assumption that neither person in the
       relationship intends to deliberately hurt the other.
   b. does not usually involve any major emotional risks.
   c. usually needs less touching and more talking.
   d. is best fostered by the use of "we" sentences.

6. Any intimate relationship that absorbs a person's time and
   emotional energy to an all-consuming level
   a. is clearly one in which communication is at its most
       effective level.
   b. helps one to get totally in touch with himself or herself.
   c. can be exhilirating but possibly damaging.
   d. is the ultimate goal in intimate relationships.

7. All of the following may contribute to a person's inability or
   unwillingness to look inward except
   a. fear.
   b. laziness.
   c. self-hatred.
   d. narcissism.

8. The intensity of intimacy
   a. rarely fluctuates once established.
   b. varies only during periods of stress.
   c. varies only in situations of pseudo-intimacy.
   d. can be influenced by external circumstances such as
       geographical separation or work pressures.

9. Self-disclosure
   a. is best achieved all at once if intimacy and communication
       are to flourish.
   b. is not a precondition of caring and sharing.
   c. should extend across a broad spectrum of things.
   d. is the willingness to tell another person what you think
       they should be thinking and feeling.

10. Sharing experiences
    a. means intimate partners should do everything together.
    b. means one shares certain things with an intimate partner while maintaining an independent identity.
    c. should include forcing your partner to engage in activities that are not inherently pleasing to that partner.
    d. always provides equal rewards to each partner.

11. Commitment within intimate relationships
    a. is an irrevocable guarantee of the future.
    b. is the same as trust.
    c. should not be expected to change over time.
    d. is usually an outgrowth of caring, sharing, and trust that develops in the early stages of intimate relationships.

12. Honesty as part of intimacy
    a. does not always mean one must make full self-disclosure statements.
    b. is not harmed by the presence of deceit.
    c. is desirable but rarely achieved in intimate relationships.
    d. can be best achieved by putting a large number of topics "off limits."

13. Hugging, cuddling, holding hands are examples of
    a. expressions of trust.
    b. expressions of commitment.
    c. expressions of tenderness.
    d. sins of commission.

14. Regarding sex differences in intimacy, it has been found that
    a. men seem more adept at self disclosure than women.
    b. boys tend to have more intimate friendships than girls do.
    c. gay men are more likely to pair off in intimate relationships than are lesbians.
    d. women have an easier time building loyal, noncompetitive friendships with other women than men do with other men.

15. All of the following are true about men and intimacy except
    a. men want "instant intimacy" more often than do women.
    b. men are not fully capable of intimacy.
    c. men become increasingly concerned with intimacy from age forty on.
    d. many men are intimacy-takers rather than intimacy-givers.

16. A common barrier to intimacy is
    a. honesty.
    b. self-disclosure.
    c. shyness.
    d. empathy.

17. Intimacy conflicts
    a. occur only in the contexts of adolescent or immature

relationships.
b. are not problematic in terms of a developing intimate relationship.
c. can cause a kind of see-saw situation in which at a certain point of contact the partners become anxious.
d. occur when the intimacy is kept under control.

18. Pseudo-intimacy describes a situation in which
a. the relationship leads to a positive, growth-enhancing relationship.
b. mutual trust is a given.
c. communication is two-way.
d. conflicts and arguments abound with resolution of key issues rarely occurring.

19. All of the following can be barriers to effective communication except
a. not saying what you mean.
b. not being specific.
c. sending mixed messages.
d. using "I" language.

20. All of the following can enhance effective communication except
a. talking at your partner.
b. thinking through what you want to say before saying it.
c. writing a letter.
d. asking for feedback from your partner.

21. One psychologist has suggested that of the total feeling expressed by a spoken message, the percentage that is verbal feeling is
a. 38.
b. 100.
c. 7.
d. 55.

22. Nonverbal messages are especially applicable to
a. business meetings.
b. sexual interactions.
c. classroom presentations.
d. negotiations with a parent about some touchy issue.

23. "I think that you..." is an example of
a. a "you" sentence.
b. "I" language.
c. a phony "I" sentence.
d. nonverbal communication.

24. The most complete, functional "I" messages should do all of the following except
a. make your partner come up with a remedy for whatever is problematic.
b. announce what or how you feel.
c. say what you think you need to maintain or change how you

147

feel.
d.   achieve clarity in intimate communication.

25. Effective listening includes all of the following <u>except</u>
     a.   undivided attention.
     <u>b.</u>   preconceived notions of what might be said.
     c.   being actively involved in the process even though one might be temporarily silent.
     d.   being willing to agree to disagree.

<u>True/False</u>

T   1.   Intimacy is sometimes situation bound.

F   2.   A person must be totally happy with himself or herself in order to be capable of intimacy with others.

T   3.   As a process, intimacy can fluctuate within any given relationship over time.

F   4.   "An attitude or feeling you have for another person which is generally related to the intensity of your positive feelings toward them" defines <u>honesty.</u>

T   5.   Most people begin the process of self-disclosure gradually.

T   6.   Telling lies is a sin of commission.

T   7.   Keeping something private is a sin of omission.

F   8.   Tenderness is best defined as "the ability to understand and relate to another person's feelings and point of view."

T   9.   Romantic intimacy needs both verbal and physical tenderness.

T   10.   The current data on whether men and women have different levels or types of motivations for intimacy are not reliable in the statistical sense.

F   11.   Some studies have found that men confide more in their mothers than in anyone else.

F   12.   Fear of intimacy is the most serious problem for women who come to see sex therapists for counseling.

T   13.   Toning down aggressive language and behavior can improve a person's chances for intimacy.

F   14.   Unfortunately, most intimate relationships are very fragile in the face of unforeseen obstacles.

148

F   15. Loneliness and being alone are the same things.

Fill in the Blanks

1. Intimacy is not precisely the same as strong affection or (romance).

2. Two people sharing and interacting together describes the mutual (caring) characteristic of intimacy.

3. The willingness to tell another person what you're thinking and feeling is (self-disclosure).

4. Working to maintain an intimate relationship in spite of frustration, crisis, or fatigue, as well as in times of joy or excitement, shows the presence of (commitment).

5. (Deceit) is a warning sign that manipulation in one form or another is occurring in an intimate relationship.

6. (Empathy) is the ability to understand and relate to another person's feelings and viewpoint.

7. One of the most neglected aspects of intimacy is the expression of (tenderness).

8. In our culture, (women) have been socialized to show their feelings.

9. (Selfishness) goes beyond self-centeredness and can be seen in people who seek to exert control within intimate relationships for purely personal gains.

10. People who can sympathize with the feelings and needs of others, and respond to these feelings and needs as well, have the skill of (empathy, empathic listening).

11. Words and sounds describe (verbal) messages.

12. (Nonverbal messages) are more "powerful" than spoken words alone, which is why it's important to avoid mixed messages.

13. Sentences that being with the word ("you") are apt to be demanding or accusatory, and may provoke defensiveness in the other person.

14. An attitude of giving up may be a hallmark of those who are (lonely, permanently lonely).

15. Social loneliness is marked by a lack of friends and support networks; (emotional) loneliness is characterized by a lack of intimate relationships.

Discussion/Essay Questions

1. Write a letter to an imaginary individual with whom you want to develop an intimate relationship. Include in it all of the factors discussed in Chapter 12 that would enhance the way in which you communicate your needs and wishes.

2. Think of all the kinds of intimate relationships you are currently involved in. Which are the most difficult to maintian for you personally? In each case, who works hardest within the context of the relationship? Is there a major difference in the nature of intimacy between sexual and nonsexual relationships?

3. What are the most important communication skills for a college student to have? Do these skills apply to non-school related activities and relationships? When you are engaged in an intimate relationship, do you think about how you are communicating or do you just "relate"? Is the process different at school or at work? Is the process different with different people?

Chapter 13

SEXUAL FANTASY

OVERVIEW

The sexual fantasies described in this chapter are the wakeful thoughts one has as distinguished from sleep-associated dreams. In this context, the emphasis is on helping students understand that sexual fantasies are not only normal but that they serve a wide variety of useful, even interesting, psychological functions. A number of examples are presented to show that having a fantasy about something is not the equivalent of desiring the real life experience depicted in the fantasy. In addition, the advantages and drawbacks of "trying out" fantasies in real life are discussed, as is the advisability of keeping sex fantasies private versus sharing them with a partner. Varying types and functions of sex fantasies are categorized and the chapter concludes with a discussion of the differences between the sexual fantasies of males and females.

While reading the chapter, the student is asked to consider these issues:

1. What functions can sexual fantasies serve in everyday life?

2. What are the possible consequences of trying out fantasies in real life, of keeping fantasies private, of sharing them with a partner?

3. What are some common types of sexual fantasies?

4. What do different researchers say about sexual fantasies?

5. How do the sexual fantasy patterns of males and females, heterosexuals and homosexuals compare?

LEARNING OBJECTIVES

At the conclusion of this chapter, the student should be able to:

1. Define sexual fantasy and distinguish it from sexual desire.

2. Describe the common kinds of sexual fantasies, and whether or not they are sex-linked.

3. Identify the situations in which preferential fantasies can become troublesome.

4. List the most common functions of sexual fantasy and explain the effects.

5. Determine whether or not sexual fantasies should be shared with a partner; understand the limitations and benefits of such disclosure.

6. Compare and contrast the gender differences in sexual fantasies; discuss whether or not such differences are substantial and meaningful or minimal and not useful to focus on.

TEACHING STRATEGIES

It is unlikely that students have been exposed to as frank a discussion of sexual fantasy as the text offers, even with the plethora of information found in other media. They might, therefore, respond to some of the content of this chapter with disbelief and astonishment.

The text states that there are many professional opinions about sexual fantasy and little scientific data. Some students may believe that sexual fantasy during intercourse is an act of infidelity to their partners. Others may believe that the content of their fantasies is "sick" or undesirable. The instructor needs to be prepared to respond to such divergent opinions, not to push the students to "believe" the book or the instructor's viewpoint, but to teach them to acknowledge alternative viewpoints about fantasy, and realize that individual morality colors their beliefs. The scientific evidence suggests that most people fantasize and use many of the scenarios listed in Chapter 13.

How is the content of fantasies established? Why are many male fantasies like pornographic movies in which the male hero conquers a helpless or seductive female? What is the effect of the men's magazine image of female attractiveness on more "average looking" men and women? Why doesn't the same fantasy used over and over for many years become boring? None of these questions have definitive answers, but there is value in allowing students to think about them.

There are numerous theories about the establishment of erotic fantasy. It appears that the seeds of erotic images are planted in childhood and early adolescence; at puberty, the "program files" are activated. The instructor can review various theories related to the development of fantasy.

Another related topic is the development of problematic erotic fantasy. The text notes that problems may develop when fantasy becomes intrusive or obsessive, or the person feels obliged to act out the fantasy. How does problematic sexual imagery become a source of sexual arousal? For example, why might a person expose his genitals as the only means of sexual arousal (exhibitionism)? Many authors have written about this subject. Once students are able to conceptualize how deviant or nondeviant fantasy becomes established, they may discover an increased acceptance and comfort with their own sexual thoughts.

The subject of homosexual thought requires some mention during a lecture on sexual fantasy. Students need to realize that a person aroused by both men and women in their sexual fantasy life is not necessarily homosexual. The label "homosexual" is best applied when a person has sexual activity with and/or forms a committed relationship with a same-sex partner. This subject is discussed more fully in the chapter on homosexuality and bisexuality.

STUDENT PROJECTS

1. Interview a sex therapist to see how sexual fantasies sometimes create guilt or conflict. In what ways can sexual fantasies be therapeutically useful?

2. Design a research survey to ascertain the frequency of use of sex fantasies by adolescents, and to determine the differences (if any) between the principal fantasy patterns of male and female teens.

3. Look at a copy of a magazine such as "Playboy" and another such as "Vogue" or "Gentlemen's Quarterly." How are the fantasy men and women depicted in these two publications, obviously geared to very different audiences? What kinds of fantasies do different publications sell?

PERSONAL REFLECTIONS

1. Did you daydream or fantasize as a young child? Perhaps you had an imaginary playmate or pretended your toys were alive. In what ways do these kinds of imaginary wanderings differ from sexual fantasy? How do you feel when you engage in sexual fantasy? in other kinds of fantasy?

2. Have you ever had a sexual fantasy that disturbed you? How did you cope with its contents? Did you use any special strategies to keep the fantasy from recurring? Did you just "go with the flow"? Would you be willing to get professional help if a fantasy really frightened you?

3. Which of your fantasies would you be willing to talk about with other people, and which would you keep entirely private? Has reading this chapter changed your attitudes about your fantasies and how you wish to deal with them?

4. Do your sexual fantasies reflect certain aspects of your personality? Do they give you any insight into yourself? When do they tend to occur? Do any patterns emerge?

CHAPTER 13 TEST QUESTIONS

Multiple Choice (* General Comprehension Questions)

1.* Sexual fantasies
    a. are destructive to one's ego.
    b. indicate mental imbalance.
    c. can help people find excitement, adventure, pleasure, self-confidence.
    d. begin at puberty.

2.* A person's sexual fantasies
    a. are rarely intentional.
    b. should not be shared with anyone else.
    c. occur only within a very narrow context.
    d. are often random, triggered by thoughts of which one may be unaware.

3.* The function of fantasy is
    a. nonexistent, serving no known psychological purpose.
    b. important only as a predictor of sexual dysfunction.
    c. important as it helps a person escape the frustrations and limits of real life.
    d. most important during adolescence, less important during adulthood.

4.* All of the following are true of sexual fantasies except
    a. fantasy provides a means of exploring a situation to get an idea of what it might really be like.
    b. the person who fantasizes wants to participate in the actual behavior at all times.
    c. fantasies may seem ridiculous when examined rationally.
    d. fantasies may be improved versions of a person's real life experiences.

5.* Sexual fantasies function on many different levels and can accomplish all of the following except
    a. boost one's self-confidence.
    b. provide a safety valve for pent-up feelings.
    c. increase sexual excitement.
    d. always indicate what a person wants to do sexually.

6. A sexual fantasy that becomes necessary for sexual arousal
    a. is the ultimate in sexual fantasy.
    b. can best be described as "sadomasochistic."
    c. can become an obsession and interfere with thinking or behavior.
    d. is typical of female sexual response, but rarely of male sexual response.

7. The "director's role" describes
    a. the way a sex therapist teaches a client about fantasy.
    b. the way a partner with whom one has an intimate relationship lets his or her sexual preferences be known.
    c. how early twentieth century psychoanalysts alluded to the role of the seducer in sleep-associated dreams about sex.
    d. part of a fantasy in which one can imaginatively control the scene, plot, and actors.

8. Sharing one's fantasies with a partner
   a. shows you are sexually liberated.
   b. proves you are sexually mature.
   c. ensures complete understanding between sexual partners.
   d. may be destructive to the relationship under certain circumstances.

9. Intruding fantasies
   a. cannot produce sexual arousal.
   b. may be so distressing that they shut off sexual feelings.
   c. rarely or never include situations the fantasizer considers abnormal.
   d. do not usually recur since they are unwanted.

10. Sexual fantasies are often used to
    a. reduce sexual arousal.
    b. teach moral lessons about sin.
    c. move from the plateau phase of arousal to orgasm.
    d. threaten a partner.

11. "Controlled rehearsal" refers to
    a. teaching women how to deal with rape situations.
    b. sex education courses in high school which offer "how to" lessons about birth control methods.
    c. practicing a given sexual situation with a partner.
    d. a way of previewing an anticipated experience and preparing oneself for what to expect or how to act via fantasy.

12. The fantasy content of homosexuals and heterosexuals is
    a. identical.
    b. totally different.
    c. remarkably similar.
    d. impossible to compare since no studies have been done on the subject.

13. People who attempt to transform fantasy to fact
    a. are usually satisfied with the results.
    b. frequently find the erotic value of the fantasy is lost.
    c. find that limited dramatization of the fantasy more psychologically satisfying than the imaginary fantasy.
    d. tend to be sexually deviant.

14. Statistics on how many people act out their sexual fantasies in real life
    a. are not available.
    b. show a figure of 50%.
    c. show a figure of 75%.
    d. have only been calculated for the lesbian/homosexual population.

15. Men who turn to prostitutes to assist them in living out a sexual fantasy
    a. are far fewer in number in the 1980's than in previous

decades due to the loosening of the sexual double
standard.
b. do so because of some deep-seated fear of sexual
performance.
c. do so because it is apt to be psychologically safe for a
number of reasons.
d. do so because they want to "shock" someone with their
fantasy.

16. The range of the erotic imagination
a. is almost limitless.
b. only begins to develop after exposure to a human sexuality
course.
c. cannot flourish if a person comes from a deeply religious
background.
d. should be controlled once one reaches adulthood.

17. Rape fantasies
a. are the most misunderstood of all sex fantasies.
b. indicate the fantasizer really wants to be raped.
c. are rarely used by men.
d. are used exclusively by homosexual men.

18. Conquest fantasies include all of the following except
a. an element of power.
b. the ability to command.
c. the ability to impregnate.
d. the ability to seduce.

19. The domination/humiliation fantasy is a subtype of the
a. switching partners theme.
b. group sex theme.
c. conquest theme.
d. idyllic encounters theme.

20. Researchers have found that the fantasy patterns of men and
women
a. are completely different.
b. are more similar than different.
c. reflect the indisputable fact that men are more interested
in sex than are women.
d. are different in type but not in frequency.

21. People who have sadomasochistic fantasies
a. tend to enjoy feeling pain.
b. are usually people who have been incarcerated at some
point in their lives.
c. are usually no different from those people who have
idyllic encounter fantasies.
d. tend to be adolescents as this kind of fantasy is usually
outgrown by young adulthood.

22. Imagining sex with a different partner
a. never results in guilty feelings because it is only a

156

fantasy.
b. always includes some version of the domination/humiliation theme.
c. is one of the commonest varieties of sexual fantasy.
d. does not include fantasizing about someone you don't know personally.

23. Many researchers disagree with the idea that sexual fantasies can be natural and creative. Their reasons include all of the following except
a. sexual fantasies can create relationship conflicts.
b. sexual fantasies can lead to a partner feeling ignored.
c. sexual fantasies can be debasing if they reduce personal involvement.
d. sexual fantasies have increased the incidence of homicides in the United States.

24. Sex researcher Robert Stoller believes that sex fantasies
a. have a flame of hostility at their core.
b. are debasing.
c. are signs of sexual alienation.
d. are pale substitutes for the real thing.

25. All of the following are common types of sexual fantasies except
a. sadomasochism.
b. masturbation.
c. group sex.
d. conquest.

True/False

T   1. Approximately 72% of women use fantasy to enhance sexual arousal.

F   2. Imagery of male sexual anatomy is the most frequent content of heterosexual female fantasy material.

F   3. The central fantasy described by Erica Jong in Fear of Flying is an example of a sadomasochistic fantasy.

F   4. Fantasy is not a useful way of dealing with sexual conflicts or confusion.

F   5. Sexual fantasies are more common during intercourse than during masturbation for both men and women.

T   6. "Celebrity sex" fantasies are a subtype of the "switching partners" fantasy.

T   7. A prostitute–client situation is apt to be psychologically safe.

T.   8. Sexual arousal can become dependent on the power of a preferred fantasy alone.

F   9. Visualization of experiences that have never been tried in real life is called the "conquest fantasy."

T 10. When sexual fantasy is transformed into a compulsion, the play element may be completely eliminated.

F 11. It is always easy to distinguish sexual fantasy from sexual desire.

F 12. An "intruding fantasy" is willfully conjured up and always pleasing.

T 13. All types of fantasies function as psychological safety-valves.

F 14. Reliable statistics are available on how many people act out their sexual fantasies in real life.

F 15. It has been found that the range of the erotic imagination is quite limited.

Fill in the Blanks

1. The most common fantasy of the (heterosexual) male and female is replacement of an established partner.

2. A fantasy that is best described as an "old familiar story" is a person's (preferential) pattern of fantasy.

3. There has been much controversy about whether fantasies should be solitary or (shared).

4. An (intruding) fantasy generally produces guilt or turmoil and can be frightening.

5. People with (low) levels of sexual desire typically have few sexual fantasies.

6. Sexual fantasies are usually (safe) because they are private and fictional.

7. The function of fantasy most prominent during adolescence, in which one previews an anticipated experience, is called (controlled rehearsal).

8. Two-thirds of the (men) interviewed at the Masters and Johnson Institute who had fantasies about unusual sex practices said they'd be willing to try them out under the right circumstances.

9. Advertising in a "swinger's magazine" may give a couple the opportunity to try out the fantasy of (switching partners).

10. The element of power is at the core of all (conquest) fantasies.

11. Voyeurism is not the equivalent of (watching) fantasies.

12. The fantasies that are in sharp contrast to rape fantasies are called (idyllic encounters).

13. Inflicting pain and receiving pain as a source of sexual arousal are called (sadomasochistic) themes of sexual fantasy.

14. Several studies have shown that the sex fantasies of women tend to be more (passive) than those of men, possibly because of socialization factors.

15. The ability to end a threatening or uncomfortable fantasy is one aspect of the (director's) role.

Discussion/Essay Questions

1. What is a fantasy? Are daydreams fantasy? Are random thoughts fantasy? Are imagined experiences fantasy?

2. When, if ever, does sexual fantasy become abnormal?

3. How are sexual fantasies related to behavior? If a person fantasizes about holding down a partner during intercourse, will that person be likely to enjoy the experience in real life?

4. You are a sex education teacher in a high school that is quite conservative, yet you have to include a discussion of fantasy because it is in your curriculum guide. How would you do it?

5. You are a dorm counselor and are responsible for holding weekly rap sessions. One group of freshmen asks for your advice about sharing fantasies with their partners. Your only experience is based on what you have learned in this class. How would you proceed?

Chapter 14

SOLITARY SEXUAL BEHAVIOR

OVERVIEW

In the not-too-distant past, masturbation was generally regarded as sick, sinful, or both. Today, in contrast, it has begun to be regarded by many people as an important and normal developmental activity, a potential source of personal learning and pleasure, an option for sexual creativity. In this chapter, the startling contrast between past and present attitudes toward masturbation is developed in detail while a variety of myths about masturbation are dispelled. Techniques of masturbation are discussed, including a Boxed Item, "What's Good and Bad about Vibrators" and some attention is paid to different mastubatory preferences of males and females. Also discussed is the topic of sexual arousal and sleep, with emphasis on the fact that female orgasms can occur just as male orgasms can during sleep. A section on the use of erotica and the effects of erotica on behavior includes a Research Spotlight on the controversial topic, "Violent Pornography and Aggression."

While reading the chapter, the student is asked to consider these issues:

1. How have attitudes toward masturbation changed from the nineteenth century to the present?

2. How have female masturbatory patterns changed in recent years and what are the likely causes for such changes?

3. What are some common techniques of masturbation for males and females?

4. What is the function of orgasm during sleep in males and females?

5. What is erotica? What forms can erotica take? How do responses to erotica differ in males and females?

6. What is the relationship of certain kinds of erotica to violent, aggressive behavior?

LEARNING OBJECTIVES

At the conclusion of this chapter, the student should be able to:

1. Define masturbation and explain the origins of the word.

2. Contrast the early cultural, religious, and medical views about masturbation.

3. Interpret the contemporary attitudes about masturbation.

4. Describe the common patterns of masturbation.

5. List the possible reasons for the reported increase in female masturbation.

6. Compare the advantages and disadvantages of using an electric vibrator as a source of sexual stimulation.

7. Analyze the process of sexual arousal during sleep and identify its most typical forms.

8. Discuss the use of erotic materials for solitary sexual arousal, and describe the four primary reasons for the use of erotica.

9. Explain the relationship between the effects of erotica and sexual behavior.

TEACHING STRATEGIES

An excellent way of initiating a lecture on solitary sex is to ask how many students have never felt any guilt related to sexual self-stimulation. The discrepancy between the degree of sexual liberation many students profess to have attained and actual fact is astonishing to students. Some of the class may be brave enough to discuss myths they may have believed to be true at some point in their lives. If not, the instructor might have students write the myths anonymously and then read them aloud in class.

Even if students never believed that masturbation could cause physical harm or was a sin, few are likely to have acknowledged that masturbation could actually be beneficial to a person. It is important that the instructor emphasize that such a fact does not mean every person should masturbate, as this implies performance standards, but -- as the text suggests -- masturbation allows a person to learn more about individual sexual response. This, in turn, can make that person more effective in the ability to communicate to a partner the kind and amount of sexual stimulation that is pleasurable (or not). To demonstrate the diversity of options, the instructor can read quotes from the Hite Report on specific ways men and women masturbate. Films can also be used quite effectively to desensitize students and make a similar point.

The topic of vibrators is usually of great interest to a class. The basic information is provided in the boxed item. Some people also choose to use vibrators as an adjunct to sexual interaction with a partner. If the vibrator is a consistent replacement or substitute for interaction with a partner, however, difficulties may result. Males are often threatened by a partner's use of a vibrator. If some of the males in the class are able to discuss their concerns, misconceptions can be alleviated.

Chapter 14 offers a review of the scientific information on sexually explicit materials. This topic is rarely discussed in such a rational manner. For example, J. Edgar Hoover stated, "The publication and distribution of salacious materials is a peculiarly vicious evil; the destruction of moral character caused by it among our young people cannot be overestimated." Similarly, Senator Keating said, in 1961, "No act of subversion planned by a Communist conspiracy could be more effective in shredding the nation's moral fabric than the lethal effects of pornography." Some scientists concur, "Unchecked pornography might influence both public and private attitudes and eventual actions" (Van der Haag, 1970).

One survey indicated that 47% of men and 51% of women in the U.S. believe that reading or viewing erotic materials causes people to commit sex-related crimes [Abelson, H., Cohen, R., Heaton, F.,& Suder, C. "Public Attitudes Toward an Experience with Erotic Materials." Technical Reports of the Commission on Obscenity and Pornography, Vol. 6. Washington, D.C.: U.S. Government Printing Office, 1971]. Thus, the students opinions will also vary widely. It is important to impress upon them that there is a need for scientific data to answer such questions. You might request that they design such a study. The data reviewed in the text indicate that pornography may actually decrease sex-related criminal activity. Obviously, the data contradicts popular opinion and therefore will not be easily accepted.

The interaction of the behavioral scientists and legal profession on this issue is remarkable. It would be valuable to have several students review court cases related to pornography and report to the class. Have the students speculate on the reactions of the courts to pornography in the next ten years. In a conservative society, does scientific data influence such decisions?

STUDENT PROJECTS

1. Visit an "adult" bookstore that deals principally in erotica. Look over the book jackets and titles to see if there are any that seem to be offensive to your taste and any that seem to be a turn-on. Also, see if there is a display of vibrators, ben wa balls, or other objects for sexual self-stimulation. If possible, discuss with the salesclerk how people react to bringing their purchases to the cash register, and find out the proportion of male to female customers.

2. (For students who have never seen an x-rated movie) Take a trip to an x-rated theater to view an erotic movie or rent an x-rated tape and play it on a VCR or BETA hook-up. Write an essay about how you responded to the movie. If you were in an actual theater, include how you felt being there. If you had to rent the tape, explore what you felt like asking for it and paying for it. Did you find the movie shocking, humorous, arousing, neutral, or offensive? How would you react if you

learned that one or both of your parents (or even your grand-parents) had seen the same movie and enjoyed it?

PERSONAL REFLECTIONS

1. Can you recall the first time you masturbated? How did you feel afterward? Happy? Curious? Ashamed? If you have never masturbated, try to remember the first time you learned about it. Who or what was your source? How did you react? Has that reaction changed as you have matured?

2. How would you discuss masturbation with your ten-year-old son or daughter?

3. Think ahead ten years. What do you think society's attitude about pornography will be? Why?

4. You are looking through a basement closet and come across a stack of sexually-explicit erotic magazines. Describe your reaction upon discovering that the magazines belong to a) your sixteen-year-old brother, b) your eleven-year-old sister, c) your mother, d) your father. How do these reactions differ and why? Do you make certain judgments and conclusions about each person based on your discovery?

CHAPTER 14 TEST QUESTIONS

Multiple Choice (* General Comprehension Questions)

1.* Solitary sexual behavior
   a. occurs between partners in the privacy of their bedroom.
   b. is a practice universally approved of by all societies.
   c. has now become an accepted practice within the context of normal sexual development.
   d. is the only sexual behavior with no known associated taboos.

2.* Autoerotic activity refers to
   a. the teenage practice of parking in cars in lovers' lanes.
   b. solitary sex.
   c. manual masturbation only.
   d. Betty Dodson's term for one's primary sex life.

3.* The activity of solitary sexual behavior has been plagued by all of the following except
   a. lack of accurate information.
   b. prohibitions.
   c. fear of discovery should one do it.
   d. a recent Congressional position paper prohibiting the dissemination of information about it in junior high schools.

163

4.* "Masturbation" refers to
   a. a sexual practice that guarantees orgasm.
   b. a sexual practice found only in the human behavioral repertoire.
   c. a sexual practice rarely utilized by females.
   d. sexual self-stimulation without regard to the outcome.

5.* "Erotica" refers to
   a. a ballet performed by the American Ballet Theater.
   b. the most kinky form of solitary sex.
   c. wakeful sexual fantasies.
   d. a blanket term used for explicit sexual material.

6. From an historical perspective about masturbation, all of the following are accurate statements except
   a. the ancient Greeks and Romans praised it.
   b. traditional Judaism and Christianity thought it sinful.
   c. the Bible actually has no clearcut prohibitions against it.
   d. 19th century physicians prescribed straitjackets at bedtime to prevent children from masturbating.

7. In today's society, masturbation is
   a. no longer a cause of concern for adolescents.
   b. no longer believed to cause sterility, memory loss, or misshapen genitals.
   c. acknowledged as habit-forming by 90% of people surveyed by "Playboy" magazine.
   d. sometimes acknowledged to be a gratifying way of releasing tension and making a person relax.

8. All of the following are accurate statements about techniques of masturbation except
   a. no two women masturbate in exactly the same way.
   b. men usually have more sameness in their masturbation patterns than do women.
   c. the commonest form of female masturbation is the use of a vibrator.
   d. there are many varieties of sexual self-pleasuring.

9. "Dildos" and "ben-wa balls" are
   a. childhood games similar to spin-the-bottle.
   b. objects inserted into the vagina during masturbation.
   c. trademarks of male prophylactics.
   d. objects used by transvestites in their cross-dressing.

10. Women who masturbate
   a. routinely insert a finger or object into the vagina.
   b. routinely include breast stimulation as part of masturbation.
   c. routinely rub the clitoral glans during masturbation.
   d. routinely stroke, rub, or apply pressure to the clitoris, mons, or vaginal lips.

11. Male masturbation typically includes
    a. performing oral sex on oneself.
    b. insertion of objects into the anus.
    c. stroking the penile shaft with one hand.
    d. stimulation of one's own nipples.

12. The preferred type of male masturbation is
    a. manual stimulation of the penis.
    b. water massage.
    c. thigh pressure.
    d. self-fellatio.

13. The least-preferred type of female masturbation is
    a. rubbing against an object.
    b. breast stimulation alone.
    c. vaginal insertion.
    d. water massage.

14. Regarding the frequency of masturbation,
    a. someone who chooses not to masturbate is abnormal.
    b. almost everyone interviewed by the authors thought their
        own personal masturbatory frequency was excessive.
    c. physical tolerance for masturbation provides a built-in
        safety valve.
    d. people who are married do not masturbate at all.

15. During sleep
    a. sexual reflexes do not function.
    b. nocturnal ejaculation creates sexual tension.
    c. people can experience orgasm.
    d. sexually explicit dreams indicate the presence of a
        psychological problem.

16. All of the following apply to erotica except
    a. it provides a source of knowledge about sexual behavior.
    b. it can produce sexual arousal.
    c. it functions similarly to sexual fantasies.
    d. it is illegal in the United States.

17. People's responses to erotica
    a. are purely psychological.
    b. are stronger for men than women.
    c. are similar for both men and women.
    d. are purely physical.

18. The effects of erotica on behavior have been
    a. found to sometimes help people overcome sexual problems or
        lessen inhibitions.
    b. researched, but no conclusions have ever been drawn.
    c. found to cause an increase in criminal behavior.
    d. found to be significant in causing men to act impulsively
        in sexual situations.

19. Almost all women who report sleep-associated orgasms
    a. have had extensive experience reading or seeing erotica.
    b. are divorced.
    c. have never been exposed to erotica of any kind.
    d. have previously been orgasmic by other means.

20. The differences in the sexual arousal induced by words, photographs, or movies are
    a. extreme and shocking with movies having the most impact.
    b. minimal, with few differences at all.
    c. nonexistent.
    d. extreme and shocking with photographs having the most impact.

21. In places where sexually explicit materials are available
    a. child molesters tend to congregate.
    b. social upheaval increases.
    c. the rates of many sex crimes decrease.
    d. the rates of many sex crimes increase.

22. A problem with sexually explicit materials is that they
    a. put women on a pedestal.
    b. undermine existing stereotypes about men and women.
    c. reinforce existing stereotypes and prejudices about men and women.
    d. are too expensive to be of use to anyone.

23. A true field study of the effects of violent pornography
    a. was done in 1953 when "Playboy" began publication.
    b. has been started and was underwritten by a grant from "Hustler" magazine.
    c. has yet to be conducted for ethical reasons.
    d. was conducted by Donnerstein and Linz and published in 1984.

24. A recent study has found that viewing x-rated violent films in laboratory settings
    a. decreases male aggressive behavior.
    b. increases male aggressive behavior.
    c. increases male sympathy and sensitivity to rape victims.
    d. makes men temporarily impotent.

25. Violent pornography, in which force or coercion against women is used in depictions of sex
    a. has decreased in the past decade.
    b. has disappeared in the past decade.
    c. has increased in the past decade.
    d. has been spearheaded by feminists as a statement against the subjugation of women.

True/False

T   1. There are many taboos about solitary sexual behavior.

166

F ✓ 2. Autoerotic activities pertain to a person's intense, often bizarre, attraction to automobiles.

F   3. Researchers have defined excessive masturbation in terms of specific behaviors, on a scale of 1 to 10.

F   4. In order to be considered masturbation, sexual self-stimulation must lead to orgasm.

T   5. Ford and Beach found that most human societies thought masturbation by adults was undesirable.

T   6. Until recently, "onanism" was synonymous with masturbation.

F   7. After the 14th century, chastity belts were never again manufactured.

T   8. Leeches, circumcision, cautery were all 19th century "solutions" to masturbation.

F   9. Masturbation can cause hair to grow on the palm of one's hand.

T   10. Masturbation is increasingly accepted as a legitimate form of sexual behavior.

F   11. "Circle jerks" is a slang term for unpopular adolescents who are sexually inexperienced.

T   12. An inflatable life-sized doll can be purchased for use as a gadget to assist in male masturbation.

T   13. Data about masturbation are very tricky to interpret.

T ✓ 14. Research data has shown that males masturbate about twice as often as females do.

F   15. According to Kinsey, only 30% of males have erotic dreams.

Fill in the Blanks

1. Recent research at the Masters and Johnson Institute found that 48% of females used manual stimulation of the (<u>clitoral/vulval</u>) area as the preferred form of masturbation.

2. Bookstores that cater to the "21 or older" crowd usually sell sexually explicit material known as (<u>erotica</u>).

3. Solitary sex is also called (<u>autoerotic</u>) activity.

4. Any act of self-stimulation without regard to outcome is (<u>masturbation</u>).

5. An American pamphleteer who believed, with Tissot, that masturbation caused insanity was (Benjamin Rush).

6. Some religions categorize masturbation as a (sin).

7. The body position most women prefer to use while masturbating is (lying on their backs).

8. Women who use vibrators usually apply them to the (external genitals).

9. Males masturbate about (twice) as often as females do.

10. (Nocturnal ejaculation) can be a physiologic safety valve for a man's accumulated sexual tension.

11. 70% of females and nearly (100) % of males have erotic dreams, according to Kinsey.

12. The sexual arousal that occurs with the use of erotica is both psychological and (physiological).

13. Men's responses to erotica tend to be (object) oriented.

14. The idea that exposure to pornography incites men to rape is most likely a (myth).

15. The "instant orgasm" induced by a (vibrator) can cause problems for a woman.

Discussion/Essay Questions

1. What are some statements made against the practice of masturbation? How does current research answer these statements?

2. Feminist Betty Dodson says, "Masturbation is our primary sex life. It is the sexual base." What does she mean by this? Do you agree or disagree?

3. How has the medical profession influenced attitudes toward masturbation throughout history?

4. You are about to present your views on violent pornography to a Congressional commission. Write out your presentation.

5. You are leading a group therapy session for young adults, both men and women, who have stated that they are having problems with the concept and practice of masturbation. What kinds of things will you try to elicit in the context of the group? What kinds of things will you actually teach them?

Chapter 15

HETEROSEXUALITY

OVERVIEW

For many students, the subject matter of this chapter will understandably be of the highest order of personal interest. The detailed opening secion, "Techniques of Heterosexual Activity," will most likely activate both fascination and some embarrassment, especially insofar as sexually experienced students seek to determine if they're "doing it right" and inexperienced students try to prepare themselves for a later sexual debut. The emphasis in the text is on sex as a matter of communication and sharing, as well as a physical act. The authors repeatedly dispel the idea that pushing the "right" buttons in the "right" sequence will invariable lead to sexual ecstasy. Both noncoital and coital techniques are considered, including a number of practical pointers related to these activities. The second half of the chapter turns to a discussion of adult heterosexual behavior and attitudes toward such behavior. This section summarizes the relevant data from a broad spectrum of sex surveys, including Kinsey's studies, Morton Hunt's research, the "Redbook" survey, the Hite Report, and Blumstein and Schwartz's voluminous American Couples. Additional studies are cited on topics such as premarital sex, cohabitation, the frequency of marital coitus, other aspects of marital sex, alternative marriage styles (triads, group marriages), extramarital sex, and nonmarital sex. The authors repeatedly emphasize that research statistics alone do not "explain" the meaning or satisfaction of a particular type of sexual experience, and they help students see the potential advantages and disadvantages within each type of sexual behavior that is discussed.

While reading the chapter, the student is asked to consider these issues:

1. What are various techniques of heterosexual activity including communication, touching, oral-genital sex, anal sex, coital sex?

2. How do current attitudes about premarital sex influence its forms and frequency among males and females?

3. What is the current status of marital sex in terms of frequency, techniques, and sexual satisfaction ?

4. What would constitute a "good" marriage? What sexual elements would or wouldn't be involved?

5. Who engages in alternative marriage styles and why?

6. What is non-monogamy and what are its characteristics?

7. What are some forms of nonmarital sex and who is likely to participate in them?

LEARNING OBJECTIVES

At the conclusion of this chapter, the student should be able to:

1. Describe various techniques used in noncoital sex play.

2. Discuss the techniques of coital sex in terms of coital positions; list the advantages and disadvantages of each position.

3. Explain how stylistic variations of timing, tempo, and setting affect coital sex.

4. Discuss the methodological shortcomings of various survey studies about sexual behaviors and attitudes.

5. Identify the changes in premarital sexual behaviors and attitudes that have occurred during the past several decades.

6. Describe the patterns of marital sex behavior in terms of coital frequency, orgasm, techniques, and satisfaction in traditional marriages. Contrast these with the sexual aspects of alternative marriage styles.

7. Explain why the practice of extramarital sex is widespread today, and discuss the variety of reaction people tend to have to it.

8. Discuss the concept of non-monogamy and why it may be a useful research subject.

9. Contrast consensual extramarital sex with nonconsensual extramarital sex. Compare the many forms of consensual sex.

10. Describe several nonmarital sexual options and what motivates people to choose them.

TEACHING STRATEGIES

This chapter presents several different challenges to the instructor. First of all, some students may feel that to study heterosexual techniques puts the emphasis on sex as a kind of mechanical interaction, while others may be obsessed with learning the "right" way to engage in a particular form of sexual activity. The material needs to be put into perspective for students as neither a mechanical checklist nor a panacea to turn sex into instant ecstasy. Discussing sexual technique need not take away the joy of sex any more than discussing musical theory would detract from playing in (or listening to) a symphony. Similarly, learning about coital positions does not make one a great lover any more than reading about art makes one a great artist.

Second, some students may be disturbed by discussion of a variety of intercourse positions and techniques such as oral sex. The lecture should emphasize that these are merely options a person has the right to choose or reject. No one should feel any pressure to explore them. You can, however, make recommendations to students wishing to feel more comfortable with sexual activity such as oral or anal sex. If they wish to experiment (and find it consistent with their personal values), they might first try the activity at a slow, individual pace. They should feel free to stop at any time. Often shutting one's eyes, imagining some positive thoughts, or using a bridge such as whipped cream with oral sex, or lotion (without lanolin) with anal sex, may help.

Third, students should also be helped to realize that in sexual relations "more" is not necessarily "better." "More" may become mechanical, fatiguing, and distracting. Different positions may be used in a continuing sexual relationship to experiment with new feelings and to prevent boredom from setting in. However, to give students a real sense of the range of sexual behavior and attitudes among their peers, and help ease any feelings of discomfort or alienation from imagining themselves to be different, the instructor can distribute anonymous questionnaires about the frequency of sexual activity, the most frequently used sexual positions, experience with a variety of sexual techniques, and so on.

One topic not discussed in the text is the planning of sexual activity. Many couples think sex must be spontaneous or it is not likely to be romantic. Point out that planning sexual activity does not necessairly take the fun out of sex by comparing sex to a picnic. If one prepares for a picnic by making chicken, checking the weather, and inviting several close friends to come along, the picnic is often better than one created on the spur of the moment. In today's hectic relationships in which both partners are often working full time, sex can become regulated to a late-night activity when both partners are exhausted. Planning can set aside a special time free from other concerns when both partners can concentrate fully on one another. Anticipation of that special time can even add to the excitement.

Extramarital sex is a particularly important (and sometimes threatening) topic for students. How would they react if they discovered their spouse had an extramarital affair? How do these reactions compare to the data reviewed in the chapter? Students could also be asked to role-play the reactions of their parents to a spouse's infidelity. What are some patterns of response common to both generations? How do the generations differ in their attitudes and subsequent actions? Is divorce more likely in the older generation? Soliciting active emotional involvement, even in a hypothetical situation, often helps students work out their own anxieties about the topic.

One last point is in order. Students are sometimes overwhelmed by statistics from various surveys of sexual behavior. Be sure to explain to the class both the usefulness of these data and their limitations. This is a particularly good spot for reviewing problems in research sampling and volunteer bias, and for helping students learn how to interpret the findings of sex research.

STUDENT PROJECTS

1. Obtain a copy of a "swinger's" magazine or newspaper (which are easily obtained from an adult bookstore) and write an essay about your reactions to reading it. Why do you think people do it?

2. Write an essay from the viewpoint of the sex opposite your own describing the ideal features of a sexual partner. What aspects of sexual technique do you imagine would be important to this person?

3. Design a study to assess the sexual satisfaction of cohabiting heterosexual couples compared to married couples of the same age and with relationships of the same duration. What variables do you think to be most critical to your study, and what is your rationale?

PERSONAL REFLECTIONS

1. The authors suggest that communication is a major ingredient in sexual relationships. To what extent have you felt able to communicate your preferences and concerns to your own sex partners? How communicative have your partners been toward you? Are you ever worried that telling your partner what you do or don't like may be taken as a subtle form of criticism? How can you deal with this?

2. How do you feel about extramarital sex? Would your attitude be different for situations in which both spouses consent, in which one spouse secretly participates, in which the extramarital involvement is only a "one-night stand," or when a long-term extramarital affair is involved? Do you think extramarital sex is likely to help or hurt a marriage?

3. Make up a rating scale of the five most important items that you believe contribute to a satisfactory sexual relationship, with "1" being the most important. What has influenced you to rate them as you have? In your own intimate relationships, were any of the five items present?

4. What do you think are the advantages and disadvantages of cohabitation? Would you live with someone without being married? What do you believe is the primary allure of cohabitation?

172

CHAPTER 15 TEST QUESTIONS

Multiple Choice (* General Comprehension Questions)

1.* Sexual technique
     a. is one-dimensional and therefore easy to master.
     b. pertains only to physical interaction.
     c. is a matter of pushing the right buttons at the right
         time.
     d. is a matter of two-way communication regarding what feels
         good or what doesn't.

2.* Foreplay
     a. refers to something one does on the golf course.
     b. is a misleading term because intercourse is not always the
         focal point of sex.
     c. is the exact opposite of noncoital sex play.
     d. is another term for onanism.

3.* Changes in premarital sexual behavior during the past three
    decades is reflected in all of the following except
     a. greater degree of sexual experimentation.
     b. fewer unmarried men being sexually initiated by
         prostitutes.
     c. decrease in frequency of oral-genital sex
     d. increase in frequency of premarital coitus among women.

4.* Changes in marital coital behavior during the past three
    decades is reflected in all of the following except
     a. increase in frequency of oral-genital sex.
     b. use of wider varieties of sexual positions.
     c. decrease in amount of time spent in sexual play.
     d. increase in number of couples trying anal intercourse.

5.* Touching
     a. is not considered an important factor in intimate
         heterosexual relationships.
     b. is always a wordless demand to make love.
     c. in terms of techniques of heterosexual activity, involves
         only the hands.
     d. is a valuable source of comfort and security in intimate
         relationships.

6. During genital touching
     a. partners always enjoy the same types of stimulation.
     b. genital sensitivity often increases as erotic excitation
         mounts.
     c. the same kinds of touching movements are arousing at the
         beginning, middle, and end of a sexual encounter.
     d. women all respond to genital play in the same ways.

7. All of the following are mentioned as useful lubricants for the
    vaginal area except
     a. baby oil.

b. saliva.
c. perfumed lotions with a high alcohol content.
d. hypoallergenic lotions.

8. The use of a vibrator during sexual activity
   a. is always disliked by men who feel threatened by it.
   b. is just one dimension of sexual stimulation in which a partner's pleasure is increased.
   c. is utilized in masturbation and not partner sex.
   d. must be infrequent or the couple will get "hooked" on its use.

9. Men's preferences regarding penile stimulation are
   a. for direct manual stimulation of the glans of the penis by a partner.
   b. for very cold lotion or oil to be applied to the genitals.
   c. for an up-and-down stroking of the penis with the partner's fingers encircling the shaft.
   d. for very vigorous stimulation of a flaccid penis by a partner.

10. Fellatio is
    a. oral stimulation of the female genitals.
    b. manual stimulation of the frenulum of the penis.
    c. a fallacious belief that a partner wants sex when in fact this is untrue.
    d. oral stimulation of the male genitals.

11. The "gag reflex" alluded to in this chapter is
    a. a woman's reaction to her partner's bad jokes during foreplay.
    b. an imagined event only experienced by sexually inhibited women.
    c. a reflex response that is a real physiologic event.
    d. a reflex response that cannot be reconditioned.

12. If a woman consistently swallows her partner's semen, she will
    a. have acne-free skin.
    b. gain weight due to the high caloric content of the semen.
    c. prevent the formation of wrinkles on her face.
    d. suffer no health risks.

13. All of the following are true about oral-genital sex except
    a. the natural secretions of the genitals are quite clean.
    b. it is no less hygienic than mouth-to-mouth kissing.
    c. people who include it in their sexual repertoires are likely to be homosexual according to recent research.
    d. almost anyone can learn to feel comfortable about it.

14. Anal stimulation
    a. can be intensely pleasurable and lead to male or female orgasm.
    b. should never be the primary focus of sexual activity.
    c. is a physically dangerous activity.

d. will obliterate one's desire for intercourse.

15. The missionary position for coitus
    a. is the least used by couples in the U.S.
    b. refers to woman-on-top, face-to-face.
    c. gives the best chance for conception.
    d. is preferred by the majority of sexually active men.

16. "Doggy style" and "spoon style" refer to
    a. side-to-side, face-to-face positions.
    b. man-on-top, face-to-face positions.
    c. woman-on-top, face-to-face positions.
    d. rear entry positions.

17. According to recent surveys about premarital coitus
    a. recreational or casual sex is most common among young adults.
    b. 80% of adults still believe premarital intercourse is always wrong.
    c. young adults believe it is justified in the context of a long-term, committed relationship.
    d. there has been no increase in frequency for either young men or young women.

18. All of the following are examples of extramarital sex except
    a. one night stands.
    b. secretive relationships.
    c. consensual relationships.
    d. nonmarital sex.

19. Cohabitation
    a. is a practice limited to college students.
    b. is undertaken by 90% of the unmarried American populace.
    c. is legally distinguished from common-law marriage.
    d. has led to an increase in the divorce rate in the U.S.

20. According to data from surveys, marital sexual techniques have
    a. remained unchanged in the last 40 years.
    b. diversified in terms of coital positions used.
    c. changed only enough to allow the husbands greater options.
    d. shown a dramatic rise in anal intercourse with most women indicating this to be a preferred type of sexual activity.

21. The correlation between the frequency of marital sex and sexual satisfaction that Blumstein and Schwartz found
    a. indicated that performing and receiving oral sex was linked to sexual satisfaction for heterosexual women.
    b indicated that intercourse was more essential to sexual satisfaction for heterosexual men than heterosexual women.
    c. indicated that heterosexual men who give and receive oral sex are happier with their sex lives than those who don't.
    d. indicated that having sex once a month or less was the hallmark of sexual satisfaction since there were no performance pressures.

22. Individuals in group marriages tend to
    a. come from conservative religious backgrounds.
    b. have a high need to be dependent.
    c. enter the marriage for the same reasons two people might get married.
    d. come from conventional backgrounds that stress togetherness.

23. All of the following are true of triads except
    a. they consist of four or more partners who genuinely regard themselves as married to each other without a legally recognized relationship.
    b. they tend to form more naturally than larger group marriages.
    c. they are likely to be formed on the basis of pre-existing sexual relationships.
    d. sex is often not the primary reason behind this choice of alternative marriage style.

24. An infrequent but interesting aspect of nonmarital singlehood is
    a. communal living.
    b. swinging.
    c. open marriage.
    d. non-monogamy.

25. Blumstein and Schwartz found that
    a. one episode of non-monogamy was sure to start a person on a career of infidelity.
    b. people who attend church or synagogue regularly are as likely as anyone else to have extramarital sex.
    c. monogamy is no longer strongly held as a moral ideal in our society.
    d. more women than men are likely to seek casual sex outside a relationship.

True/False

F   1. Many people are permanently substituting living together arrangements for a marital relationship.

F   2. In swinging situations, female homosexual relationships are rare while male homosexual relationships are frequent.

T   3. An open marriage does not have to involve outside sexual relationships.

F   4. People who engage in extramarital sex almost always tell their spouses.

T   5. Triads often form more naturally than do larger group marriages.

T   6. How a married couple communicates is correlated with the

176

quality of their marital sex.

F   7. "Confused nonvirgins" refers to women who engage in sexual activity only while under the influence of drugs like cocaine.

T   8. The term "premarital sex" implies marriage is a logical goal of every person in our society; thus, it is misleading.

T   9. Many couples like a set sexual routine and do not find it to be boring.

F   10. Rear-entry intercourse is the most intimate form of intercourse.

T   11. Fellatio is often called a "blow job."

T   12. There are many similarities between male and female sexuality in terms of genital touching preferences.

F   13. In general, sexual behavior is very different outside of marriage than within a marriage.

T   14. Working married women engage in extramarital sex more often than do married housewives.

F   15. Sexual activity is primarily a matter of excellent technique.

Fill in the Blanks

1. Unmarried couples living together in heterosexual arrangements is called (cohabitation).

2. Almost (50%) of all marriages today will end in divorce, if present trends continue.

3. (Communal living) is where a group of people pool economic resources and personal energies; it involves emotional and sometimes sexual sharing.

4. A form of consensual extramarital sex where married couples exchange partners with other couples is called (swinging).

5. Most women do not enjoy (direct, sustained) stimulation of the clitoral glans during noncoital play.

6. Thr profile of people who engage in (group marriage) includes individuals with liberal, nonreligious backgrounds who have a high need for autonomy.

7. More than (90) % of Americans have married by their early thirties.

177

8. Since Kinsey's day, the average frequency of premarital coitus has (<u>increased</u>), particularly among women.

9. People who firmly believe that intercourse before marriage is improper are called (<u>adamant</u>) virgins.

10. (<u>Recreational</u>) sex is less common than relationship sex among today's teenagers.

11. (<u>Timing</u>) and tempo are important ingredients of lovemaking.

12. Penile-vaginal intercourse is also called (<u>coitus</u>).

13. K-Y jelly is an (<u>artificial lubricant</u>) that can be used as an aid in lovemaking.

14. A one-man, one-woman marriage is also called (<u>monogamy</u>).

15. A wordless way to communicate a willingness to make love is also known as (<u>touching</u>).

<u>Discussion/Essay Questions</u>

1. What is the importance of good communication in a sexual relationship?

2. Describe the four most common positions of coital sex.

3. How does our society feel about singlehood and sexual activity for a 27-year-old man? a 27-year-old woman? a 65-year-old man? a 65-year-old woman?

4. Discuss the positive and negative ways that extramarital sex can affect a marriage.

5. Compare cohabitation to marriage. What benefits are unique to each? How could the best of each lifestyle be successfully combined?

6. Why do so many people feel uncomfortable about oral-genital sex? What, if anything, should be done about it?

7. Given the changes in patterns of premarital sexual behavior during the past three decades, can you make any predictions about the future? What concerns might you have for your own children?

Chapter 16

HOMOSEXUALITY AND BISEXUALITY

OVERVIEW

Attitudes toward homosexuality have changed dramatically during the last quarter-century, and this chapter offers students a succinct but complete picture of homosexuality and bisexuality. Beginning with definitions of each, the chapter then examines homosexuality in historical perspective by tracing attitudes from biblical times through times in which homosexuality was relatively accepted or strongly opposed. Discussion then shifts to two important areas, theories on the origins of homosexuality (including biological theories, psychoanalytic views, behavioral theories) and dispelling the notion that homosexuals are psychologically maladjusted. A Research Spotlight examines the question of how sexual preference develops by focusing on the research protocol of Bell, Weinberg, and Hammersmith and their surprising findings. Next is a thought-provoking section on techniques of homosexual arousal, discovering homosexuality and the complexities of being gay in a straight society, the problems surrounding "coming out" (or the decision to "stay in the closet"), homophobia and its impact on homosexual individuals, homosexual couples, and homosexual relationships. There is discussion of the gay world, legal issues involving homosexuality, homosexual teachers, bisexuality, and bisexuals and gays in heterosexual marriages.

While reading the chapter, the student is asked to consider these issues:

1. What are homosexuality, bisexuality, ambisexuality, lesbianism, homophobia?

2. What have been the attitudes of different societies to homosexuality in times past? How do these contrast with current attitudes?

3. What are some theories about the causes of homosexuality?

4. How do the predominant sexual techniques of gay men and women compare with those of heterosexual men and women?

5. How does the diversity of homosexual lifestyles in fact compare with the widely held stereotypes about homosexual men and women?

6. What circumstances are conducive to bisexuality?

7. What factors are critical if bisexual or homosexual individuals are to maintain functioning heterosexual marriages?

LEARNING OBJECTIVES

At the conclusion of this chapter, the student should be able to:

1. Define the terms homosexual, bisexual, ambisexual, heterosexual, homophobia.

2. Outline the history of homosexuality from early Jewish tradition through the present day.

3. Identify and discuss the prevalent theories about the origins of sexual preference.

4. Discuss the prominent research studies and their conclusions about the psychological adjustment of homosexuals.

5. Describe some techniques of homosexual arousal and compare them to those used by heterosexuals.

6. Discuss stereotypes attributed to homosexuals and their lifestyles, and contrast these with facts presented in the text.

7. Describe the nature of the gay world.

8. Explain the underlying attitudes toward homosexuality that affect laws and law enforcement practices.

9. Compare and contrast homosexuality, bisexuality, heterosexuality.

10. List the types of homosexual feelings and behaviors that are included in Bell and Weinberg's typology of homosexualities.

11. Explain the rationale behind the practice of gays and bisexuals entering into heterosexual marriages.

TEACHING STRATEGIES

Many students have developed an attitude of sexual self-determination -- "You do your thing, I'll do mine." However, when confronted with an intimate interview with a homosexual couple or a film of explicit homosexual activity, strong prejudices are likely to surface. Therefore, an important goal of a human sexuality course is to help students learn more about their own feelings regarding all forms of sexuality. Another goal is to provide accurate information and exposure to a variety of sexual behaviors and attitudes in order to neutralize prejudices. Lectures on homosexuality should promote an attitude of respect for and increased comfort with sexual activity between mutually consenting same-sexed persons.

The text offers basic information for establishing such nonjudgmentalism by addressing the most common questions: What determines homosexuality? What are typical patterns of homosexual lifestyles? How accurate are the stereotypes? What are the processes of self-discovery, labeling, and coming out? Each of these questions can be explored in depth in the context of the class lecture.

Causation can be approached from the perspective of increasing the students' understanding of development of individual differences rather than from a viewpoint of deviance or illness. As the text notes, some homosexuals have intimacy problems with the opposite sex that are related to childhood traumas, just as some heterosexuals do. Common childhood interactions leading to such intimacy difficulties can be one topic of this presentation.

It is also important to emphasize the absence of a cause-effect relationship between childhood events and adult behavior. There may be numerous other manifestations of similar childhood experiences, and neurologic factors may eventually be shown to influence these manifestations. Postnatal events may also have an influence. It is valuable to map out some possible permutations of contributing factors. For example, homosexual activities which are quite common during childhood may continue after puberty if a same-sex partner is readily available and an opposite-sex partner is not. This may result in primarily homosexual fantasies during masturbation. If other factors are added, such as physical unattractiveness to the opposite sex, awkward dating skills, great fears about sexual performance, severe prohibitions or punishment related to coitus, or extreme fear of pregnancy, then homosexual interactions may become far more comfortable than heterosexual interactions. Describing these influences will further unravel some of the factors contributing to sexual development.

The process of labeling can also be the topic of a lecture. Some individuals who experience homosexual imagery (which is common among heterosexuals) label themselves as homosexual and then to polarize themselves from heterosexual contact. Once labeled, some male homosexuals may develop effeminate mannerisms as they begin to identify with their limited perception of the deviant groups [see C.A. Tripp, The Homosexual Matrix, New York: McGraw-Hill, 1975]. Ask students how mannerisms such as the limp wrist or the lisp have become established as homosexual gestures. After students are able to see the connection between labeling, gestures, and behavior, ask them how such polarization might be reversed through behavioral therapy. What components of heterosexual interaction do homosexuals need to learn or relearn? Also, how might self-esteem be enhanced when individuals begin to dislike themselves following same-sex sexual encounters? Suggestions for improving self-esteem may prove to be indirectly helpful to many class members.

Bisexuality is also a controversial discussion topic. Bisexuality can be positively considered "the best of both worlds" and "double the opportunity" or the bisexual can be negatively described as belonging to neither orientation, an outcast from both the straight and gay communities. Discuss these cognitive approaches and their different effects on the individual. It's rather incredible that whether one feels good or bad may be a result of how one cognitively labels the experience. Ask the class how a bisexual male who falls in love with and marries a woman is different from a married heterosexual male who occasionally experiences homosexual fantasies. Somehow, a common belief lingers that if a married man is aroused by fantasies of sex with other males, he will be forced to act on these fantasies, yet if he is aroused by other women he may not choose to commit adultery! Ask students to explain the logic of this.

The subject of homosexuality and bisexuality lends itself particularly well to the use of one or more guest speakers, since many groups in the gay community have speakers' bureaus to help combat homophobia and to assist students in seeing the gay perspective on social, legal, and sexual issues. Be certain to allow time for class discussion, and also discuss the presentation in advance with the guest speaker in order to outline the topics you would like him or her to cover.

One final note must be made. Many instructors have found that using films depicting gay male sexual activity provokes strong negative feelings in a sizable number of their male students. While, theoretically, this can help to desensitize students, in actuality it often provokes male students into further stereotyping homosexuals as sick, evil, loathsome. Each instructor must assess the potential risks and benefits here very carefully, for there can be a definite down-side to the use of explicit films about homosexual activity. A "compromise" solution is to use a film about lesbian sex, which seems to be far less threatening to both males and females.

STUDENT PROJECTS

1.   Attend a meeting of a gay liberation group. Did the experience change any of your attitudes about homosexuals?

2.   Read an issue of "The Advocate," a national homosexual newspaper. What insights into the gay lifestyle did this give you? Was the material discussed in the paper surprising to you?

3.   Role-play a discussion between two gay college students about the wisdom of "coming out." Suppose that one student is pre-med and the other is a musician and that both are from conservative, middle class families. What issues would be uppermost in their minds?

PERSONAL REFLECTIONS

1.   Are any of your friends, classmates, relatives homosexual? How did you learn of their sexual orientation? Did this knowledge alter your feelings about them?

2.   Imagine you are a homosexual who recently moved to a medium sized, conservative city and who is trying to meet someone with whom you could form an intimate relationship. How would you go about it? What might you be most worried about?

3.   Consider how your parents would feel if you told them you were homosexual or bisexual, and compare it to your reaction at being told that one of your parents is homosexual or bisexual.

4.   If you were a senior partner in a small law firm about to hire a new lawyer, and you had to choose between two applicants -- equally qualified in every respect but one of whom had candidly admitted to being gay -- what would you decide and why?

CHAPTER 16 TEST QUESTIONS

Multiple Choice (* General Comprehension Questions)

1.*   A person who considers himself or herself to be homosexual
      a.   must have had prior sexual experience in order to state the preference.
      b.   cannot be aroused by heterosexual partners.
      c.   is classified as mentally ill by the American Psychiatric Association.
      d.   has a preferential sexual attraction to people of the same sex over a significant period of time.

2.*   Homosexuality has
      a.   never been the preferred pattern of any culture.
      b.   only developed during the last hundred years.
      c.   is accepted or even expected in some societies.
      d.   never been a basis for a judicial decision.

3.*   Heterosexuality, homosexuality, and bisexuality
      a.   exist along a continuum in real life.
      b.   are equivalent behaviors.
      c.   have nothing in common with one another.
      d.   are learned behaviors only.

4.*   The cause of homosexuality
      a.   is genetic.
      b.   is due to prenatal hormonal exposure only.
      c.   is due to trauma in the birth canal during labor.
      d.   is not really known.

5.*   Research studies conducted to determine the psychological adjustment of homosexual and lesbian subjects have found
      a.   homosexuals are always emotionally healthy.
      b.   the majority of homosexuals are well-adjusted, productive people.
      c.   homosexuals have a very high rate of alcoholism.
      d.   homosexuality is typically associated with manic-depression.

6. Many of the negative attitudes about homosexuality that dominated Western thought until the 18th century were
   a. expressions of a medical viewpoint.
   b. described in the <u>Wolfenden Report.</u>
   c. promulgated as a contradiction to the Inquisition's approval of homosexuality.
   d. derived from the writings of St. Augustine and Thomas Aquinas.

7. Bieber's research found that homosexual
   a. women generally had strong affection for their mothers.
   b. men were typically only children.
   c. women were low achievers in school.
   d. men often had passive fathers and dominant mothers.

8. Behavioral theories about sexual orientation state all of the following except
   a. sexual fantasies can be conditioned.
   b. homosexuality is primarily a learned phenomenon.
   c. people who experience unpleasant heterosexual encounters usually become hypersexual with opposite-sex partners.
   d. children who show atypical gender-role behavior may have a greater likelihood of becoming homosexual.

9. Homophobia
   a. is a variant of fellatio performed by homosexuals.
   b. is a variant of cunnilingus performed by lesbians.
   c. is the hostility and fear many people have towards homosexuals.
   d. refers to the gay liberation movement's legal status.

10. The physiological responses of homosexual men and women, according to Masters and Johnson
    a. are no different from those of their heterosexual counterparts.
    b. differ only in laboratory settings, but not when tested at home.
    c. differ in both quality and quantity.
    d. seem to differ only in intensity of response.

11. The erotic techniques of homosexual couples
    a. are more bound by convention than those of heterosexual couples.
    b. tend to pay greater attention to stylistic matters than do those of heterosexual couples.
    c. bear no relationship to the techniques of heterosexual couples.
    d. lead to totally different physiological responses than are found in heterosexual couples.

12. Committed lesbian couples tend to engage in all of the following except
    a. extended periods of breast touching and caressing.
    b. manual stimulation of the genitals in a teasing pattern.

c.   cunnilingus as the preferred technique for reaching orgasm.

d.   use of a dildo or insertion of a finger deep into the vagina as the preferred technique for reaching orgasm.

13.   Committed male homosexual partners tend to engage in all of the following except
a.   anal intercourse.
b.   fellatio.
c.   cunnilingus.
d.   nipple stimulation.

14.   Blumstein and Schwartz surveyed 772 lesbian couples and 3,547 married heterosexual couples and found
a.   lesbians had genital sexual activity more often than married heterosexuals.
b.   lesbians had genital sexual activity less often than married heterosexuals.
c.   only 2% of lesbians had any form of genital sexual activity, preferring full body contact instead.
d.   lesbian sexual activity was exactly the same as heterosexual sexual activity.

15.   Male homosexuals who are committed couples
a.   are more goal-oriented in their sexual behavior than heterosexual counterparts.
b.   usually stop having sex at about the five year mark in their relationships.
c.   tend to take their time in whatever form of sexual interaction they are involved in.
d.   generally move quickly through both the excitement and plateau stages of arousal.

16.   A common stereotype about homosexual behavior is that
a.   homosexuals start out as pedophiles.
b.   homosexuals all engage in masochistic sexual games such as "bondage."
c.   male homosexuals almost all become hairdressers or interior decorators.
d.   homosexuals are afraid of sex.

17.   "Fisting" or "handballing" refers to
a.   athletic games many homosexual health clubs offer their members.
b.   the practice of hitting the male partner's testicles to achieve an intense orgasm.
c.   a form of anal sex that has many associated health risks.
d.   the practice of homosexual intercourse in which one partner stands on his head, supported by his hands, while the other inserts a dildo in the partner's mouth.

18.   Discovering one's homosexuality is a process that
a.   occurs definitively during childhood.
b.   is likely to occur during adolescence for males.

c. does not include trying to fit a heterosexual mold.
d. occurs only if the person is exposed to gay role models.

19. Open-coupled homosexuals
    a. have no sexual problems and few sexual partners.
    b. live in one-to-one same-sex relationships similar to heterosexual marriages.
    c. tend to spend a relatively large amount of time cruising.
    d. are not "coupled" and are low in sexual interest and activity.

20. According to Bell and Weinberg, "coming out" regarding one's sexual orientation
    a. is less likely to occur in people with more education or higher income than those with lower social status.
    b. is only possible when the person is involved in a long-term committed homosexual relationship.
    c. is easier when one comes out first by telling heterosexual friends and family, then their gay friends.
    d. is a simple, straightforward matter.

21. Gay men have increasingly been choosing monogamy or close-coupled relationships probably because of
    a. the herpes scare.
    b. the AIDS epidemic.
    c. tax benefits to committed couples.
    d. the mumps epidemic.

22. The legal rights accorded to homosexual individuals now include
    a. the right to be employed by the F.B.I. and C.I.A.
    b. tax exempt status for gay organizations.
    c. automatic child custody to lesbian mothers in spite of their sexual orientation.
    d. the right to leave the military with honorable discharges.

23. Bisexuals are sometimes called all of the following except
    a. switch-hitters.
    b. ball and chainers.
    c. AC/DC.
    d. people who swing both ways.

24. All of the following are circumstances that are conducive to bisexuality except
    a. group sex.
    b. experimentation in a relationship with a close friend.
    c. a personal belief system that translates into a bisexual philosophy.
    d. incest.

25. According to Masters and Johnson, ambisexual individuals were
    a. the same in every way as the bisexual group they studied.
    b. very picky about the physical attractiveness of their potential partners.
    c. had divided preferences for the gender of their partners.

    d.   never became involved in committed sexual relationships.

True/False

T   1.   Until recently, laws in our society have been strongly anti-homosexual.

F   2.   "A form of experimentation which adds spice to one's life but doesn't become the main course" describes celibacy.

T   3.   Relatively few of the people who are aware of their same-sex feelings prior to marriage disclose them to their prospective spouse.

T   4.   Homosexual teachers do not molest or seduce students more frequently than heterosexual teachers do.

F   5.   One-half of homosexual men and two-thirds of homosexual women have been married at least once according to research surveys.

F   6.   Heterosexuality, bisexuality, and homosexuality are distinct biological phenomena with no possible overlap.

T   7.   There is no firm agreement as to the cause or causes of homosexuality.

T   8.   In Western society, socialization tends to orient both straight and gay men to sexual variety.

T   9.   Male homosexuals may be at a disadvantage in learning intimacy and relationship skills because they have few role models to follow.

F   10.   Homosexual women tend to have more sexual partners than homosexual men do.

T   11.   Many homosexuals choose to pass as heterosexuals to avoid social stigma and economic repercussions.

F   12.   Lesbians are more likely to have difficulty accepting their homosexuality than are gay men.

T   13.   Homosexual couples frequently discuss genital stimulation techniques with their partners to learn what is most pleasing.

T   14.   No current psychological tests are able to distinguish between homosexuals and heterosexuals.

F   15.   There is no difference between discovering homosexuality and accepting it.

Fill in the Blanks

1. A "6" on Kinsey's Heterosexual-Homosexual Rating Scale indicates (exclusive homosexuality).

2. The Greek root "homo" in the word "homosexual" means (same).

3. The work of (Evelyn Hooker) in 1957 was one of the first studies to demonstrate that homosexuality was not necessarily a form of psychological maladjustment.

4. A study by Kallman found (100) % concordance in identical twins for male homosexuality. However, this finding has not been replicated.

5. Some studies of hormone levels in homosexual men found higher estrogen levels and lower (testosterone) levels than in heterosexual men.

6. Freud believed that homosexuality was an outgrowth of an innate (bisexual) predisposition in all people.

7. Wolf believed that female homosexuality arose from a girl's receiving (inadequate) amounts of love from her mother coupled with a poor relationship with her father.

8. Many psychoanalysts believe that homosexuality results from incapacitating fears of (castration).

9. The (stereotypes) about homosexuals and lesbians are largely inaccurate.

10. One of the health risks of "fisting" is (damage to the anus, or contracting hepatitis B).

11. One study found that (lesbians) had more frequent orgasms, a greater number of partners, and a higher degree of sexual satisfaction than heterosexual women.

12. Deliberately searching for a sexual partner in the gay community is known as (cruising).

13. (Coming out) is the process of announcing one's homosexuality to family and friends.

14. (Functional) homosexuals weren't coupled, had few sexual problems, and had a high number of sexual partners in the Bell and Weinberg study.

15. A deadly disease that is afflicting the gay community predominantly is (AIDS).

Discussion/Essay Questions

1. Statistically speaking, male homosexuals are less likely to form long-term monogamous bonds than are lesbians. Why is this the case?

2. In what ways, and why, has society become more tolerant of homosexuality during the past twenty years?

3. What are some common homophobic prejudices? Do they have any basis in fact?

4. Why are bisexuals often rejected by both the homosexual and heterosexual communities?

5. How might the developmental factors contributing to lesbianism differ from those contributing to male homosexuality?

6. What are some of the current legal issues homosexuals are battling and trying to change? In what areas has change occurred; in what areas does change seem to be far off?

7. Why do some male homosexuals have difficulty becoming intimate with a woman while others choose to marry and maintain a dual life? Do male homosexual's intimacy problems differ at all from those of a male heterosexual?

8. What are the necessary conditions for a heterosexual marriage to survive and flourish with one of its members "out of the closet?"

9. How do men and women tend to react when they discover their marital partners are homosexual or lesbian?

Chapter 17

THE VARIETIES OF SEXUAL BEHAVIOR

OVERVIEW

Diversity is the hallmark of human behavior, and in few realms is this diversity more apparent than in studying sexual behavior. After initially acquainting students with the complexities of defining sexual normality and the impact of labeling and stigmatization, this chapter surveys some of the less well-known forms of sexual behavior. In addition to familiarizing students with the various paraphilias (fetishism, transvestism, voyeurism exhibitionism, sadomasochism, pedophilia, and so on) and their psychological meanings, the authors discuss hypersexuality, celibacy, and the various types of prostitution. The chapter concludes with an examination of the legal aspects of sexual behavior.

While reading the chapter, the student is asked to consider these issues:

1. Why is defining "normal" sexual behavior difficult? How do labeling and stigmatization influence a definition?

2. What are some common fetishes, and who is likely to become a particular kind of fetishist? How can a fetishist be helped?

3. What are some common and bizarre paraphilias? What sort of person is likely to become a particular kind of paraphiliac? How can paraphiliacs be helped?

4. What are the ways in which nymphomania and satyriasis are distinguished from a hearty sexual appetite?

5. Why is celibacy a viable sexual option for some people and not for others?

6. How can prostitution be defined from the legal, cultural, and psychological perspectives? How do forms of female and male prostitution differ?

7. What are some legal aspects of sexual behavior, current United States statutes, and changes underway in the law?

LEARNING OBJECTIVES

At the conclusion of this chapter, the student should be able to:

1. Discuss the complexities inherent in determining sexual normalcy, describe patterns of labeling and stigmatization, and explain why labels often lead to stigmatization.

2. Describe the continuum of sexual behavior in terms of the factors that affect normalcy or abnormality.

3. Define paraphilia and distinguish it from sporadic sexual experimentation.

4. Identify the major types of paraphilias and describe their characteristics.

5. Discuss the causes of paraphilias.

6. Identify the most common therapeutic approaches for the treatment of paraphilias and discuss the ethical questions raised by their use.

7. Define hypersexuality and identify the labels assigned to men and women considered to be oversexed.

8. Describe celibacy and discuss its characteristics including motivations and purposes.

9. Discuss male and female prostitution in terms of motivations, advantages, disadvantages.

10. Outline the categories of sexual behavior that are regulated by law.

TEACHING STRATEGIES

Students tend to have a fascination for details about unusual people and unusual practices. For this reason, the chapter on sexual variations is likely to be the most interesting to them. Nobody knows the incidence of paraphilias, but the frequency with which the problem is found in clinics and police reports suggests that the rate is probably higher than most students would guess. Paraphilias can be distinguished as noxious or benign. A benign paraphilia does not (1) involve imposing oneself on another, (2) interfere with establishing a mutually satisfying relationship, (3) include inflicting physical or psychological harm on oneself or another. Cross-dressing is an example of benign sexual behavior. Should transvestites be treated by the psychiatric profession, be locked up by the legal profession, or simply be left alone? Should they be labeled as "deviant," "perverse," "disturbed," or "variant"? The fact is that the psychiatric profession has been notoriously unsuccessful in curing fetishes, and rehabilitation programs within prisons and mental institutions are practically nonexistent. The best solution may be to <u>allow</u> people to be different. One goal of this course should be to encourage such an accepting and tolerant attitude, until programs and procedures exist that can reliably reverse such problems.

It is much more difficult to be nonjudgmental about the noxious paraphilias (those involving coercion or harm). What should be done with the exhibitionist or child molester? If they are imprisoned, they usually are released and may reoffend. Some authorities believe that a prison term may maximize the probability of reoccurrence because it is so unlikely that rehabilitation will be achieved or interpersonal skills learned there. Ask students to discuss rationales for imprisonment and potential alternatives. It has been documented that some noxious paraphilias can be rehabilitated. How might the government choose individuals with the highest probability of being rehabilitated, and provide treatment in each community? When one child molester reoffends, ask students to speculate about what political pressures might be placed on such treatment centers. Can the public be educated about paraphilias or is the issue too sensitive?

The instructor should explain and demonstrate how difficult it can be to avoid stigmatizing certain kinds of people. For example, few of us are able to set aside our moral values in order to uncritically accept the woman who makes her living as a prostitute. Yet in our age of increasing premarital and extramarital sex, it is often the individual who is unable to find partners for conventional sexual activity who gains sexual release through prostitutes. This outlet, however undesirable, can be superior to a life with no sexual activity. Having the students wrestle with such issues from the standpoints of client, prostitute, lawmaker, and citizen can provide a valuable perspective about human behavior, hopefully increasing the students' abilities to be objective about sensitive issues.

Stigmatization can be further discussed when examining hypersexuality. Why do males seem to joke so much about nymphomania? Why is the woman labeled as a nymphomaniac likely to be seen as "deviant" while her male counterpart is probably just labeled as "macho"? What is the difference between a person with a hearty sexual appetite and a person labeled hypersexual?

At the opposite end of the frequency spectrum is celibacy. Some students are unwilling to consider the possibility that celibacy, even as a temporary lifestyle choice, has any potential benefits. Other students may endorse celibacy as an ideal. Encourage students to discuss the pros and cons of celibacy and see if a class consensus develops about the subject.

Legal aspects of sexual behavior can be approached in several different ways. You can prepare a synopsis for your students about the local and state laws that apply to sexual behavior in your own college jurisdiction. You can invite a lawyer or a law enforcement official to give a lecture on the topic. Ideally, it would be helpful to have someone who represents a conservative approach and someone who is more liberal presenting at the same time to ensure the broadest coverage of the subject. A panel discussion involving a vice-squad policeman, a district attorney, a judge, and a representative of the American Civil Liberties Union would be ideal. Another way of teaching this topic would be to focus on the details of one or two recent court cases in your own vicinity that involve sex crimes, using these concrete examples as a springboard for fuller discussion. Offering an outline of the American Bar Association's Modern Penal Code that pertains to this area can help your students immensely.

STUDENT PROJECTS

1. Interview a judge, a lawyer, a court-appointed social worker to find out how people convicted of child molestation are dealt with. What criteria determine whether someone is sentenced to prison or put on probation? What treatment programs exist? What aspects of existing treatment programs seem to work and which seem less successful? How are repeat offenders handled? What are the stresses of dealing with such individuals?

2. Interview a district attorney or a police officer from the vice squad to discuss "victimless" crimes. Is it valuable to prosecute prostitutes or is it a waste of time and taxpayers' money? Are statutes forbidding nonmarital sex or certain types of marital sex ever enforced in your locale? If so, under what circumstances, and how can evidence be collected?

3. Write an editorial for your college newspaper opposing or favoring the legalization of prostitution.

PERSONAL REFLECTIONS

1. Do you consider your own sexual behavior normal? Why?

2. If your brother or sister told you that he or she was experiencing symptoms of one of the paraphilias, what would you do? Would you try to obtain help? What people or agencies would you go to for help? What kind of personal advice would you offer? What kinds of relevant questions would you ask to make sure your sibling really suffered from a paraphilia?

3. How do you feel about the legalization of prostitution? Do you think this would be beneficial or detrimental to American society? At the present time, do you think there are any effective ways of curbing prostitution?

4. What was your reaction to reading about the types of paraphilias and the variety of sexual behavior? Were you repulsed or did you end up empathic, sympathetic, objective? How do you think society's understanding of the many forms of unusual sexual behavior might affect their actual occurrence?

CHAPTER 17 TEST QUESTIONS

Multiple Choice (* General Comprehension Questions)

1.* One of the most perplexing problems in sexology today is
  a. trying to define homosexuality.
  b. trying to define what is sexually normal and abnormal.
  c. trying to find the G-spot.
  d. trying to define orgasm.

2.* Learning about the less typical variations of sexual behavior
  a. decreases one's tolerance for others.
  b. desensitizes a person so that he or she can try out the atypical sexual behavior.
  c. increases one's tolerance for others.
  d. puts one at risk for paraphilias.

3.* Anyone who attempts to define "normal" should understand that
  a. no definition is possible since one person doesn't have the right to judge another.
  b. the definition can be arbitrary since it involves value judgments.
  c. there is always a clearcut separation between abnormal and normal.
  d. the definition is time-specific and does not apply to behavior viewed in a continuum.

4.* The process of labeling
  a. can lead to stigmatization.
  b. is the same as stigmatization.
  c. is the result of stigmatization.
  d. never fosters acceptance, always fosters rejection.

5.* The term "paraphilia" refers to
  a. the process of stigmatization a person can be subjected to.
  b. sexually oriented paraphernalia of any sort from the 1960's.
  c. a condition in which a person's sexual arousal depends on an unusual fantasy theme.
  d. a collection of pornographic reading materials from the 1950's.

6. A person with a full-blown paraphilia
  a. is so anxious to get to do it that he or she becomes exceptionally competent in other areas of life.
  b. is more likely to be a woman than a man.
  c. is usually so inventive that the paraphilia changes from week to week.
  d. is so psychologically dependent on it that other areas of sexual activity lose their turn-on potential.

194

7. In fetishism, sexual arousal occurs principally in response to
    a. young boys.
    b. young girls.
    c. an inanimate object or body part not primarily sexual in nature.
    d. animals.

8. An object that has served as a fetish is likely to be
    a. something that has never been worn.
    b. something used to produce a sexual high, such as a vibrator.
    c. some kind of specific material as rubber, leather, silk, or fur.
    d. something very obvious or loud that will call attention to the fetishist.

9. A transvestite is
    a. a lesbian female "in drag."
    b. a male who is in the process of deciding whether or not to undergo transsexual surgery.
    c. a female impersonator.
    d. a heterosexual male who cross-dresses for sexual arousal.

10. All of the following are true about transvestites except
    a. most transvestites are exclusively homosexual.
    b. the wives of many transvestites help their husbands with make-up or clothing.
    c. they can be distinguished from female impersonators.
    d. their behavior usually begins in childhood or early adolescence.

11. Voyeurs are people who
    a. are always harmless since they avoid personal contact.
    b. often have difficulty forming heterosexual relationships.
    c. are generally older men, past the years of male menopause.
    d. are attracted to nudist camps and nudist beaches.

12. An exhibitionist
    a. is usually someone in his or her forties or fifties.
    b. is usually very sexually active in other facets of heterosexual activity.
    c. seems to be pushed by an "uncontrollable urge" which leads to impulsive behavior.
    d. is rarely caught by the police and does not want to be caught.

13. Sadism is best defined as
    a. intentional, repeated infliction of pain on another person in order to achieve sexual excitement.
    b. a condition in which a person derives sexual arousal from being hurt.
    c. engaging in sexual contact with animals.
    d. a sexual attraction to amputations.

14. All of the following are true about pedophilia and pedophiles except
    a. the majority of pedophiles are male.
    b. most of the victims are boys between the ages of eight and eleven.
    c. the child molester is a relative of the victim about 15% of the time.
    d. most pedophiles are heterosexual.
15. The paraphilia that is the cause for the most police arrests is
    a. voyeurism.
    b. obscene phone calls.
    c. zoophilia.
    d. exhibitionism.

16. All of the following are examples of hypersexuality except
    a. satyriasis.
    b. nymphomania.
    c. Don Juanism.
    d. celibacy.

17. Women who become prostitutes usually
    a. do so because they truly enjoy sexual encounters.
    b. have orgasms in their business contacts as well as in their private lives.
    c. are closet lesbians.
    d. do so because of economic necessity.

18. In the United States, laws about sexual behavior
    a. are uniform between the states.
    b. have defined both "victimless" and "victim" crimes in a uniform manner.
    c. are mostly found at the state or local level.
    d. are enforced in a strict and uniform manner.

19. All of the following are illegal in some states except
    a. seduction.
    b. fornication.
    c. cunnilingus.
    d. celibacy.

20. The laws against prostitution are often
    a. directed against decoys who roam the streets.
    b. directed against loitering in public places for the purpose of solicitation.
    c. on the verge of changing to decriminalize the business by 1986.
    d. structured so that when convicted, the prostitute must pay a large fine, often as high as 50% of her annual wages.

21. Sexual arousal resulting from rubbing the genitals against the body of a fully clothed person in crowded situations such as subways, buses, or elevators is
    a. necrophilia.
    b. coprophilia.

c. frotteurism.
d. apotemnophilia.

22. The paraphiliac
    a. actively seeks therapy for the problem.
    b. gets little or no real pleasure from the behavior.
    c. gets such intense pleasure from the behavior that giving it up is unthinkable.
    d. can be treated with drugs to drastically increase testosterone on a temporary basis.

23. The adult who is accused and/or convicted of having sex with a child is usually labeled a
    a. pedopsychopath.
    b. public nuisance.
    c. exhibitionist.
    d. child abuser.

24. Abnormal sexual behavior is usually judged as severe when
    a. it operates within cultural norms.
    b. it occurs infrequently but with explosiveness.
    c. it becomes a matter of great psychological dependence.
    d. the person outwardly appears to be normal in terms of psychosocial functioning.

25. Noncoital acts
    a. are considered illegal even if done in private by consenting adult partners in many states.
    b. do not include cunnilingus and fellatio in the legal definition.
    c. do not include homosexual acts in the legal definition.
    d. include fornication and adultery in the legal definition.

True/False

T 1. Behavior that is defined as "normal" may vary from culture to culture and may vary over time.

F 2. The negative effect of paraphilias is called stigmatization.

F 3. A fetish refers to sporadic sexual experimentation.

T 4. Transsexuals are not usually sexually aroused by cross-dressing.

T 5. Most transvestites are exclusively heterosexual.

F 6. Exhibitionists are usually sexually active, extroverted men.

F 7. All current sex researchers are in agreement that there is a positive side to pedophilia.

T   8.   The voyeur is most sexually excited in situations in which the risk of discovery is high.

F   9.   Bestiality and zoophilia are the same things.

F   10. A regressed pedophile is often an antisocial person who may feel hostility toward women.

T   11. There is no single pattern of sexual activity that fits all pedophiles.

F   12. Klismaphilia is sexual excitement resulting from contact with urine.

F   13. There are several serious health risks known to result from celibacy.

T   14. Seduction is legally defined as a situation in which a woman is enticed into sexual intercourse by a promise of marriage.

T   15. Noncoital sexual acts are often referred to as "crimes against nature" in legal statutes.

Fill in the Blanks

1.   A behavioral technique used to treat paraphiliacs that can include use of electric shocks is called (aversion) therapy.

2.   Engaging in sex for pay is called (prostitution).

3.   Legal statutes define (adultery) as extramarital intercourse.

4.   A number of states have adopted the (Modern Penal Code) which recommends the abolition of laws that regulate private sexual behavior between consenting adults.

5.   A paraphilia peculiar to the 20th century is (obscene telephone calling).

6.   Another term for a voyeur is a (Peeping Tom).

7.   Sexual arousal from viewing or having sexual contact with a corpse is called (necrophilia).

8.   (Hypersexual) people have high sex drives which rarely lead to more than fleeting gratification.

9.   Self-mutilation can be an extreme form of (masochism).

10. "Sexual psychopath" is the legal term for a (paraphiliac).

11. (Anti-androgens) are drugs that temporarily lower testosterone levels and are used to treat paraphiliacs.

12. In (fetishism) sexual arousal occurs primarily in response to an inanimate object or body part that isn't primarily sexual.

13. (Coprophilia) is sexual arousal deriving from contact with feces.

14. The intentional infliction of pain on another is a form of (sadism).

15. "Scores" is one term for a (prostitute's) customers.

Discussion/Essay Questions

1. Explain what is meant by labeling and stigmatization. Give several examples drawn both from the text and from your own experiences.

2. Explain five types of paraphilias and list them in order from least to most socially offensive. Why did you rank them this way?

3. How could periodic celibacy in a relationship be beneficial? Do you know of any religions in which celibacy in marriage is required?

4. What are some possible cultural reasons that the incidence of paraphilias is much higher in males than in females?

5. Some paraphiliacs appear to be addicted to obtaining sexual gratification in an atypical manner. What is an addiction? How does a paraphilia compare with a drug addiction?

6. What are some biological and developmental explanations for paraphilias?

7. Data suggest that some exhibitionists spontaneously stop exposing themselves around the age of 30. If this is true, speculate about the possible reasons for it.

8. Prostitution is illegal in most of the U.S., yet it occurs everywhere. Given unlimited resources, how would you stop the practice of illegal prostitution? What would be the possible consequences to society of no longer being able to purchase sexual favors?

9. What would be the consequences of changing all laws regulating sexual behavior in America to legalize any form of private sexual activity between consenting adults? Explain why you think this would be a wise or unwise reform.

Chapter 18

COERCIVE SEX: THE VARIETIES OF SEXUAL ASSAULT

OVERVIEW

The subject of sexual assault is steeped in myth and laden with emotionalism. This chapter provides an objective, up-to-date review of current research, opinion, legislation, and social trends in this controversial area. The opening section discusses rape from an historical perspective, then debunks several of the most common myths about rape, and describes typical patterns of rape including a Research Spotlight on the "Rape of Men by Women" and a lengthy discussion of date rape and marital rape -- two forms of violence that are much more common than previously realized. Attention is then turned to the plight of the rape victim (from medical, legal, and psychological viewpoints) before describing what is known about men who rape. By juxtaposing discussions of incest and sexual harrassment at work and at school with discussion of rape, students are helped to see the parallel dimensions of coercion in these situations. The current legal definition of sexual harrassment is presented and what steps to take should you be a victim are elucidated. Similarly, a Boxed Item, "If You Have Ever Been Involved in Incest" offers practical suggestions about dealing with the experience of incest. The concluding section of the chapter examines the cultural underpinnings of coercive sex and what is necessary to reduce the frequency of sexual victimization in our society.

While reading the chapter, the student is asked to consider these issues:

1. What are the elements of coercive sex?

2. What is rape? What are the types of rape? Who are likely targets for the rapists? What is the profile of the rapist?

3. What are the medical, legal, and psychological needs of the rape victim, the family members of the victim?

4. How have law enforcement agencies and the legal system been deficient in handling rape cases in the past, and what changes have recently occurred to rectify these deficiencies?

5. What are the three stages of psychological reaction to rape? What are some long-term effects of rape for the victim and her (his) spouse or sexual partner?

6. How can incest affect a person's later sexual behavior?

7. Why is sexual harassment at work and school sexual coercion? How do victims of such coercion usually react? How can gender role stereotyping contribute to sexual harassment or coercion?

8. What children are most likely to be found working in the child pornography business? How can participation in this affect them psychologically? What do situations of incest and child pornography have in common?

LEARNING OBJECTIVES

At the conclusion of this chapter, the student should be able to:

1. State the legal definition of rape and incest.

2. Describe the early laws against rape and the myths about rape.

3. Identify the patterns of rape.

4. Explain the legal considerations facing rape victims.

5. State the phases of the aftermath of rape.

6. Outline the general characteristics of convicted rapists and discuss their patterns of rape.

7. Identify the common myths about incest and state the facts that override these myths.

8. Discuss the various patterns of incest and the research findings about the effects of incest on its victims.

9. Identify the situations in which sexual harassment occurs.

10. Discuss the current laws against sexual harassment.

11. Discuss the cultural and societal attitudes and practices that foster sex victimology.

TEACHING STRATEGIES

College students need to discuss in detail the following questions about sexual assault: What causes a person to force himself or herself physically on another person? What are the consequences of assault to the victim? How frequently do such events occur? How can the trauma of coercive sex be minimized? What should the student do if she or he directly or indirectly encounters an incident of sexual assault? How has media coverage of sexual offenses changed in the last few decades, and what are the political consequences of these changes? The instructor can use the text as a solid starting point for discussion and analysis of these questions.

A human sexuality class should help students not only to achieve a sympathetic appreciation of the plight of <u>victims</u> of coercive sex but also to the plight of the <u>offenders</u>. What, for example, should society do with offenders? The most common public attitude is to lock them up and "throw away the key." However, most sex offenders are given a limited prison sentence and eventually return to the streets to commit further offenses. Most rapists are on the street -- not in prison. Forgetting economic restraints for a moment, what would be a more rational approach to the problem? What types of rehabilitation for the rapist would make intuitive sense? Keep in mind that the text emphasizes that rape is a crime of hostility and rage rather than of sexual passion. The typical offender is an emotionally weak and insecure person who has learned to cope with life's stresses by striking out. For the rapist, sex has become intertwined with rage, frustration, and revenge against women. Some rapists actually believe that women invite assault. Help students create a behavioral profile of the offender who has other specific deficits. Designing such a profile will spark additional ideas for rehabilitation. Students will begin to appreciate the task confronting many behavioral therapists and their varied approaches to the same questions.

Another aspect of discussing the topic of rape has to do with very practical issues. Should a woman scream, fight, run, or resign herself to cooperation if she is assaulted? Should she carry a weapon, knife, aerosol tear gas, or take a self-defense course? There are many professionals who offer contradictory advice. This can be frightening, since a woman may react as she has been trained but thereby increase her chances of being injured or even killed. The Boxed Item in the text, "Rape and Self-Defense," reviews some of the experts' advice. Discussion should cover the range of particular reactions in different rape situations: for example, reaction to rape on a dark, lonely street would probably be different than one's reaction to date rape in one's own home.

Incest is an emotionally charged subject that can be made even moreso because some students may have been sexually approached by an adult during their own childhoods. The discussion can be quite sensitive. Some state laws require that anyone who knows of a sexual offense to a child must report it to authorities. This includes health professionals who are trying to help the offender. How can a psychotherapist help a patient if the therapist/patient confidentiality has been breached? What are the possible effects on a child who is asked to testify against a parent in an incest case? What other alternatives are feasible?

The subject of sexual harassment at work or school is one that has not generally been discussed in depth and so the students may be surprised or even shocked by the material, especially as it applies to school. You can help the class consider the dimensions of this problem by defining several hypothetical situations of varying degrees of coercion. For example, if a secretary wears tight-fitting sweaters and skirts to work does this mean she is inviting her boss to make a sexual pass at her? What is the difference between a boss dating an employee and developing a sexual relationship and a boss who demands sexual "favors" as a condition of employment. How does the class feel about Phyllis Schlafly's remark quoted in the photo caption? What would the students do if they found out about sexual harassment occuring in one of their classes?

The concluding segment of the lecture or class discussion should turn to the question of how to prevent coercive sex and its resulting sexual victimization. While it is unlikely your students will develop a perfect blueprint, try to encourage them to hypothesize about areas needing further attention and social change. Awareness can be an important first step towards prevention!

STUDENT PROJECTS

1. Attend a court trial of a sexual assault case and report to the class about it. Include in your discussion how you felt emotionally as well as your intellectual response to the case.

2. Visit a rape crisis center (these can be located either through the Yellow Pages or by contacting the National Center for the Prevention and Control of Rape, Room 10003, Parklawn Building, 5600 Fishers Lane, Rockville, MD 20857) to review the programs and pamphlets that are available in your community. Is there a 24-hour rape hotline? Do they sponsor any rape prevention programs? Do they arrange for long-term counseling? Review their statistics on patterns of rape in your community. Report all this to your class.

3. Interview a social worker from a local family and children's agency who specializes in dealing with incest. What types of treatment programs are available for incest victims and their families? What are the most common patterns of incest that they encounter? What is their counseling success rate?

4. Interview a woman executive from a large corporation. How does her company familiarize employees with the problem of sexual harassment at work? How are complaints handled? Have there been any instances of firing or demoting employees because of sexual harassment?

5. Prepare a questionnaire about sexual harassment to be administered at your school. Administer it. What were the results? What was your reaction to the results?

PERSONAL REFLECTIONS

1. If your best female friend had been raped, how would you react? What would you do or say to try to help her? What would you want a friend or relative to do or say for you if you had been raped or otherwise sexually assaulted?

2. Have you ever experienced sexual harassment at work or school? Did you do anything about it? Did you feel in any way responsible? After having read this chapter, do you feel

differently about the experience? If you were to now encounter sexual harassment, how might you react and in what ways would this be different from your prior reactions?

3. Do you think that rapists and other individuals who victimize through the use of coercive sex should be punished? Do you believe in rehabilitation? Compare your feelings about these sex offenders with your attitude about people with paraphilias. Is there any difference? Explain.

4. Do you think that incest can ever be a benign, even a positive experience?

CHAPTER 18 TEST QUESTIONS

Multiple Choice (*General Comprehension Questions)

1.* Rape is
   a. an intellectual act.
   b. directed only against women.
   c. an expression of violence, anger, or power.
   d. no longer clouded by myth.

2.* Coercive sex includes all of the following except
   a. rape.
   b. incest.
   c. sexual harassment.
   d. masturbation.

3.* Major problems with sexual coercion in its many forms
   a. no longer exist due to the E.E.O.C. regulations.
   b. occur when passive men conflict with aggressive women.
   c. will continue if society continues to socialize women to be sexual victims and program men to see sexual aggression as "manly."
   d. have been eradicated due to special police "teams" trained to cope with these situations.

4.* Incest is
   a. sexual contact between consenting adults.
   b. sexual contact between relatives.
   c. punishable by death.
   d. not implicated as a cause of a person's later sexual problems.

5.* Rape occurs
   a. only to women.
   b. only when poorly educated men have no other sexual outlet.
   c. under a variety of circumstances, by a variety of individuals who cannot easily or accurately be categorized.
   d. primarily in situations where prostitutes are not orgasmic, thus angering their customers.

6. The legal definition of rape says it is sexual assault with
   a. penile penetration of the vagina or anus.
   b. penile penetration of the vagina or mouth.
   c. penile penetration of any orifice.
   d. penile penetration of the vagina without mutual consent.

7. The earliest rape laws
   a. viewed rape first and foremost as a crime against women, not honor or property.
   b. provided for a trial by women jurists.
   c. dropped the distinctions between raping virgins and raping married women by the end of the 13th century.
   d. provided for guilt to be determined by "trial by combat" through the end of the 17th century.

8. All of the following are commonly held myths about rape except
   a. it is impossible to rape a woman who physically resists.
   b. women seduce men into rapes and get what they deserve for being provocative.
   c. women frequently make false accusations of rape.
   d. unattractive women are practically immune to rapes.

9. The most common form of rape that is reported is
   a. statutory rape.
   b. rape of mentally ill women.
   c. rape through coercion such as blackmail.
   d. forcible rape.

10. Forced intercourse between husband and wife
    a. is the most severely punished form of rape.
    b. has not been included in rape statistics.
    c. does not "count" as rape in 38 of the 50 American states.
    d. has been all but eliminated due to the impact of feminism and the "consciousness raising" of the Women's Movement.

11. Men who have been raped by women
    a. tend to report the crime immediately.
    b. were sexually responsive, "proving" they enjoyed the experience.
    c. tend to brag about the experience as if they were the "chosen" ones.
    d. suffer from post-rape trauma reactions.

12. Many women choose not to report rapes. All of the following might be reasons for this except
    a. in all states, a woman's past sexual behavior may be introduced into the trial.
    b. she has a fear that the police won't catch the rapist anyway and he may not go to trial.
    c. she has a fear of retribution by the rapist.
    d. she may be pressured by family members not to report it.

13. A woman reacts to a rape with shock, fear, disbelief, shame, anger, emotional turmoil, even apparent calmness. She is

205

experiencing
a. the post-trauma "recoil" phase.
b. the long-term regrowth and recovery phase.
c. the acute reaction phase.
d. the resolution phase.

14. Sexual problems that may occur as a consequence of rape
    a. rarely involve the victim's sexual partner or spouse.
    b. are reflected in the victim's desire to have sex much more frequently than prior to the rape in order to "prove" she's okay.
    c. are often manifested in a woman's development of sexual aversions or vaginismus.
    d. do not usually involve a woman's sexual satisfaction when with her chosen partner.

15. Recent research and data about incest have revealed that
    a. father-daughter incest is the most frequent pattern.
    b. sexual activity between siblings is the most frequently treated form of incest.
    c. only about 5,000 children a year are sexually abused by their parents or guardians.
    d. the most frequently reported cases of incest are those between adults and children.

16. All of the following are widely believed myths about incest except
    a. incest occurs only where there is opportunity for long-term interaction.
    b. incest is usually committed by a sexually degenerate father.
    c. children usually make up their claims of incest.
    d. incest occurs primarily in poor, uneducated families.

17. Within reconstituted families, the incidence of incest
    a. is all but nonexistent.
    b. is particularly common.
    c. occurs primarily between stepmothers and stepsons.
    d. is reported by one in forty women according to researcher Diana Russell.

18. When incest occurs
    a. it is rarely in a religious family.
    b. it is rarely something that begins as a teasing or playful activity between participants.
    c. it is typically initiated by the mother.
    d. it rarely takes the father-son or mother-daughter form.

19. Title VII of the Civil Rights Act of 1964 addresses
    a. sex discimination issues.
    b. abortion issues.
    c. affirmative action issues.
    d. the rights of black rape victims.

20. According to the 1980 E.E.O.C. Rules and Regulations an employer
    a. has no legal responsibility for sexual harassment that occurs at his or her office.
    b. is only responsible for sexual harassment he or she knew of.
    c. is responsible for any sexual harassment regardless of whether he or she knew of or should have known of it.
    d. is only responsible for sexual harassment committed by non-supervisory personnel.

21. Boys who end up being sexually coercive were most likely
    a. socialized to believe women should be the sexual aggressors.
    b. programmed to be dependent and passive.
    c. trained to be demure in sexual situations.
    d. taught to believe females mean "maybe" when they say "no"; "yes" when they say "maybe".

22. Improvements in the police and legal system regarding rape situations include all of the following except
    a. specially trained police rape units.
    b. victim advocates.
    c. training in administering lie detector tests to women who claim they have been raped.
    d. lawyers specially trained to deal with rape victims and rape issues.

23. Sexual harassment at work
    a. does not invovle harassment of males.
    b. traditionally has been viewed as even more shocking than rape.
    c. may involve sexual compliance as a condition for keeping a job.
    d. always starts in pre-employment situations.

24. A study of 170 convicted rapists showed that sexual dysfunction during rape
    a. was nonexistent among the rapists but common in the victims.
    b. included only premature ejaculation.
    c. was so widespread that 58% of the men were sexually dysfunctional.
    d. did not occur when the women didn't resist.

25. The scope of sexual harassment on college campuses
    a. is estimated at one in five college coeds victimized in this way.
    b. has never been studied in a systematic fashion.
    c. has recently attracted enormous publicity, culminating in a national campaign to rid schools of the problem.
    d. seems to be much greater at the graduate level, minimal at the undergraduate level.

True/False

F   1.   Legally speaking, penile penetration of the mouth without mutual consent, is rape.

T   2.   A man is unlikely to be charged with raping a prostitute.

F   3.   Women's rape fantasies usually indicate a desire to be raped in real life.

F   4.   A woman who resists cannot be raped.

T   5.   Corroboration as proof is often required in rape cases.

F   6.   The rape of men by men is frequent among homosexuals.

F   7.   Under present rape laws in most jurisdictions, a husband may be charged with raping his wife.

T   8.   A 1980 study suggests one woman in six will be a victim of attempted rape, and one in twenty-four is a victim of completed rape during her lifetime.

T   9.   Rape trials often make the woman feel <u>she</u> is on trial, not the rapist.

F   10.   98% of rapists have been found to be unmarried.

F   11.   Rapists are usually oversexed men.

T   12.   Anger rape is committed by men whose motive is to punish and get revenge on women in general.

T   13.   Most men who get involved in incest are devoted to their families.

T   14.   Sexually exploited children often grow up to become sexual exploiters of children.

F   15.   Father-daughter incest is more common than brother-sister incest.

Fill in the Blanks

1.   The Latin origin of the word "rape" -- the term "rapere" means (<u>to steal, seize, carry</u> away).

2.   The Hammurabi Code set the penalty for a man who raped a betrothed virgin as (<u>death</u>).

3.   (<u>Pair or gang</u>) rape involves two or more men, often with a female accomplice, who take turns raping a victim.

4.   One woman in 25 has been victimized by (<u>date</u>) rape, which might

have occurred at a party or when in a social situation.

5. The commonest form of incest is between (siblings).

6. Statutory rape is a kind of (nonforcible) rape.

7. The aftermath of rape may be divided into three psychological phases. The second phase is known as (post-traumatic recoil) phase.

8. (Mother -daughter) incest is the rarest form of nuclear family incest.

9. When a rapist tries to intimidate a victim by using a weapon, force, or threats of bodily harm, this is known as (power) rape.

10. A person who is tortured by cigarette burns, bites, and whippings as well as rape may be said to have been a victim of a (sadistic) rape.

11. Sexual activity between a person and a close relative is called (incest).

12. When a boss makes (sexual compliance) a condition for obtaining or keeping a job, this is sexual harassment.

13. In coercive sexual situations, (men) are often the victimizers due in part to gender role socialization.

14. Rape victims should be medically checked to be sure they have not been injured or exposed to (venereal) disease.

15. Children who pose for nude photos, who are filmed engaging in sexual acts, are victims of (child pornography), a form of child abuse.

Discussion/Essay Questions

1. Discuss the history of rape laws.

2. Who are the most frequent victims of rape?

3. List three deterrents a woman can use to escape an attempted rape. Give your opinion on the advisability of resisting rape.

4. What can be done to improve the rate of reporting actual or attempted rapes?

5. Are most rapists convicted? Do you think if rape against men was more common, this might change?

6. Make some suggestions to a person who believes he or she is a victim of sexual harassment but who does not want to leave the

job.

7. How can families with patterns of incest be helped?

Chapter 19

SEXUAL DYSFUNCTIONS AND SEX THERAPY

OVERVIEW

In a society where adept sexual performance is often considered desirable and, moreover, expected as a norm, people can be vaguely uneasy or terribly anxious about what happens if things go wrong. This chapter examines the nature of sexual dysfunctions by first discussing their diagnostic classification, natural histories, and impact on the individual and relationships, followed by a section delineating what is currently known about the causes of sexual dysfunction. The second half of the chapter summarizes the methods and results of sex therapy, focusing on the Masters and Johnson model but also examining the approaches of other sex therapists such as Helen Singer Kaplan, Jack Annon, Albert Ellis, Lonnie Barbach. Chapter 19 concludes with practical discussions on "Choosing a Sex Therapist" and "Preventing Sexual Dysfunction."

While reading the chapter, the student is asked to consider these issues:

1. What are some common male and female sexual dysfunctions, their possible causes, and ways they can be treated or prevented?

2. What are some of the relatively uncommon male and female sexual dysfunctions, their possible causes, and ways they can be treated or prevented?

3. How do organic and psychosocial factors each contribute to any given kind of sexual dysfunction? Do they interact? If so, how?

4. What is the concept behind the Masters and Johnson model of sex therapy? What is the actual format? What are its salient features?

5. How are other approaches to sex therapy practiced? How do they compare to the Masters and Johnson model?

6. What guidelines should be used in choosing a sex therapist?

7. What is sexual fakery and how might it contribute to sexual dysfunction?

LEARNING OBJECTIVES

At the conclusion of this chapter, the student should be able to:

1. Describe the various forms of male and female sexual dysfunction.

2. List the organic and psychosocial factors that are involved in male and female sexual dysfunction, and explain their effects on the individual and society.

3. Describe the Masters and Johnson model for treating sexual dysfunction; outline the therapy format used in treatment.

4. Explain the squeeze technique and why it is used; explain the form and function of sensate focus exercises.

5. Describe the additional methods used within the Masters and Johnson treatment model for handling problems of erectile dysfunction, premature ejaculation, ejaculatory incompetence, vaginismus, anorgasmia.

6. Explain other treatment approaches and compare and contrast them to one another and to the Masters and Johnson model.

7. Explain the problems that make evaluation of sex therapy difficult.

8. State the general guidelines recommended for minimizing the risk of falling victim to unqualified sex therapsits.

9. Discuss the recommended practices and attitudes that help prevent sexual dysfunction.

TEACHING STRATEGIES

In a college human sexuality course, some students might ask, "Why do the authors include so much detail about sex therapy?" With the high incidence of sexual problems in our culture, it is likely that a majority of students in the class will be directly or indirectly confronted with a sexual difficulty. Whether the experience involves a relative, a client, a date, or the student, information about sexual dysfunction can potentially prevent a serious problem or provide information about where to turn to for competent help.

Class discussion about fears of performance can further clarify this complicated, important topic. Since performance concerns can become a self-fulfilling prophecy, the content and style of presentation of this lecture is critical. All men and women experience performance concerns from time to time. A man may have a fleeting doubt about whether he will be able to attain an erection with a certain desirable partner or whether he will ejaculate too rapidly. Similarly, with the increased performance pressures on women recently, some female students may question if they will be orgasmic, if their partners will be satisfied, or why they do not become aroused as easily as they have been led to believe they should. The critical factor is the method used to ease such concerns. The instructor should stress during class discussion that self-doubts are normal, and they are usually fleeting. Once two people get involved in touching each other's bodies, "natural" bodily responses ordinarily take over. Students who become distracted by their thoughts may be helped by recommendations to get reinvolved in touching or stroking. If they continue to be distracted, explain that their bodies may be sending them messages to forget about coitus during a specific intimitate interlude, and to try to just enjoy one another without performance pressures or spectatoring. Offer the analogy that they wouldn't be likely to force themselves to eat at a banquet once they felt satiated, "full."

It is natural for men to lose erections and rapidly ejaculate when they are not at ease (for whatever the reasons) with their partners. The same is true about the female response. A woman who is overly concerned with having an orgasm may discover a lack of vaginal lubrication during the early stages of touching. If she can focus on the moment rather than anticipating orgasmic success or failure, performance pressures may dissolve into genuine enjoyment. The instructor should emphasize that no one should feel personal inadequacy if faced with a sexual problem. This kind of detailed information can prevent fleeting performance concerns from becoming obsessive, debilitating fears. The instructor is not becoming a therapist by providing such information, but is trying to prevent the development of difficulties that might later require therapeutic intervention.

In defining the nature of sexual dysfunctions and explaining what is currently known about their etiologies, it is helpful to point out to students that a particular background factor (such as severe religious orthodoxy or childhood sexual trauma) does not invariably lead to sexual dysfunction. It can be enlightening to students to speculate about why certain pscyhosocial factors affect one person negatively and have little or no effect on another person. Students can also benefit from the classroom discussion of a few case histories because by using a "real life" case example, abstract concepts can be made concrete and usable.

An article by Zilbergeld and Evans ("Psychology Today," August, 1980, pp. 29-43) challenged many of the findings of Masters and Johnson's sex therapy research. A detailed reply to this critique by Robert C. Kolodny, M.D. can be found in "The Journal of Sex Research," volume 17, number 4, November, 1981 and may be of interest to students.

STUDENT PROJECTS

1. Visit a sex therapy clinic in your area (national listings can be obtained from the organizations listed elsewhere in this manual). Compare the format and methods of this program with those used by Masters and Johnson. What are the most and least

common problems treated? Do the therapists ever use surrogates in their work? Are the therapists M.D.s, nurses, social workers, psychologists? Where did they get their training? Do they do only sex therapy or is sex therapy just one component of the therapy their office offers?

2. Design a research study to determine the percentage of students on your campus who have a sexual dysfunction. What measures could be employed to assure anonymity for those who participate? What would you do with your results?

PERSONAL REFLECTIONS

1. Have you ever experienced "fears of performance" in any of your sexual encounters? In what ways have you dealt with such pressures?

2. Have you ever lapsed into "spectatoring" while involved in a sexual situation? How does it feel? Does your partner know? What does it do to or for your own response?

3. If you had a sexual problem and decided to seek help, what qualities or characteristics would you look for in selecting a therapist?

4. Knowing what you do now about sexual dysfunctions, do you think you have ever been afflicted with one? How would you now deal with it? Do you think reading this chapter would be enough to help you overcome it?

5. Would you give this chapter to your parents to read? Do you think they would learn anything? Could you ever discuss sexual problems with them? Do you think they would ever confide their sexual problems in you? How could you help them if they did?

CHAPTER 19 TEST QUESTIONS

Multiple Choice (* General Comprehension Questions)

1.* Sexual dysfunctions
   a. rarely occur in married women.
   b. occur only in those people who consistently engage in "spectatoring."
   c. are said to occur when ordinary physical responses of sexual function are imparied.
   d. can begin prenatally.

2.* Among the psychosocial causes of sexual dysfunction are all of the following except
   a. developmental problems.
   b. personal problems.
   c. interpersonal problems.

        d.   organic problems.

3.* Sex therapy as a distinct speciality originated with the   work
     of
     a.   Masters and Johnson.
     b.   Lonnie Barbach.
     c.   Albert Ellis.
     d.   Sigmund Freud.

4.* All of the following are principal sexual dysfunctions in males
     except
     a.   ejaculatory incompetence.
     b.   dyspareunia.
     c.   retarded ejaculation.
     d.   premature ejaculation.

5.* All of the following are principal sexual dysfunctions in
     females except
     a.   vaginismus.
     b.   anorgasmia.
     c.   dyspareunia.
     d.   FSH and LH suppression.

6.   The male who is sexually dysfunctional usually
     a.   ignores the problem.
     b.   changes his behavior to avoid sexual situations.
     c.   admits that the problem is his and not his partner's.
     d.   is a heavy drinker.

7.   Erectile dysfunction means that a man
     a.   is sterile.
     b.   is a victim of gonorrhea.
     c.   cannot ejaculate during intercourse.
     d.   cannot have or maintain an erection firm enough for
           intercourse.

8.   Fears of sexual performance can
     a.   cause a man to lose his erection.
     b.   enhance sexual arousal due to tension.
     c.   enhance sexual spontaneity.
     d.   increase self-esteem as a way of coping with the fear.

9.   The "spectator role" can
     a.   occur only in cases of erectile dysfunction.
     b.   enhance a couple's involvement in sexual activity.
     c.   affect both men and women.
     d.   decrease any performance fears that might exist.

10. The man who ejaculates prematurely
     a.   cannot participate in any sexual activity, coital or
           noncoital, without ejaculating.
     b.   is impotent.
     c.   has total voluntary control over the timing of his
           ejaculation and ejaculates prematurely by choice.

d. is one who ejaculates unintentionally during noncoital play, or during coital activity soon after intercourse begins.

11. All of the following are methods men may use to overcome premature ejaculation except
    a. use of condoms to cut down on genital sensations.
    b. use of the "nipple squeeze" technique to reduce sexual arousal.
    c. imbibing of alcoholic beverages prior to intercourse.
    d. use of creams and ointments that are supposed to desensitize the penis and deaden sensations.

12. Ejaculatory incompetence is
    a. a very frequent disorder seen mainly in men over age 35.
    b. exactly the same as retrograde ejaculation.
    c. something that occurs almost always during masturbation.
    d. a potential source of sexual pleasure due to the man's ability to prolong coitus.

13. Vaginismus refers to a condition that
    a. occurs mainly in partners of men who have problems with ejaculatory incompetence.
    b. affects only postmenopausal women.
    c. can cause pelvic pain in certain women when intercourse is attempted.
    d. accounts for approximately 80% of cases of female sexual dysfunction.

14. Women with vaginismus usually experience
    a. abnormal or reduced vaginal lubrication.
    b. little or no difficulty with sexual arousal.
    c. a cessation of any orgasmic response.
    d. no difficulty in conceiving children.

15. Situational anorgasmia refers to a condition of women who
    a. have never experienced orgasm.
    b. were regularly orgasmic at one time but no longer are.
    c. have had occasional orgasms, but under certain circumstances.
    d. have experienced orgasm in different types of sexual activity, but very infrequently -- such as once a year.

16. Dyspareunia refers to
    a. painful intercourse.
    b. cessation of menses.
    c. rapid orgasm.
    d. a category of psychosocial sexual dysfunction.

17. All of the following types of sexual dysfunction commonly have organic causes as the major contributing factors except
    a. female dyspareunia.
    b. erectile dysfunction.
    c. premature ejaculation.

216

d. complete inability to ejaculate.

18. Research has discovered that sexual dysfunctions can be caused by all of the following <u>except</u>
   a. severely negative parental sex attitudes.
   b. blind acceptance of cultural myths.
   c. poor communication.
   <u>d.</u> childhood exposure to adult nudity.

19. The Masters and Johnson model of sex therapy includes
   a. the idea that the partner always causes the problem.
   b. the use of psychosocial data only.
   <u>c.</u> a co-therapy team to increase objectivity.
   <u>d.</u> a six-week format of twice-a-week therapy.

20. The major treatment concepts of the Masters and Johnson model include all of the following <u>except</u>
   a. therapy individualized to meet each couple's needs.
   b. an assumption that sex is a natural function, involving reflex responses.
   c. therapy approached at several levels.
   <u>d.</u> a checklist for couples to assess everything they do in terms of success or failure.

21. At the start of sensate focus exercises the couple is told
   a. that the purpose of touching is to be sexual.
   <u>b.</u> to refrain from genital contact at the start.
   c. to use the touching as a stimulating form of massage.
   d. to communicate verbally throughout the exercise.

22. The "squeeze technique" is used to treat
   <u>a.</u> premature ejaculation.
   b. vaginismus.
   c. erectile dysfunction.
   d. ejaculatory incompetence.

23. The use of various sized plastic dilators is part of the treatment strategy aimed at overcoming
   a. anorgasmia.
   b. ejaculatory incompetence.
   <u>c.</u> vaginismus.
   d. rapid orgasm.

24. Helen Kaplan's triphasic approach to human sexual response includes all of the following phases <u>except</u>
   a. desire.
   b. arousal.
   c. orgasm.
   <u>d.</u> ovulation.

25. Behavioral therapy for sexual difficulties can include all of the following <u>except</u>
   a. desensitization.
   b. relaxation training.

c.   directed masturbation.

d.   dream analysis.

True/False

T   1.   If lack of interest in sex is the predominant problem, it is classified as inhibited sexual desire (ISD).

F   2.   If a sexual problem occurs, the first thing someone should do is abstain from further sexual activity for at least a month.

T   3.   Sexual aversion refers to the lack of participation in sex due to overwhelming fear.

F   4.   When choosing sex therapists, seek out only those who guarantee cures.

T   5.   Goal-oriented sex creates performance demands which can lead to spectatoring.

T   6.   Sex therapy has been criticized as being mechanistic and dehumanizing.

F   7.   Surrogate partners are no longer used in any kinds of sex therapy.

F   8.   The "stop-start" method advocated by Helen Kaplan is used to treat vaginismus.

T   9.   The use of thought-blocking techniques can be helpful to women who are anorgasmic due to disturbing fantasies.

F   10. Any man can will an erection on demand.

T   11. Premature ejaculation can be more distressing to the woman than the man in the relationship.

F   12. The sensate focus technique starts out with an exercise known as "hand-riding."

F   13. The round-table session used by Masters and Johnson occurs on the last day of therapy.

T   14. Rapid orgasm is the female counterpart of premature ejaculation.

T   15. Some sexual dysfunctions are maintained by positive reinforcement.

Fill in the Blanks

1.   Many women require additional stimulation beyond that of (intercourse) in order to have coital orgasms.

2. When semen spurts backwards into the bladder and is mixed with urine, this is called (retrograde) ejaculation.

3. (Anorgasmia) is the largest category of female sexual dysfunction.

4. The two most prominent organic causes of erectile dysfunction are diabetes and (alcoholism).

5. Prior to 1970, sexual dysfunctions were usually treated by (psychiatrists).

6. Occasional difficulty with ejaculation is not a sign of sexual disturbance and is often related to (fatigue, tension, alcohol or drug use, sexual satiation, illness).

7. Environmental and cultural factors are among the (psychosocial) causes of sexual dysfunction.

8. Erectile failure can lead to performance fears which lead to the (spectator) role.

9. (Learning theory) says that sexual dysfunction is a conditioned or learned response.

10. Within the framework of the Masters and Johnson therapy model, a majority of time in the therapy sessions is usually spent on (nonsexual) issues.

11. (Lonnie Barbach) pioneered the use of women's groups for the treatment of anorgasmia.

12. A four-level model for treating sexual problems suggested by Jack Annon is represented by the acronym (PLISSIT).

13. Masters and Johnson began their revolutionary program for treating sexual dysfunctions in the year (1959).

14. Masters and Johnson believe the focus of therapy should be on the (relationship, couple), not the individual.

15. The "bridging technique" is used as part of the treatment for (anorgasmia).

Discussion/Essay Questions

1. Explain how fears of sexual performance can create sexual problems.

2. Why is the statement that "Sex is a natural function" the core concept in treating sexual dysfunctions?

3. How can sexual dysfunction be prevented?

4. What is the difference between impotence and infertility?

5. What is ISD and what are the ramifications for a couple?

6. Distinguish between organic and psychosocial causes of sexual dysfunction and give examples of each for males and females.

7. What was revolutionary about the Masters and Johnson model of sex therapy? Why has it been successful? Why and how has it been criticized?

8. Why is it so important that one picks a sex therapist who fulfills all the criteria listed in the chapter? What are the dangers if one doesn't?

Chapter 20

SEXUAL DISORDERS AND SEXUAL HEALTH

OVERVIEW

This chapter covers a broad range of clinical and practical information that acquaints students with common problems of sexual health, sex and disability, sexual infections, and the impact of illness and drugs on sexuality. The opening section of the chapter explains how various medical conditions -- spinal cord injury, multiple sclerosis, mental retardation, blindness, deafness, diabetes, heart disease, alcoholism, cancer can lead to sexual problems. The emphasis here is on reminding students that a person's sexual feelings and needs don't cease when illness or disability disrupts their ordinary sexual functioning. Next, the effects of commonly used prescription and recreational drugs on sexuality are discussed, including a careful look at research on the sexual effects of alcohol and marihuana. The focus of the chapter then shifts to coverage of sexual infections providing not only "academic" knowledge about these infections (including vaginitis, cystitis, prostatitis) but also a number of practical pointers related to personal prevention. A discussion of the effects of DES and toxic shock syndrome include the most recent research findings. Several Boxed Items familiarize students with information important to their personal health, such as the how-to's of breast self-examination for females and testicular self-examination for males, as well as information about pelvic exams and Pap smears.

While reading the chapter, the student is asked to consider these issues:

1. What physical illnesses commonly affect sexual functioning and by what mechanisms?

2. Why is it important to recognize the sexual feelings and needs of people with chronic illnesses or disabilities? What special educational techniques can be immensely helpful?

3. What sexual side-effects are commonly encountered with prescription drugs and other pharmacological substances people use? Is there such a thing as an aphrodisiac?

4. What are the symptoms and treatments of the most common sexual infections? In what ways can these diseases be prevented?

5. How can alcoholism affect sexual functioning?

6. What methods of self-examination and medical care are useful in

preserving one's sexual health?

LEARNING OBJECTIVES

At the conclusion of this chapter, the student should be able to:

1. List the common myths and stereotypes about sex and disabled people.

2. Describe the direct and indirect ways that illnesses can affect sexuality.

3. Explain how diseases or injury to the nervous system can lead to sexual difficulties and identify the most common types of neurologic conditions that affect sexuality.

4. Describe the special steps that should be taken to alleviate the potential sexually related problems of blind, deaf, and mentally retarded individuals.

5. Identify types of cancer and heart disease that can impact on sexuality and how resulting problems can be alleviated or eliminated.

6. Describe the effect of alcoholism and substance abuse (cocaine, marihuana, and so on) on sexuality and discuss why problems usually develop.

7. Compare the effects of various prescription and nonprescription drugs on sexual desire and function.

8. List some common infections of the sex organs and identify their symptoms, diagnosis, and treatment.

9. Explain the mystique of the aphrodisiac and then de-mystify it.

10. Describe the recent research about diethylstilbestrol (DES) and toxic shock syndrome (TSS).

TEACHING STRATEGIES

The old adage that "an ounce of prevention is worth a pound of cure" provides the most important backdrop to teaching this chapter. Students should be made aware of the fact that learning about issues of sexual health is advisable for their own personal welfare and for the welfare of their sexual partners. The practical ramifications of this point become quite clear when students realize that sexually transmitted diseases and sexual infections are second in annual frequency only to the common cold in America today. Similarly, realizing how common disorders like breast cancer, heart disease, prostatic disease, diabetes, and alcoholism can affect sexuality helps to forewarn students whose families are quite likely to face one or more serious health problems without necessarily realizing the sexual impact they may have. This is true also of other catastrophic health problems such as spinal cord injuries, blindness, deafness, mental retardation -- which often are not discussed in terms of their sexual ramifications.

Two primary points should be made in teaching about the effects of illness or injury on sexual health. First, the impact of such conditions generally depends on both the altered physiology that occurs and the person's psychological responses to the health problem. Second, even severely disabled or ill people continue to have sexual needs and feelings, yet these needs and feelings have, in the past, been largely ignored by the health-care community. In addition to helping students learn about how physical problems can adversely affect sexual function, try to help students come to grips with the emotional side of disability. Suggest that students try some role reversal exercises (for example, by imagining for five minutes how their lives would be changed by an auto accident that led to quadriplegia) and use this as a springboard for further discussion. It can be illuminating to read passages from Sexuality and Physical Disability: Personal Perspectives, edited by Bullard and Knight [St. Louis: C. V. Mosby, 1981] to the class to give them a very personal glimpse at how disabilities can create frustrating sexual pressures, as well as to see how these pressures can be overcome.

Students will be eager to learn as much as possible about drugs and sex, and it is particularly important in this area to offer them objective, data-based information. While there's lots of interest in finding an effective aphrodisiac, none yet seems to have surfaced! Help the class consider the complexities of research in the area of drugs and sex, including concerns for confidentiality in dealing with illicit drug use and the difficulty in interpreting subjective "self-reports" on sexual arousal while using a drug. It is equally important to point out areas in which little research exists. Why are people under the influence of a drug notoriously poor observers of that drug's effects? What sorts of studies are needed to provide careful documentation of the sexual effects of a "recreational" drug such as marihuana or cocaine? Is it likely that such studies will be done in today's research climate?

Another key topic to cover is that of sexual infections. Students must be taught to seek medical help and not be ashamed if faced with such a problem. It is important to teach students about cancer, since many of them will be terrified by the word alone. In spite of the fact that cancer of the cervix and uterus may be nearly 100% curable if detected in the early stages (see text), students may be reticent to discuss the disease. Discussing the fears, social stigma, actual signs and symptoms and what can be done if detected, can help students ease into an open discussion. Ask how women could be encouraged to have regular Pap smears and pelvic exams. Have students design their own ad campaigns. Furthermore, stress to students the importance of self-examination (of the breasts, for women, and the testes, for men) in helping to combat cancer through early detection. Accompanying the discussion of cancer you should include the DES data and explore people's often-angry feelings about the entire DES scenario. It is critical that students understand that cancer (and other diseases that can negatively impact on sexuality) can be cured only if fears of learning the truth from a physician are first overcome.

STUDENT PROJECTS

1.   Contact a local Vietnam Veteran's Group and get permission to interview someone who has experienced a spinal cord injury. How did he cope at first? With the passage of time, what things have changed? Does he agree with the image presented in the film, "Coming Home"? What were his major obstacles?

2.   Interview a urologist who performs penile implantation surgery. How are patients selected for surgery? How satisfied are patients after this operation? What problems are commonly encountered pre- and post-operatively? What counseling do such patients get?

3.   Attend a meeting of a local self-help group for victims of cancer, heart disease, spinal cord injuries. What themes seem to dominate their discussions? Are they willing to speak about sexual issues or do sexual topics seem off-limits?

4.   Speak with the parents of a disabled teenager. What have been the most difficult situations for those parents in coping with their child? How have they dealt with sexual topics? If possible, speak with the teen. Asking the same kinds of questions, see if teen and parents share similar perspectives or not.

PERSONAL REFLECTIONS

1.   If you are female and had a mastectomy, would you have breast reconstruction surgery? If you are male and could no longer attain erections (due to physical problems), would you opt for a penile implant? What factors would you consider before making such decisions? How do you think you might feel about this "artificial" part of yourself? Or is it no different from choosing to have a nose job or face lift?

2.   Imagine that your fiancé was involved in a car accident and his or her spinal cord was injured leading to paralysis from the waist down. How would you feel? What would you want to discuss with your partner? How would his or her reaction to the accident affect your feelings? In what ways could you best help one another through such an ordeal? Would you be able to go ahead with your wedding plans?

3.   What would be your first reaction if you discovered you had a sexual infection? If you were sexually active, would you tell your partner or partners? Would you go for treatment or ignore the problem? Would you confide in a parent? Would you feel it

was no one's business but yours? In what ways would a sexual
infection affect your sexual responsiveness and subsequent
behavior? Why?

CHAPTER 20 TEST QUESTIONS

Multiple Choice (* General Comprehension Questions)

1.* Until recently, the medical illnesses that can cause sexual
    problems were largely overlooked because
    a.   the doctor's Hippocratic Oath prohibited such discussion.
    b.   the issue of doctor-patient confidentiality prevented such
         discussion.
    c.   professionals were often uncomfortable with the subject as
         well as uninformed about it.
    d.   sexual health is not really interwoven with total health.

2.* The sexuality of disabled people
    a.   is inhibited.
    b.   is destroyed by the nature of any major disability.
    c.   is characterized by a broad range of sexual expression.
    d.   is always problematic and in need of sex therapy.

3.* Illnesses associated with anxiety about sex that limit sexual
    enjoyment include all of the following except
    a.   drug abuse.
    b.   heart attacks.
    c.   breast cancer.
    d.   conditions requiring hysterectomies.

4.* Vaginitis is an example of
    a.   toxic shock syndrome.
    b.   an infection of the bladder.
    c.   a neurologic problem.
    d.   an infection caused by an overgrowth of microorganisms
         normally residing in the vagina.

5.* A significant loss of sexual function along with a loss of
    bowel and bladder control is usually the result of
    a.   monilia.
    b.   toxic shock syndrome.
    c.   spinal cord injuries.
    d.   radical mastectomy.

6. The sexual bill of rights for the disabled includes
    a.   the right to engage in prostitution.
    b.   the right to refused sexual therapy.
    c.   the right to deny one's disability by refusing to discuss
         it openly.
    d.   the right to have access to needed services related to
         sexuality.

225

7. "Stuffing" is a technique to facilitate
   a. the movement of a paraplegic's limbs to prevent atrophy.
   b. oral sex.
   c. intercourse in cases of incomplete spinal cord injuries.
   d. bowel and bladder control in cases of quadriplegia.

8. "Phantom" orgasms often occur in individuals who have
   a. spinal cord injuries.
   b. cerebral palsy.
   c. cancer of the cervix or uterus.
   d. multiple sclerosis.

9. The most accurate statement about the impact of SCI on people is
   a. women with such injuries lose their fertility.
   b. men with such injuries may be able to have brief reflex erections.
   c. men with such injuries lose the ability to ejaculate.
   d. women with such injuries experience increased vaginal lubrication output.

10. Blindness and/or deafness
   a. produce physical limitations on the body's sexual responsivity in and of themselves.
   b. make it all but impossible for sex education to have any lasting, positive impact on people so afflicted.
   c. often make it easier for people so afflicted to express themselves sexually.
   d. can create a predisposition toward sexual and relationship problems if the individuals so afflicted have not had access to special sex education materials designed to meet their special needs.

11. The best birth control method currently available for sexually active retarded women seems to be
   a. the IUD.
   b. the pill.
   c. the diaphragm.
   d. contraceptive foams.

12. Painful intercourse in women is a very common symptom of
   a. brain tumors.
   b. epilepsy.
   c. multiple sclerosis.
   d. polio.

13. The most accurate statement about the diabetic person is
   a. retrograde ejaculation occurs in about 75% of diabetic men.
   b. about 33% of diabetic women experience secondary anorgasmia.
   c. sex therapy can cure the sexual dysfunction related to the nerve damage that is a complication of diabetes.

226

        d.   circulatory problems related to diabetes cause the largest
              percentage of sexual dysfunctions in diabetics.

14.   The capacity for sexual activity in a person with heart disease
       a.   should not be limited even if the disease is severe and
             chronic.
       b.   rarely is negatively affected one year after recovery.
       c.   is less likely to be negatively affected if the person is
             male rather than female.
       d.   may be negatively affected because of mental rather than
             physical factors.

15.   The surgical removal of a breast to treat cancer is
       a.   likely to cause sexual problems in a direct, physical
             sense.
       b.   likely to cause a women to become sexually aggressive in
             an attempt to overcompensate.
       c.   likely to encourage the female-on-top position for
             intercourse after surgery.
       d.   less likely to create sexual problems if the woman and her
             partner receive appropriate counseling.

16.   Cancer of the testis is
       a.   rare in men under 40 years of age.
       b.   accompanied by pain and is thus easy to detect.
       c.   often incorrectly blamed on an overactive sex life by a
             guilt-ridden man.
       d.   likely to cause erectile problems due to the spread of
             cancer to the penis.

17.   The alcoholic person may experience all of the following except
       a.   lowered testosterone (in men) or lowered estrogen (in women)
       b.   shrunken testes and breast enlargement in men.
       c.   problems with erections in 40% of alcoholic men.
       d.   increased sexual desire in alcoholic women.

18.   Aphrodisiacs are
       a.   medications used to treat high blood pressure.
       b.   sinus medications that affect sexuality.
       c.   substances alleged to increase a person's sexual prowess
             or desire.
       d.   nonprescription drugs of any kind.

19.   Each of the following facts about sex and alcohol is true
       except
       a.   alcohol is a depressant to sexual reflexes.
       b.   in moderate or high amounts, alcohol impairs erections.
       c.   alcohol increases the intensity of orgasms.
       d.   alcohol lowers a person's ordinary sexual inhibitions.

20.   Recent research data indicates that DES and DES-like drugs have
       been responsible for all of the following except
       a.   increased incidence of multiple births in women whose
             mothers took the drug while pregnant.

b. cell adenocarcinomas in daughters whose mothers had taken DES during pregnancy.
c. incomplete testicular development in sons whose mothers had taken DES during pregnancy.
d. abnormalities of the cervis in DES-daughters.

21. Cystitis or infection of the bladder
    a. is closely associated with sexual activity in women.
    b. is more common in men than in women.
    c. can only be diagnosed by x-ray exam.
    d. is best treated by douching and sitz baths.

22. Penile implants are
    a. used to improve the appearance of the penis much as a nose job can improve the appearance of a nose.
    b. completely natural in feeling to both the man and his partner.
    c. devices used to restore sensation to the penis or restore normal ejaculation if either has been lost due to organic causes.
    d. devices used to provide firm enough erections for intercourse when illness or injury has prevented this.

23. Self-examination of the breasts
    a. is an overrated procedure because breast lumps are rarely self-discovered.
    b. does not need to be done by women who have stopped having periods.
    c. should be done once a month in a lying down position and a sitting or standing position.
    d. only needs to be done on one breast each month.

24. According to recent research studies, the use of marihuana
    a. increases vaginal lubrication in women making orgasm occur too quickly.
    b. accelerates a person's reflex reactions.
    c. increases touch sensitivity in nonsexual situations.
    d. can improve the users' sexual experiences.

25. Vaginitis can be prevented by
    a. wearing nylon or synthetic fiber underpants.
    b. frequent douching.
    c. having your physician prescribe antibiotics for long-term use.
    d. maintaining good habits of personal hygiene.

True/False

T 1. Diabetes can lead to sexual dysfunctions because of nerve damage or circulatory problems.

T 2. Spinal cord injured women often lose their genital sensations and orgasmic responsiveness.

F   3.   People with paralysis from polio are almost always impaired in their sexual function.

F   4.   Pap smears are an almost foolproof way of detecting cancer of the lining of the uterus.

T   5.   Hysterectomy does not usually have any negative effects on female sexual function.

T   6.   Erectile dysfunction may be a result of a prostatectomy for prostate cancer.

F   7.   Antihistamines used in allergy pills and sinus medications do not affect sexuality in any way.

T   8.   Amounts of alcohol well below legal levels of intoxication suppress erections.

T   9.   Vaginitis is not usually sexually transmitted.

T   10. Women using birth control pills have an increased incidence of monilial (or yeast) infections.

T   11. TSS is actually a rare form of scarlet fever.

F   12. Cocaine is a fool-proof aphrodisiac, the only "true" aphrodisiac.

F   13. The relationship between TSS and Rely tampons was never proven.

T   14. Aldomet, a drug used to treat high blood pressure, often causes erectile dysfunction in men.

F   15. Disorders of the pituitary, thyroid, or adrenal glands are not commonly associated with sexual difficulties.

Fill in the Blanks

1.   The paralysis of the legs that results from a spinal cord injury is called (paraplegia).

2.   The most common endocrine disorder that affects 4% of the U.S. population is (diabetes).

3.   Ginseng root, Spanish fly, animal testicles are examples of substances that were thought to be (aphrodisiacs).

4.   (Alcohol) has a depressant effect on the nervous system.

5.   SCI people often find that the (unaffected) regions of their bodies become extraordinarily sensitive and erotic.

6.   A person with lifelong (blindness) may be uncertain about the anatomic relation of one part of the body to another.

7. Sign language and the (touch) method are techniques for teaching anatomy and other facets of sex education to the deaf.

8. A disease that involves patchy damage to the protective covering of nerves throughout the body is (multiple sclerosis).

9. A disease that affects muscular function but not sensations and that is very rare today is (polio).

10. Surgical removal of a cancerous breast is called (mastectomy).

11. DES is a form of synthetic (estrogen).

12. Over (98) % of individuals exposed to DES have been found to be cancer-free.

13. An unusual side effect of cocaine use found by Kolodny (1983) was that 4% of men in the study experienced (priapism), painful, persistent erections.

14. Drugs such as amyl nitrate which are inhaled are widely used to prolong or intensify the sensation of (orgasm).

15. Trichomonas, monilia, and hemophilus are implicated as causes of (vaginitis).

Discussion/Essay Questions

1. Discuss the impact of four physical illnesses on sexual functioning.

2. For the same four illnesses, outline appropriate courses of psychological counseling.

3. What are the sexual effects of alcohol, marihuana, cocaine, heroin, amyl nitrate? Is any one more dangerous than any other? Why?

4. Why is it so important for non-handicapped people to understand the problems of handicapped people regarding sexual issues? What myths need to be debunked? How can we begin to change attitudes now?

5. Why are self-examinations as described in this chapter important? Why might students, in particular, be reticent to try them?

Chapter 21

SEXUALLY TRANSMITTED DISEASES

OVERVIEW

This chapter expands on the information provided in the preceding chapter by focusing on another aspect of sexual health, sexually transmitted diseases. The focus here is on accurate, no-nonsense factual information about the STDs and straightforward pointers on how to prevent them as well as what to do should you contract them. One of the goals of the chapter is to broaden knowledge of the scope of infections included in this group: gonorrhea, syphilis, genital herpes, AIDS, pubic lice, NSU, hepatitis A and B, and so on, and to minimize the sense of stigmatization that often accompanies discussions of sexual infections. Psychosocial aspects of STDs are discussed as are specific preventive strategies. There is also an analysis of the media's impact on the recent genital herpes hysteria and a Personal Perspective of an AIDs victim's reaction to his disease.

While reading the chapter, the student is asked to consider these issues:

1. What are the symptoms of gonorrhea, syphilis, genital herpes, AIDs, pubic lice, NSU, hepatitis A and B, venereal warts, and so on?

2. What is the preferred treatment for each of the STDs mentioned in (1) and what can happen should a given STD go untreated?

3. What is the psychosocial impact of each of the STDs mentioned in the chapter?

4. What can a person do to lower the risk of contracting any kind of STD?

5. What is the nature of individual responsibility regarding STDs? Should only sexually active people be held accountable?

6. Why must people be educated about STDs?

LEARNING OBJECTIVES

At the conclusion of this chapter, the student should be able to:

1. Identify the most common forms of sexually transmitted diseases.

2. Describe their symptoms and how they are spread.

3. Explain how they are diagnosed.

4. Discuss how they are treated.

5. Analyze the psychosocial effects STDs can have for the victim and the victim's sexual partner.

6. Outline the ways to prevent and/or minimize the risks of complications from STDs.

7. Discuss why educating the public about STDs is so important.

TEACHING STRATEGIES

Sexually transmitted diseases are not particularly pleasant to teach or learn about so the instructor must be careful to present the material in as objective a fashion as possible. Many students may shy away from the topic because it is scary for them to contemplate, or because (as with the subject of cancer) it is riddled with myth and misinformation. Also, many students may be new to the process of sexual interaction and thus may be hypersensitive to the idea that they or their partners could be transmitters of STDs, preferring instead to ignore the entire issue. It is also possible that during their high school years, students were taught about venereal disease in a way designed to terrify and induce chastity, and so may have incorrect notions about the treatment options available for STDs. Such scare tactics in the past were, almost always, completely ineffectual in changing sexual behavior although they may have been very effective in heightening sexual anxieties or reinforcing in some people's minds the notion that sex is dirty.

Therefore, the first task of the instructor is to set the record straight. Describe the symptoms of each disease and show slides. Ask some students to devise flashy advertising and marketing ideas to replace scare tactics and to encourage college students to recognize and seek treatment for the STDs. Then ask students why a large number of young people, even those who take this course, will not have their symptoms treated. Discuss fears of doctors, denial of illness, hope that symptoms will vanish, and social stigma, as you may have done when teaching Chapter 20. Such discussion can and should increase the likelihood that students will have their early symptoms diagnosed properly and treated promptly. Most important, however, will be the fact that you will be encouraging young adults to be responsible both for themselves and their sexual partners by being honest about the state of their sexual health and doing something about it when treatment is indicated. By demystifying the subject of STDs and replacing myth or misinformation with facts, you as the educator can play an important preventive role that can have long-term, positive consequences within our society.

STUDENT PROJECTS

1. Interview three males and three females in your human sexuality
    class about what their prior levels of information about STDs
    had been. Who taught them? Was there any bias in the
    teaching? Based on your results, write a proposal for a
    curriculum for high school students regarding STDs.

2. Visit your student health clinic and interview a staff member
    about people's reactions to the discovery of a sexually
    transmitted disease. Find out what counseling techniques are
    offered in addition to the medical treatment. How are
    additional cases traced? How is the stigma issue dealt with?
    Is complete confidentiality possible?

3. Do some research about the psychosocial impact of STDs in
    history. Have attitudes changed much over the centuries? Has
    modern medicine contributed to changing attitudes? Do males or
    females tend to get more stigmatized by any STD? Why?

PERSONAL REFLECTIONS

1. What was your initial, gut reaction upon reading this chapter?
    Why?

2. Do you think you could tell a sexual partner if you had any
    kind of STD? What would be the things you'd be most worried
    about? Would they pertain to yourself or to your partner?

3. How would you feel if you found out your sexual partner had
    contracted any kind of STD? Would your feelings change
    depending upon the severity of the infection?

4. If you were a parent, would you be willing to teach your
    children about STDs? How would you do it? At what ages?

5. What is the most important thing anyone should know about STDs?

CHAPTER 21 TEST QUESTIONS

Multiple Choice (* General Information Questions)

1.* Sexually transmitted diseases were previously called
    a. sexual infections.
    b. venereal diseases.
    c. sexual dysfunctions.
    d. molluscum contagiosum.

2.* Sexually transmitted diseases include all of the following
    except
    a. gonorrhea.
    b. granuloma inguinale.

c. syphilis.
d. yeast infections.

3.* When symptoms of any STD appear or are suspected, one should
   a. wait several weeks to make sure the problem is real.
   b. attempt self-treatment such as heavy doses of aspirin to relieve symptoms.
   c. be promptly tested to ensure appropriate diagnosis and treatment.
   d. tell noone until diagnosis is certain to avoid inducing hysteria among one's sexual partners.

4.* STDs are occurring in epidemic numbers in the U.S. today. This fact is reflected in the figure of
   a. 200,000 new cases of gonorrhea annually.
   b. 80,000 new cases of gonorrhea annually.
   c. 4 million new cases of gonorrhea annually.
   d. 2.5 million new cases of gonorrhea annually.

5.* The impact of any STD on a person's sexuality is usually
   a. catastrophic, all but destroying one's sex drive.
   b. minor in terms of its physical effect, assuming proper detection and treatment is implemented.
   c. major in terms of its physical effect, since most STDs lead to fertility problems.
   d. destructive only when people have had long-term, committed relationships and feel betrayed by the partner who has been the carrier of the STD.

6. The oldest and most common form of STD is
   a. gonorrhea.
   b. NSU.
   c. pubic lice.
   d. hepatitis B.

7. The first indications of gonorrhea in men are
   a. high fever and vomiting.
   b. infrequent urination and chills.
   c. a yellowish discharge from the tip of the penis and frequent urination.
   d. frequent fainting spells and vertigo.

8. If left untreated in women, gonorrhea can
   a. stretch the Fallopian tubes.
   b. cause pelvic inflammatory disease.
   c. totally stop menstrual bleeding.
   d. cause cancer of the cervix to develop.

9. The only reliable means of establishing the diagnosis of gonorrhea in women is
   a. culture tests.
   b. pelvic exams.
   c. Pap smears.
   d. eye examinations to check for the presence of infection.

10. The most effective treatment for gonorrhea is
    a.   sulfa drugs.
    b.   butazolydine.
    c.   penicillin G.
    d.   norepinephrine.

11. The earliest sign of syphilis in its primary stage is the
    a.   pubic louse.
    b.   granuloma inguinale.
    c.   condyloma lata.
    d.   chancre.

12. In infants, congenital syphilis can cause all of the following except
    a.   kidney problems.
    b.   bone and teeth deformities.
    c.   reproductive organ malformations.
    d.   anemia.

13. The accuracy with which secondary syphilis can be detected is
    a.   100%.
    b.   75%.
    c.   50%.
    d.   25%.

14. The herpes family of viruses cause all of the following except
    a.   chickenpox.
    b.   shingles.
    c.   cold sores.
    d.   mumps.

15. The most common symptom of a first episode of genital herpes is likely to be
    a.   fever blisters.
    b.   eye infection.
    c.   clusters of blisters on the genitals.
    d.   chancres.

16. The genital herpes virus can
    a.   never lapse into a dormant state so must be treated continuously for the life of the patient.
    b.   give immunity to any infant born of a herpes-infected mother.
    c.   can cause death or serious damage to the brain or eyes of an infant born to a herpes-infected mother.
    d.   offer immunity to certain forms of cervical cancer.

17. The most promising drug to date in the treatment of genital herpes is
    a.   polysporin.
    b.   acylovir.
    c.   penicillin G.
    d.   aspirin.

18. All of the following seem to be sources of transmission of AIDS except
    a. sharing needles (among drug addicts).
    b. sharing "poppers" (amyl nitrate).
    c. sexual contact.
    d. transfusions of contaminated blood products.

19. All of the following are symptoms of AIDS except
    a. swollen lymph nodes.
    b. unexplained weight loss.
    c. bouts of chills and shivering.
    d. reddish-purple coin-sized spots on the skin.

20. Nonspecific urethritis (NSU) is
    a. a form of bladder dysfunction in women.
    b. a form of gonorrhea.
    c. any inflammation of a male's urethra not caused by gonorrhea.
    d. a symptom of the secondary stage of syphilis.

21. The most effective treatment of NSU is
    a. tetracycline.
    b. penicillin.
    c. immune serum globulin.
    d. darvocet-N.

22. Recent data suggests that the population most likely to be afflicted with hepatitis B is
    a. college men.
    b. college women.
    c. homosexual men.
    d. lesbian women.

23. Chancroid, granuloma inguinale, and lymphogranuloma venereum are STDs that are most commonly found in
    a. subtropical climates.
    b. tropical climates.
    c. temperate climates.
    d. arctic climates.

24. PID refers to a complication of
    a. syphilis.
    b. gonorrhea.
    c. genital herpes.
    d. AIDS.

25. Pubic lice can be best treated by
    a. application of lanolin-based ointments on the affected areas.
    b. shaving the hair from the pubic area.
    c. application of gamma benzene hexachloride on the affected areas.
    d. douching with a vinegar and water solution for women, and sitz baths in the same kind of solution for men.

True/False

F   1.   Gonorrhea can be transmitted only by sexual intercourse.

T   2.   Pubic lice can be easily treated with little chance of long-lasting ill effects.

F   3.   The second most frequent infectious disease in America is syphilis.

T   4.   Molluscum contagiosum can be treated by applications of liquid nitrogen or frozen carbon dioxide to the skin lesions.

F   5.   Non-A and non-B hepatitis are sexually transmitted.

T   6.   The laboratory measurement of acid-labile alpha interferon may be helpful in early detection of AIDS.

F   7.   Kaposi's sarcoma is associated with hepatitis-B.

F   8.   HELP is a support group for AIDS victims and their families.

T   9.   Avoiding tight underwear or clothing can actually be beneficial during an initial herpes episode.

T 10. Recurrence of genital herpes episodes are sometimes preceded by warning symptoms up to 36 hours before blisters appear.

F 11. Natural childbirth is always recommended to women who have genital herpes.

F 12. Genital herpes is caused by a single form of the herpes simplex virus, namely herpes virus type 1.

F 13. In the latent stage of syphilis, the disease is highly contagious though dormant.

T 14. PID is the most common cause of female infertility.

F 15. A blood test to reliably identify gonorrhea has recently been developed.

Fill in the Blanks

1.   Paralysis, insanity, blindness, and death may be the result if syphilis is allowed to reach the (tertiary) stage.

2.   A "Papillon d'amour" is more commonly known as a (pubic louse).

3.   The most reliable means of diagnosing (gonorrhea) in women is by a culture test.

4. The oldest and most common form of STD is (gonorrhea).

5. In 75% of cases of syphilis, chancres form on the genitals and (anus).

6. In 1983, the male to female sex ratio of cases of syphilis was (two to one).

7. The risk of infecting the baby with genital herpes during childbirth if the mother is infected and is experiencing a first attack may be as high as (50) %.

8. Acyclovir ointment is not recommended for use in (recurrent) attacks of genital herpes because of the concern that it may cause resistant strains of the virus to emerge.

9. The number of new cases of (AIDS) is doubling every six months according to the most recent evidence.

10. Unfortunately, the negative effect of AIDS publicity on the general public has been to increase (homophobia).

11. The eggs of pubic lice can survive (six) days if they fall off into sheets or clothing.

12. Chlamydia trachomatis is found in 30-50% of women who are sex partners of men with chlamydia-positive (NSU).

13. Viral hepatitis is an infection of the (liver).

14. (Venereal warts) are greyish-white in color with a cauliflower-like surface.

15. In addition to homosexuals, intravenous drug abusers, and hemophiliacs, (Haitians) seem to be at great risk for contracting AIDS.

Discussion/Essay Questions

1. List the ways in which STDs can be prevented.

2. Devise a counseling program for sexually active college students who have contracted genital herpes. What topics would be most important to cover and most difficult to discuss?

3. Why is discussion of STDs likely to be met with resistance, even disgust? How can these attitudes be changed?

4. Is there such a thing as a minor STD? Must every STD be dealt with seriously and cautiously? Is there ever any justification for not revealing an STD and not seeking medical help?

Chapter 22

SEXUAL THEMES IN POPULAR CULTURE

OVERVIEW

The central thesis of this chapter is that the ways in which a society deals with sexual issues are mirrored in the everyday visibility of erotic themes. An adequate understanding of contemporary societal attitudes toward sex requires an examination of the freedom with which sex is portrayed and how this freedom is exercised. Chapter 22 begins with a discussion of legal aspects of pornography and obscenity, followed by a concise review of sex in literature. Next, the portrayal of sex in various types of media -- newspapers, magazines, cinema, television -- is examined, along with the ways in which sex is used in advertising. The chapter concludes with a discussion of sex in rock 'n' roll and Boxed Items discuss computer sex and sex via telephone.

While reading the chapter, the student is asked to consider these issues:

1. How can pornography and obscenity be compared?

2. What major legal decisions have affected our culture's concepts and definitions of obscenity?

3. What are some sexual themes in contemporary literature? How has our culture accepted or rejected sexual themes in literature at different times in history?

4. What role do newspapers and magazines play in transmitting and shaping popular attitudes about sexuality? What are some publishing events that were turning points?

5. How did changes in censorship that gradually occurred during the 20th century affect treatments of sexual topics in films, television, and music?

6. How do sexual themes function in advertising?

LEARNING OBJECTIVES

At the conclusion of this chapter, the student should be able to:

1. Define pornography and obscenity.

2. Identify the historical antecedents of the U.S. obscenity laws

and give examples of the materials to which they were applied.

3. Discuss the U.S. Supreme Court decisions that have both clarified and confused our current obscenity standards.

4. Summarize the findings of the 1970 Report of the Commission on Obscenity and Pornography.

5. Cite examples of the prominent literary sexual themes of several cultures throughout history.

6. Describe the recent changes in the use of erotic themes and explicit sex in the media.

7. Trace the evolution of sexual content in motion pictures and contrast the censorship practices in cinema with those in both literature and the media.

8. Explain the reason(s) behind the more stringent censorship practices in the television industry over those in cinema.

9. Discuss the effect that sexual themes has had on advertising practices.

10. List several artists and musicians who have used sexual themes in their works.

11. Discuss the opposition to sexual openness and pornography by pressure groups.

12. Give examples of new cultural settings in which sexual themes are becoming part of the electronic revolution.

TEACHING STRATEGIES

Students tend to quickly forget, or lose their perspective about, the changes in cultural attitudes toward sex and sexuality that marked the 1960s and 1970s. This chapter can be used to provide a sense of "living history" and to help students examine the meaning of these changes. One useful approach to teaching this chapter is to begin by reading to students brief excerpts from literature that illustrate some of the stylistic differences between modern works and older writings. For instance, passages from a Henry Miller novel (Tropic of Cancer, Tropic of Capricorn), Erica Jong's Fear of Flying, or a current novel on the best-seller list can be compared to passages from Rabelais, Walt Whitman, or John Cleland's Fanny Hill. Rather than discussing the literary merits of these works, ask the class to consider the social and political implications of censorship. What are the ramifications of banning the sale of a particular book or removing a book from library shelves? Why does our U.S. Constitution provide specific protection for freedom of expression? Should there be limits to the extent of this freedom?

Even broader issues of censorship can be addressed by asking the class to consider the reasons some groups try to limit or suppress sexual themes in movies, television, and other forms of entertainment. Are the primary arguments of these groups religious ones? If so, does our constitutional guarantee of freedom of religion supersede these arguments? Is there evidence that portraying sexual themes frankly leads to an increase in certain types of sexual behavior? Are children somehow contaminated or negatively influenced by watching television shows with a high sex quotient? Point out to the class the concerns voiced by some feminists that a majority of pornographic materials portray women as objects and so dehumanizes sex. Also consider the differences, if any, between frank portrayals of sexual activity between adults and so-called "kiddie porn."

Next, ask the class to consider the reasons people seem so interested in entertainment with frank sexual content. In many locales, X-rated movies have more cable TV viewers than all other movies combined. The best-seller lists are usually peppered with books about sex. Dozens of glossy men's magazines with explicit sexual photographs and stories sell well. Does this mean that most people are sexually dissatisfied? Does it mean that people are titillated by some of the forbidden aspects of sex? Does it just represent a healthy curiosity? Illustrate the way in which business decisions -- "sex sells" -- can occur in real life by posing the following example for discussion. You are president of a company about to market a major new perfume. Your advertising agency has test-marketed two different ad campaigns, one with a strong sexual innuendo, and one with a more direct appeal to youthfulness. The responses to the two ads show that consumers viewing the sexually motivated ads would buy your product at twice the rate of those viewing the other ads. Which campaign would you choose for your national marketing effort?

Another strategy that can be used to enliven class discussion is to play several rock 'n' roll records with sexual themes for the class. Could the Pointer Sisters' 1981 recording, "(I Want a Man With a) Slow Hand" have been played on the radio 25 years ago? What messages does it convey about male and female sexuality? Is this an effective form of sex education for preteens and teens? What about the depiction of such records on MTV? Contrast this record with Meatloaf's 1977 hit song, "Paradise by the Dashboard Light" (found on the "Bat Out of Hell" album), which frankly presents a stereotypical, albeit realistic, story of teenage seduction. Instructors who are connoisseurs of rock 'n' roll may also want to play a few records from the "golden oldies" category ("Come On Baby Let the Good Times Roll" genre) to illustrate how an undercurrent of sexual innuendo was present in those hits.

It seems that U.S. culture has moved long distances in changing sexual prudery and prohibitions, but is this really the case? School sex education in the 1980s, as recently estimated by a government study, is offered to a mere 10% of students. Antipornography campaigns are commonplace. Homosexuality is a horror to most parents. Many men and women believe that masturbation after marriage is abnormal, and that sex after age sixty is improper or even impossible. Thus, although out culture may be talking about it, seeing it, and hearing it more, actions and underlying attitudes about sexuality seem to remain almost static. Confront students with this important question toward the end of this course: Has there really been a major revolution in human sexual behavior?

STUDENT PROJECTS

1. Assume that you are a lawyer defending "Playboy" magazine against charges of obscenity in a small, rural community in the Southwest. At the start of the trial, before jury selection begins, you file a motion with the judge to dismiss the charges. What would you say in support of this motion to dismiss?

2. Read two weeks' worth of advice columns in your local newspapers. What sorts of sexual issues are addressed? Do you agree with the columnists' advice?

3. Listen to a local rock 'n' roll station for a few hours to make up a list of songs with definite sexual connotations. Do you think such songs have any impact on teens' sexual attitudes? Then spend a few hours watching MTV. What impact do visuals have on that same sexual content? (MTV and Top 40 radio stations usually play the same songs.)

4. Visit an art museum or an art library to find examples of erotic art from different countries and different historical periods. What can you tell about a culture from its art?

PERSONAL REFLECTIONS

1. Have you ever seen an X-rated movie? Recall your reaction to it. If you have never seen one, why not? How do you think our society would be different if X-rated movies were not allowed to be produced or shown in this country?

2. Do you think that sexually explicit rock 'n' roll lyrics or videos have any influence at all on teenage sexual behavior? Have you ever been sexually aroused to the point of excitation just by listening to music?

3. Suppose you are the author of a novel that includes several sex scenes which are pivotal to the plot. Your editor tells you the scenes are too explicit and should be eliminated. What would you do?

4. If you were a member of a city council that was holding hearings on whether or not a local cable TV company should be allowed to show X-rated movies after 11:00 P.M., what would you decide and why?

CHAPTER 22 TEST QUESTIONS

<u>Multiple Choice</u> (* General Comprehension Questions)

1.* Cultural attitudes and uncertainties about sex
   a. are not accurately reflected by censorship in everyday life.
   <u>b.</u> can be judged by the openness and visibility of erotic themes in popular culture.
   c. are rarely expressed in the literature of the time.
   d. are expressed universally within a given society: all groups endorse the prevailing trends.

2.* Pornography is best defined as
   a. childhood erotica.
   b. anything designed to incite lust or depravity.
   <u>c.</u> any form of communication intended to cause sexual excitement.
   d. blasphemy.

3.* Obscenity is best defined as
   a. anything sexually detrimental to underage minors.
   b. anything designed to incite to riot.
   <u>c.</u> anything abhorrent to morality, disgusting to the senses.
   d. pornography.

4.* Denmark's experience with the repeal of laws limiting the availability of pornography
   a. was instrumental in Nixon's decision to veto a similar proposal in the United States.
   b. proved that pornography caused an increase in unintended adolescent pregnancy.
   <u>c.</u> was positive insofar as their rates of several sex offenses declined.
   d. led to the legalization of prostitution.

5.* The current trend toward sexual openness
   a. is applauded by all feminist organizations.
   b. is approved by most fundamentalist religious groups.
   <u>c.</u> reflects the fact that the public tends to get what it wants in a democratic society.
   d. has, unfortunately, been demonstrated to program many men toward coercive sex.

6. During the 19th century in the United States
   a. there was much enforcement of the obscenity laws at both state and local levels.
   b. New York was the first state to convict booksellers of selling obscene literature.
   c. the mailing of birth control information was encouraged.
   <u>d.</u> Anthony Comstock got Congress to broaden its federal mail act.

7. The 1933 Woolsey decision lifted the ban on

243

a. Ellis's Studies in the Psychology of Sex.
b. Margaret Sanger's works on population control.
c. The Archbishop of Talavera's Little Sermons on Sin.
d. James Joyce's Ulysses.

8. A major problem with the 1957 and 1966 decisions regarding obscenity is
a. there has never been a definition of "community."
b. there has never been a definition of "standards."
c. there has never been a delineation of the scope of literary forms to be considered when deciding about obscenity.
d. they were reached at a state level and the issues were never considered by the U.S. Supreme Court.

9. The President of the United States who lobbied hard for the abolition of pornography and obscenity laws as well as for the inclusion of sex education in public schools was
a. John F. Kennedy.
b. Lyndon B. Johnson.
c. Dwight D. Eisenhower.
d. Gerald Ford.

10. An interesting ordinance passed in 1983 by the Minneapolis City Council but later vetoed by the Mayor, would have defined pornography
a. as a form of blasphemy.
b. as a form of sex bias.
c. as a harmless though foolish form of recreation.
d. as a tool for sex education to be made available to public school sex educators under controlled conditions.

11. Sexual themes in literature
a. are primarily an invention of the 20th century.
b. can be found as early as the 5th century B.C. in the writings of Aristophanes.
c. were censored in Shakespeare's times.
d. did not exist at all during the Victorian era.

12. My Secret Life was an 11 volume sexual autobiography
a. published by Henry Miller in France.
b. written by Walt Whitman and not found until after his death among his posthumous papers.
c. written anonymously by an Englishman in Victorian England.
d. written by Rabelais and circulted widely in 18th century France.

13. Tropic of Cancer and Tropic of Capricorn were
a. written by Grace Metalious.
b. used as models for Nabokov's Lolita.
c. almost immediately banned in all English-speaking countries after their publication.
d. precursors to Ulysses.

14. One of the most successful and prolific writers of popular novels with sexual themes in the U.S. today is
    a. Philip Roth.
    b. John Updike.
    c. Harold Robbins.
    d. Stanley Elkin.

15. Sex in the media is
    a. on the wane.
    b. utilized only rarely as a marketing device.
    c. pervasive in almost every media format.
    d. not subject to any of the controls that literature is.

16. The words "penis" and "vagina" first appeared in many newspapers
    a. in April, 1966 when Masters and Johnson published Human Sexual Response.
    b. when the Woolsey decision was implemented.
    c. when Denmark abolished its anti-pornography laws.
    d. when Johnson lobbied for sex education in the schools.

17. The role of newspapers in transmitting or shaping popular attitudes about sex has been
    a. minimal.
    b. nonexistent.
    c. a gradual response to a changing society.
    d. irrelevant since most people get their news from T.V. or radio.

18. All of the following are true about sex in the cinema except
    a. in 1935, the American motion picture industry lifted its ban on the use of erotica.
    b. in the early 1960s, courts ruled many major censorship boards unconstitutional.
    c. in the 1970s, X-rated theaters began to cater to a new clientele.
    d. in the 1980s, sex seems to be woven into the story lines of movies, yet with less explicit sexual content than one would expect.

19. The television event that marked the change from shows being heavily censored to shows being more sexually explicit was
    a. the appearance of Elvis Presley on the "Ed Sullivan Show."
    b. Norman Lear's "All in the Family."
    c. the PBS special on the birth of Louise Brown, the first test-tube baby.
    d. the development of the Playboy Channel on cable.

20. The use of sex in advertising has been found to
    a. be amusing but insignificant in terms of actual sales.
    b. be utilized only for personal products, never for business-oriented products.
    c. enhance the potential customer's identification with the actors and the products they are selling.

d.   reduce gender role stereotyping.

21. When one studies the role of sex in rock 'n' roll music, it
     becomes clear that all of the following were true except
     a.   the sexuality of the Beatles was more in their appearance
           than their songs.
     b.   there was no sexual innuendo in pre-rock 'n' roll records.
     c.   the real sexual revolutionaries of the 1960s were the
           Rolling Stones.
     d.   the lyrics of Elvis Presley's records were tame.

22. Explicit sexual lyrics in rock 'n' roll songs are
     a.   one indication of how mindless the media can be.
     b.   a direct result of the Motion Picture Association rating
           system.
     c.   a primary source of sex education for school-age children.
     d.   a reflection of a general cultural trend toward more
           sexual openness.

23. Computer sex is
     a.   only a factor on college campuses.
     b.   facilitated by the use of a modem.
     c.   on the wane.
     d.   currently outlawed in twenty-five states.

24. Telephone sex services
     a.   cannot be regulated because of first amendment rights.
     b.   is only subject to scrutiny by authorities if a particular
           service is reported to the Better Business Bureau.
     c.   can be declared illegal by the F.C.C. if obscene or
           indecent language is available to people under the age of
           18.
     d.   so far, only exist on the east and west coasts of the U.S.

25. The magazine editor most responsible for the change in women's
     magazines from homemaker orientations toward sexual themes was
     a.   Letty Cottin Pogrebin.
     b.   Gloria Steinham.
     c.   Helen Gurley Brown.
     d.   Christy Hefner.

True/False

F   1.   Even in cultures that are pro-sex, censorship is still
           very prominent.

T   2.   In the 1600s, obscenity was considered an offense against
           religion.

F   3.   In 1821, booksellers in Massachusetts were convicted of
           selling The Tropic of Cancer.

T   4.   The Comstock Act addressed the issue of mailing obscene

246

literature.

F 5. Judge Woolsey said that the difference between literature and pornography was "in the groin of the beholder."

T 6. You cannot have computer sex without a modem. *ha, ha*

F 7. President Richard Nixon accepted the findings of the 1970 Report of the Commission on Obscenity and Pornography.

F 8. Children's literature has been exempt from the pervasive increase of sex in literature.

F 9. Citicorp lost millions of dollars because of an ad campaign that was clearly sexually offensive to its clientele.

T 10. In 1948 and 1953, many newpapers refused to discuss the Kinsey Reports.

T 11. The start of a new era in magazine publishing occurred when Hugh Hefner brought out the first issue of "Playboy" in 1953.

F 12. X-rated movie theaters haven't been noticeably affected by the availability of pornographic films on cable or video cassettes.

F 13. The upsurge in sexually oriented programming on television was an easy process after the success of "All in the Family."

F 14. All products, even laxatives and dog foods, have been marketed through the use of sexy advertising.

T 15. Art, more so than literature, has had an abundance of sexual themes.

Fill in the Blanks

1. (Cosmopolitan), under the leadership of Helen Gurley Brown, was the first woman's magazine to deal frankly with sexual issues.

2. A novel by Grace Metalious that shocked 1950s America was (Peyton Place).

3. A 5th century play by Aristophanes that told about a group of women withholding sex from their husbands and lovers until the latter voted for peace was (Lysistrata).

4. (Charles Rembar) is a well-known lawyer who has defended many books against charges of obscenity.

5. The erotic environment both reflects the attitudes found in a

society and helps to (shape) these attitudes.

6. In cultures that are strongly antisexual, (censorship) is prominent.

7. According to U.S. law, although obscenity is illegal, (pornography) is not.

8. Anthony Comstock was most angered by the mailing of (birth control information).

9. In a 1973 Supreme Court case, (Miller v. California), it was ruled that local community standards could be used to obtain obscenity convictions.

10. Current television shows featuring attractive women in tight-fitting, revealing clothing have been dubbed (T and A or jiggle) programs.

11. Primitive art from many cultures shows a fascination with the (genitals).

12. According to Bradley Smith, the heyday of erotic art has been during the (20th) century.

13. A controversial newpaper devoted entirely to sex and published by Al Goldstein is called (Screw).

14. A novel about the seduction of a 12-year-old girl by a middle-aged man that stirred a great deal of controversy in the late 1950s is (Lolita).

15. Sex in the cinema in the 1980s is exemplified by (Personal Best), a film about the lesbian experiences of a young female athlete.

Discussion/Essay Questions

1. How did the novel Ulysses affect the course of U.S. publishing history?

2. Discuss the findings of the 1967 President's Commission on Obscenity and Pornography.

3. Outline some trends in sexual explicitness in the cinema and on television.

4. Why and how do advertisers use sex in their ads?

5. Is television censorship necessary? If so, who should control television programming?

6. How would sexual behavior be affected if laws could effectively ban sexual themes from books, t.v., movies, and magazines?

Chapter 23

RELIGIOUS AND ETHICAL PERSPECTIVES ON SEXUALITY

OVERVIEW

Although most people realize that sexual behavior has been
tremendously influenced by religious teachings, there is often a
great deal of confusion about each religion's specific stance on
sexual matters. This chapter summarizes the sexual teachings of the
world's major religions and addresses the ways in which sexual
ethics and sexual decision making are intertwined. Included are
discussions of three sexual issues that are sources of ethical and
religious controversy: abortion, homosexuality, and contraception.
Throughout the chapter the complexity of making sexual choices
consistent with one's religious beliefs and ethical value system is
stressed.

While reading the chapter, the student is asked to consider these
issues:

1. How do Jewish, Christian, Islamic, Hindu, and Buddhist beliefs
    and teachings about human sexual behavior compare with one
    another?

2. What are some of the problems inherent in making sexual
    decisions?

3. How can one distinguish between decisions that are ethically
    value free and those that involve ethical issues?

4. What are the differences between pro-life, pro-choice, and
    middle-of-the-road positions on abortion?

5. What are some of the ways in which religious views about
    homosexuality and contraception have changed from prior
    clerical positions?

LEARNING OBJECTIVES

At the conclusion of this chapter, the student should be able to:

1. Outline the basic views of sexuality expressed in Jewish,
    Catholic, and Protestant thought.

2. Describe the similarities and differences in the ways
    particular religions have handled sexual issues.

249

3. Contrast ethical questions about sex with those based on personal taste and preference.

4. Identify the four moral views by which educated people judge the moral appropriateness of a sexual act.

5. Discuss the historical background and attitudes about abortion and state the three primary positions that people take on abortion.

6. Explain the position(s) most religions take with regard to homosexuality.

7. Compare and contrast the views regarding contraception methods held by different religious groups.

8. List the major ethical questions concerning contraception.

9. Briefly summarize the religious teachings about sexuality included in Islam, Hinduism, and Buddhism.

TEACHING STRATEGIES

Many students may have rejected or distanced themselves from the practice and teachings of formal religion and so may approach this chapter reluctantly. However, the content is critical to a course in human sexuality and should not be skipped. One major goal of this course is to help students make sexual decisions more objectively, without residual guilt or discomfort. It has been noted in previous chapters that almost all people at some time experience ambivalence and guilt relative to sexual decisions. The instructor can ask students to think about the following questions. Should I masturbate? Should I masturbate after marriage? Should I use fantasies of another person when I'm having sex with my spouse? Should I have an abortion? Should I have an extramarital affair? As noted in the text, a person's value system has some influence on all moral choices made by that person. Religions, in turn, may directly or indirectly influence values. Since some people reject formal religion, its effects on their values are often not articulated and cause conflict for them. Articulation may therefore lead to more objective decision making and reduced guilt and anxiety. Some of the more common methods of sexual decision making are listed in the text. The instructor can suggest various situations as examples to help the students delineate their values. For example,

> Bill and Sue have a committed marriage and they love one another. Bill asks Sue to have sex with his depressed, lonely bachelor friend Joe. Sue, at first reluctant, eventually seduces Joe without confessing that it was at Bill's request. However, Sue enjoys the sex and continues to visit Joe weekly for an additional six weeks without telling Bill. Bill finds out and is furious. He physically assaults Joe and threatens to divorce Sue.

Who is right? Who is wrong?

The power of religion is strong. It is estimated that 40% of people throughout the world attend church regularly. Despite the fact that churches may be losing their influence in people's daily decision making, the total number of church members does not decrease. This suggests that fewer people get involved in the church or synagogue out of a sense of obligation, and there is now more voluntary religious participation than ever before. Why might this be true? If voluntary participation has increased, and the frequency of so-called "immoral behaviors" is on the rise, do these signs mean that sexual guilt is increasing? One important but controversial question for class discussion is whether or not formal religion is harmful to sexual development. If some students answer "yes," what do they propose as a solution?

In this discussion, it is important to emphasize that most societies do have some form of religious worship. One purpose of religion may be to persuade individuals to internalize rules and regulations that control their own behavior for the good of all. From this persepctive, every society has some sanctions on certain types of sexual behavior, often pertaining to procreation and libido. Perhaps regulating natural functions such as these give authorities greater control over other human behaviors. Consider whether sanctions against certain sexual behaviors alleged to be "for the good of society" are still useful and applicable to modern situations as in the case of sanctions against incest.

Have students think about the ways in which sexual morality is defined in countries that reject formal religion, as Russia or Communist China. As sexual morals become more relaxed in a country, what are the implications for individual freedom? If a country swings to conservatism, how might sexual values change?

Also have the class consider what realistic and workable positions might be developed regarding sexuality for our contemporary religions. Should priests or nuns be celibate? Should a priest or nun be permitted to pursue a homosexual lifestyle? Should religions provide formal rules of who does what, with whom, where? Should they focus instead on "values" in order to foster the belief that "relationships require care, concern, and nonexploitation?"

Chapter 23 discusses a number of ethical dilemmas that involve sexuality, and tries to show that there are no simple solutions to the dilemmas. While recognizing that some students will feel strongly about a particular ethical issue (with the risk of class discussion turning into an emotion-laden debate), the instructor should try to help the class look at varying viewpoints to see just how complex these issues are. For example, should abortion be freely available to all females without restrictions? Should abortions be permitted only when the mothers' lives are endangered? Ask those who hold the latter position to consider what they would suggest should a twelve-year-old sister (or other relative) become pregnant as a result of forcible rape. Is it usually the case that making the "right" ethical choice is a matter of choosing between the lesser of two evils? Other topics for class discussion might include whether prostitution should be legalized, if extramarital sex is always wrong, if premarital sex is right or wrong, whether it is ever possible to change one's mind about such things within the framework of one's personal religious beliefs.

STUDENT PROJECTS

1. Interview a minister, priest, or rabbi to find out the most common types of sexual problems that their congregants come to them to discuss. What sorts of advice do they give? What kind of training have they had to qualify them to discuss sexual issues? Would you feel comfortable discussing a personal sexual question or problem with this particular clergyman? What impact do you think his or her advice or admonitions might have on a given congregant?

2. Attend a "Pro-Life" or "Pro-Choice" meeting. Do the discussions seem to be thoughtful and objective or do they seem based on emotion? Is your response in any way colored by whether or not you agree with the position of the group about abortion?

PERSONAL REFLECTIONS

1. How have your own religion's teachings about sexuality influenced your sexual value system? Do you follow all or most of the teachings of your religion regarding sexual behavior? If not, what reasons have you used to justify your choices?

2. How would you make a decision to have an abortion? How would you make a decision to carry an unplanned, unwanted pregnancy to term? Is the decision-making process the same for the two situations? What role does emotion play? What role does logic play?

3. Would you attend religious services conducted by an avowed homosexual? Would you attend religious services if it was alleged that the clergyman had been seen propositioning teenage boys? Would you react the same way about attending a theatrical production performed by the same individuals? Why?

4. What are your sources of authority regarding sexual thoughts and actions? Who or what do you turn to for advice in sexual matters? Why? Ideally, who or what would be the best sexual authority for your needs?

CHAPTER 23 TEST QUESTIONS

Multiple Choice (* General Comprehension Questions)

1.* The two major ways individuals and societies approach questions of values are by the teaching and analysis of
a. sociology and religion.

b. religion and ethics.
c. biology and ethics.
d. psychology and ethics.

2.* Sexual issues that currently provoke considerable controversy include all of the following except
a. homosexuality.
b. contraception.
c. abortion.
d. transsexualism.

3.* The various moral issues discussed, in Chapter 23
a. have clearcut solutions for the times they become problematic.
b. are rarely problematic since they are so closely intertwined with popular cultural trends.
c. represent problems that involve individual and social judgments about the nature of responsible sexual behavior with no easy answers.
d. seem to be problematic only for those who do not attend organized religious worship services.

4.* According to this chapter, ethical analysis can be applied effectively when
a. one set of values conflicts with another.
b. the values of a Judaeo-Christian religion conflict with those of an Eastern religion.
c. the values of a non-religious culture conflict with the values of a religious culture.
d. the values of a pagan culture conflict with the values of missionaries trying to convert the pagan people.

5.* The way people make sexual decisions in real life
a. often conflicts with the teachings of their church or synagogue.
b. rarely causes people any feelings of guilt.
c. should hinge on the cut-and-dry pronouncements by clergy about moral issues.
d. should not involve religious teachings at all.

6. Jewish views of sexuality
a. are derived from the New Testament.
b. indicate that marriage exists only for the purpose of procreation.
c. indicate that celibacy is a virtue.
d. indicate that sexuality is a positive force, a gift of God.

7. According to Jewish beliefs and teachings
a. sexual activity is seen as proper only within marriage.
b. sexual activity between husband and wife is not mandatory.
c. a woman cannot reject her husband's sexual advances.
d. divorce is not permitted if sexual problems exist in the marriage.

253

8. All of the following are forbidden or discouraged by Judaism except
   a. adultery.
   b. incest.
   c. prostitution.
   d. bestiality and pedophilia.

9. The Laws of Niddah in Orthodox Judaism state that
   a. abortion is prohibited.
   b. female homosexual behavior is prohibited.
   c. forcing daughters into prostitution is prohibited.
   d. sexual contact between husband and wife during menstruation and one week after is prohibited.

10. Early Christian teachings about sexuality
    a. were strongly influenced by Greek ideas separating physical and spiritual love.
    b. saw sexuality as a very positive force in one's life.
    c. rejected all of Judaism's teachings about sexuality.
    d. said only sexual acts were not contaminated by original sin.

11. The Catholic Church teaches that
    a. masturbation is morally acceptable under some circumstances.
    b. chastity, celibacy, or abstinence is virtuous.
    c. premarital sexual activity is acceptable for engaged couples.
    d. all forms of sexual behavior are good.

12. Some modern Catholic clergymen would like to see all of the following changes occur regarding teachings about sexuality except
    a. development of new attitudes toward female sexuality.
    b. development of procedures to judge sexual behavior as self-liberating, honest, socially responsible, joyful.
    c. the dissolution of all teachings about original sin.
    d. acceptance of the idea that the primary role of sexual union is to enable people to reach fulfillment.

13. In 1983, Pope John Paul II said
    a. sex education of Catholic children was the primary responsibility of the religious schools.
    b. cohabitation without marriage was permissible under certain circumstances.
    c. marriages should be indissoluble.
    d. homosexuality could be condoned.

14. The conservative Protestant perspective about sexuality says
    a. masturbation and homosexuality are excusable behaviors.
    b. marriage does not have to be a life-long commitment.
    c. priests may marry.
    d. abortion is completely acceptable.

15. Protestantism, developed by Martin Luther, evolved from
    a.   Orthodox Judaism.
    b.   Unitarianism.
    c.   Catholicism.
    d.   Calvinism.

16. A question that is ethically value-free might be
    a.   "Am I being honest?"
    b.   "Might I hurt my partner?"
    c.   "Am I doing the right thing?"
    d.   "Am I in the mood?"

17. All of the following are possible ways of judging the moral
    appropriateness of a sexual act except saying
    a.   anything between consenting adults is moral.
    b.   good sexuality is anything that enhances interpersonal
         relationships.
    c.   there are no absolute rules to use.
    d.   the right time and place are the parameters for judging.

18. The "Pro-Life" position about abortion is
    a.   that abortion should be banned under all circumstances.
    b.   that abortion should be available to any pregnant woman.
    c.   that abortion should be restricted to situations of rape
         or incest.
    d.   that first trimester abortions are allowed.

19. The "Pro-Choice" position about abortion states that
    a.   human life begins at the moment of conception.
    b.   abortion is an abuse of human power.
    c.   male domination is responsible for stringent abortion laws.
    d.   there is no distinction between the legal problem and the
         moral problem of abortion.

20. Most religions today teach that homosexual behavior
    a.   is a criminal offense even between consenting adults.
    b.   is just cause for denial of the person's care.
    c.   should be considered an orientation and not mainly a
         matter of free choice.
    d.   should be considered an illness.

21. A study which defined a measure for sexual morality as the
    integrity of the relationship between the people involved was
    published a generation ago by
    a.   the Catholics.
    b.   the Quakers.
    c.   the Protestants.
    d.   the Reform Jews.

22. A Protestant denomination that is completely conservative in
    its sexual views and seeks to follow the Bible literally is
    a.   the Jehovah's Witnesses.
    b.   the Quakers.
    c.   the Unitarians.

255

d.   the Calvinists.

23. In reference to contraception, most religious groups today
     a.   pay   very   little   attention   to   questions   about
          contraception.
     b.   favor male methods of contraception.
     c.   agree that contraception is morally justifiable.
     d.   condemn the development of the morning-after pill.

24. The Islamic religion
     a.   encourages celibacy.
     b.   is tolerant of adultery.
     c.   is intolerant of homosexuality.
     d.   regards sexuality as a gift from God.

25. The religion that treats sex as a form of spiritual energy is
     a.   Buddhism.
     b.   Islam.
     c.   Hinduism.
     d.   Evangelical Baptist.

True/False

T   1.   In Judaism, the family has a great deal of religious
          significance.

F   2.   Kosher law regulates the sexual activity between husband
          and wife.

F   3.   Judaism   doesn't permit divorce in cases of sexual
          dysfunction.

F   4.   The "Laws of Niddah" are part of the orthodox Catholic
          tradition.

T   5.   Some of the early Christian teachings about sex which seem
          negative today were probably meant as temporary measures.

F   6.   The teachings of the Popes have had little, if any, impact
          on the Catholic position regarding sexuality.

F   7.   The many denominations of the Protestant faith are in
          agreement about sexual matters.

T   8.   Generally, denominations of religions are classified as
          conservative, moderate, and liberal for purposes of
          discussing their ethical or moral positions.

T   9.   Some clergy feel uneasy about traditional religious
          viewpoints on sexuality.

F   10. Ethical   decision making   in sexuality is a   process
          requiring faith, and is based solely on religion.

F   11. The Catholic Church, Orthodox Jews, and the Eastern
         Orthodox, conservative Protestants are among the
         denominations supporting the "Pro-Choice" movement.

T   12. Most religions today take the position that it is not
         sinful to have a homosexual orientation.

T   13. Various religious denominations have been debating about
         the exact ways in which contraception should be used.

F   14. For every question about responsible sexual behavior,
         there is only one right answer.

T   15. Every known religion has teachings that relate to sexual
         ethics.

Fill in the Blanks

1. The (Jewish) tradition says companionship between spouses is of
    major importance.

2. The "Declaration on Certain Questions Concerning Sexual Ethics"
    was issued in 1976 by the (Catholic) religion.

3. "Salvation by faith through grace" and a rejection of celibacy
    were changes in belief instituted by a man named (Martin
    Luther).

4. A branch of Protestantism that is traditional and seeks to find
    Biblical rules for sexual behavior by following the Bible
    literally is (the Jehovah's Witnesses).

5. A religious group that published a study which defined the
    integrity of a relationship as a measure for sexual morality is
    (the Quakers).

6. (Ethical) questions have to do with the moral quality of a
    particular course of action.

7. Kinsey determined that people in the 1940s and 1950s judged
    what was "proper" sexual behavior differently depending on
    their (educational) background.

8. (Situation) ethics, an approach to sexual decision making based
    on assessment of facts, was developed by Joseph Fletcher.

9. (Abortion) was originally disapproved of as far back as 4600
    years ago in China because it was a health risk.

10. "The love that dared not speak its name" was once the way
    people described (homosexuality).

11. In (Hinduism), the oldest religion of India, sex is considered
    a form of spiritual energy.

12. People of the (Buddhist) faith don't condemn prostitution because of the belief that prostitutes are working out their karma.

13. Judith Jarvis Thomson's story of the famous violinist is meant to point out some of the ethical dilemmas of (abortion).

14. Whatever one's attitudes toward sexuality, choices are always made in terms of some (values).

15. All religions agree that pastoral care should be available to (homosexual) individuals, though the religions may not openly approve of such people's sexual behaviors.

Discussion/Essay Questions

1. Explain the most important teachings regarding sexuality from the perspectives of Judaism, Catholicism, and Protestantism.

2. Which of the following religions -- Buddhism, Islam, and Hinduism -- is the most sexually uninhibited and why?

3. What is an ethical sexual decision? Give an example and compare it to a decision that does not pose an ethical question. Are certain issues ethical for everyone, or is defining what is ethical a personal decision?

4. Discuss the legalization of abortion from the point of view of Pro-Life and Pro-Choice. Construct an analogy along the lines of the one cited in this chapter to illustrate each side's position.

5. If the Catholic Church allowed the ordination of avowed homosexuals as priests, would the stance of the church toward homosexuality have to change? Why? How?

6. According to recent statistics, three-quarters of Catholic women use artificial methods of birth control, thus going against the teaching of the church. What does such defiance suggest about the influence of religion on sexual behavior?

7. What are the major differences between the conservative, moderate, and liberal Protestant perspectives on sexuality?

Chapter 24

SEXUALITY IN CROSS-CULTURAL PERSPECTIVE

OVERVIEW

Quite appropriately, the last chapter in the book synthesizes studies of human sexuality around the world by surveying cross-cultural issues. While students may be surprised or entertained by reading about sexual customs that differ drastically from their own, they are also helped to develop a more tolerant sexual viewpoint and new insights into the sexual practices of their own society. This guest-authored chapter by Paul Gebhard, Ph.D., begins by explaining how anthropology adds to the study of sexuality while defining the limits of the anthropological approach. The chapter then discusses cross-cultural aspects of sexual attraction, childhood and adolescent sexuality, premarital sex customs, and sex in and out of marriage. The chapter concludes with sections on cross-cultural aspects of homosexuality, and ritualized sex.

While reading the chapter, the student is asked to consider these issues:

1. Why is sex well-suited for cross-cultural studies?

2. How do different societies define what is sexually arousing and attractive?

3. What are the functions of puberty rites? What are the attitudes of different cultures toward petting, foreplay, and premarital coitus?

4. Why, from an anthropological perspective, do marriage, incest taboos, exogamy, and endogamy benefit a society? What are some different types of marriages that occur cross-culturally?

5. When would the frequency of sexual activity be limited or increased by a culture? When would extramarital and postmarital sexual activity be encouraged or discouraged by different cultures?

6. What is the anthropological perspective on homosexuality? How do attitudes toward male and female homosexual behavior differ?

LEARNING OBJECTIVES

At the conclusion of this chapter, the student should be able to:

1. Explain why sex is particularly well-suited for cross-cultural studies.

2. Describe the physical characteristics of sexually attractive persons in all cultures, the sexual attractiveness of other physical attributes that depend on the values of the culture, and the behavioral patterns of sexually attractive persons in most cultures.

3. Compare and contrast the culturally approved and condemned forms of sexuality among cultures during childhood and puberty.

4. Identify the premarital heterosexual behaviors practiced in our European-American culture and shared by other cultures.

5. Discuss the relationship between sex and marriage in those cultures in which the union of sexual partners is legitimized and list the benefits of marriage and the societal rules and regulations for marriage.

6. Compare the types of marriages and the attitudes toward them by various cultures.

TEACHING STRATEGIES

A large amount of basic information about human sexual behavior awaits more extensive anthropologic research. Students should be impressed with what is known as well as what is unknown about sexual behavior in other cultures. Only recently has the study of sexual behavior been a legitimate topic among professional anthropologists. Thus, practically nothing is known about masturbation or sexual difficulties and dysfunctions in various societies. With more basic information, it might be possible to contrast extremes of sexual taboos and freedoms in order to determine how they affect a population. For example, many Polynesian and African cultures are more sexually permissive than the U.S., while the Irish of Inis Beag are extremely prudish [Marshall, D.S. and Suggs, R.C. (Eds.). Human Sexual Behavior. New York: Basic Books, 1971]. Unfortunately, no data exist on the prevalence of sexual problems in these diverse cultures.

It might also be possible to contrast societies that permit childhood sexuality. The scant data suggest that the incidence of sexual problems are low in Polynesian-like cultures [Marshall and Suggs]. Study of the differences in sexual development between these cultures and our own might identify components of the sociocultural climate in Western cultures that produce sexual difficulties. The test notes cross-cultural evidence that clearly reveals childhood sexual responses. Permission or prohibition of the expression of this drive may eventually be identified as one critical component.

Another illustration of the importance of anthropological research in sexology is related to homosexuality. If some cultures have no members who are exclusively homosexual in adulthood, what is the implication for our own society? What sociocultural factors in our society might encourage exclusive homosexuality?

Anthropologic study is one more unique resource to help untie the nature/nurture knot. The text notes that some cultures do not have kissing between members. Does that mean the extreme pleasure experienced by kissing is mainly psychological? Does a behavior have to be recorded in every culture to have a biologic basis? Inversely, if a phenomenon such as transvestism is recorded in most cultures, does that imply a major genetic etiology? There are no factual answers to these questions and discussion should point to the difficulty of conducting cross-cultural research.

If this chapter is taught at the conclusion of the course, it provides an ideal vehicle for asking students to make predictions about cultural attitudes toward sex 100 years from now. Will the 20th century be viewed by our descendants as a guilt-laden time with archaic sexual beliefs (as we tend to describe the Victorian era)? Will sex become less important in people's lives? Will reproductive behavior become increasingly controlled by governments? Will marriage survive? Students are likely to be amazed at how much they have learned in the course and questions such as these will help them to recognize the amazing perspective they have gained about human sexuality.

STUDENT PROJECTS

1. Write a 1,000 word description of key sexual customs of contemporary America to be placed in a time capsule to be opened 500 years from now.

2. Conduct a library research project on rites of pubertal passage in three different societies.

3. Design a study to investigate patterns of extramarital sexual behavior in three different countries.

PERSONAL REFLECTIONS

1. If you could have been raised in any type of culture, what type would you pick? How might you be different today had you been raised with a different set of cultural standards?

2. How do you think living in a nudist camp would influence your sexual behavior?

3. Does the study of sexual behaviors and beliefs that are very different from our own culture's enable you to see your own values in terms of a wider cultural perspective? Do you get a sense of values and attitudes being relative to the time and place of your upbringing? Does this mean value systems are too changeable and imprecise and should be discarded? Try to imagine a society in which no one had any values or standards. Would it be a society?

4. If America in the 22nd century has succeeded in eliminating sexual health problems and unwanted pregnancies, what sort of cultural attitudes toward sex might there be?

CHAPTER 24 TEST QUESTIONS

Multiple Choice (* General Comprehension Questions)

1.* Anthropology is
   a. a study of unique plant forms.
   b. a branch of medicine.
   c. a study of humanity.
   d. a study of skeletal bones and other ancient human artifacts.

2.* Sex is suited for cross-cultural studies for all of the following reasons except
   a. differences in sexual behavior and capacity are less than differences in other behaviors and capacities.
   b. it is not greatly influenced by environmental factors.
   c. it is an impulse shared by almost all humans.
   d. the limits to sexual capacity are set by one's genetically determined physiology.

3.* All human societies agree that
   a. the female navel is sexually arousing to males.
   b. the female breasts are sexually arousing to males.
   c. exposed female genitals are sexually arousing to males.
   d. total nudity is sexually stimulating.

4.* Anthropology developed
   a. in ancient Greece.
   b. after World War II.
   c. in Europe and the U.S. during the Victorian era.
   d. in ancient Egypt.

5.* Early records of the sexual lives of women were incomplete because early anthropologists
   a. studied only men.
   b. believed women were basically asexual beings.
   c. believed women were the inferior sex and not consistent enough in their behaviors to be able to make conclusions about.
   d. were almost always men, unwilling to risk their reputations or be charged with being overinterested in sex if they published their data.

6. What is considered sexually stimulating to see
   a. is always in terms of the female's response to male genital exposure.
   b. can only be guessed at by sociobiologists who really have no scientific basis for their judgments.
   c. is always in terms of the male's response to female

genital exposure.
d. is determined by both male and female response to exposed
    genitalia.

7. All of the following are accurate statements about sexual
    attractiveness except
    a. being reared together increases sexual attractiveness
        between those thus reared.
    b. male sexual attractiveness is enhanced by behavior showing
        he is a good provider and socially successful.
    c. female sexual attractiveness is enhanced by behavior
        suggesting she will be a good wife and mother.
    d. novelty is sexually stimulating.

8. Childhood sexual activity
    a. is necessary to ensure better adult sexuality.
    b. is not ordinarily detrimental.
    c. is always a turn-on to adults.
    d. is always distinct from adult sexual activity in primitive
        societies.

9. Puberty rites in primitive societies are characterized by all
    of the following except
    a. discomfort and pain to the adolescents.
    b. attention to the genitals of the adolescents.
    c. sexual acts serving symbolic or educational purposes.
    d. ceremonies held for males and females together, for
        educational purposes.

10. Incubi and succubi are
    a. strains of viruses that cause genital infections and are
        common in primitive societies.
    b. primitive sex manuals originally written about by Margaret
        Mead.
    c. evil demons or spirits that are said to victimize men or
        women.
    d. sex games played by adolescents in the Celebes Islands.

11. All of the following are universal or nearly   universal
    components of premarital heterosexuality except
    a. kissing.
    b. embracing.
    c. manual stimulation of genitalia.
    d. petting.

12. From a cross-cultural perspective, masturbation
    a. is not tolerated in children but is tolerated in adults.
    b. is considered the ultimate form of sexual behavior.
    c. is lauded as proof that one is sexually stimulated and a
        good potential marriage partner.
    d. is usually regarded as an admission of one's inability to
        obtain a sexual partner.

13. A society that allows cunnilingus
    a. always allows fellatio.
    b. rarely allows fellatio.
    c. encourages anal intercourse.
    d. always has sunna circumcision as part of their puberty rites.

14. Exogamy and endogamy refer to
    a. childbirth practices among most primitive people.
    b. legal appeals of those accused of incestuous behavior.
    c. the tendency to marry outside or within one's group.
    d. universal taboos adhered to by all human societies.

15. The double standard of sexual morality probably exists because
    a. women are usually more promiscuous than men.
    b. men are usually more promiscuous than women.
    c. it is harder to get a consensus on punishment for women who err sexually.
    d. women make most of the social rules.

16. Ceremonial license refers to
    a. a formal paper obtained from a local court to hold a ceremony.
    b. a ceremony that licenses a village elder to judge sexual offenders.
    c. ceremonies in which sexual rules are temporarily abandoned.
    d. a part of almost every primitive society's puberty rites for girls.

17. Sleep crawling refers to
    a. exercizes done by Polynesian girls to learn to become sexually responsive.
    b. an extramarital affair in Polynesian cultures.
    c. what an adolescent Polynesian girl does right after she has lost her virginity in a puberty rite.
    d. a Polynesian practice in which adolescent boys steal sex with unmarried girls.

18. Female virginity is highly regarded in many societies for all of the following reasons except
    a. females are viewed as property.
    b. men like to perform the mutilative genital operations on the women who are virgins as proof of their masculinity.
    c. men want proof that any children will be their own.
    d. men do not want experienced females who could compare them to former lovers.

19. Considered cross-culturally, it can be said of marriage that
    a. some cultures do not have any known form of marriage.
    b. all cultures have some form of romantic love as the basis for marriage.
    c. all peoples have some form of marriage.
    d. no culture allows a child as young as an infant to be

264

earmarked as a future spouse by another family.

20. Extramarital sex from a cross-cultural perspective
    a. is usually forgiven in females rather than males who are supposed to "know better."
    b. is never allowed with relatives since this is part of the universal incest taboo.
    c. is usually forgiven when engaged in by males since it is harder to restrain or punish men.
    d. is always subject to censure of some sort.

21. All of the following are accurate statements about the sexual freedoms of postmarital persons except
    a. postmarital persons are expected to remain celibate for long periods of time.
    b. postmarital persons in preindustrial societies are under greater social pressures to remarry.
    c. postmarital persons usually have greater sexual freedom than never married or married persons.
    d. even in industrialized civilizations such as ours, most postmarital persons will remarry.

22. Anthropology's investigation of homosexuality has concluded that
    a. predominant homosexuality as a lifetime pattern is common in pre-industrial societies.
    b. homosexuality and heterosexuality are mutually exclusive.
    c. expectations of how one should behave cannot overcome prior conditioning.
    d. male homosexuality is often divided into the "penetrator" and "penetrated" roles.

23. All of the following are common forms of homosexuality except
    a. the Greek form.
    b. homosexuality accompanied by transvestism.
    c. the Egyptian form.
    d. homosexuality expected under specifically defined conditions.

24. The joking relationship refers to
    a. the relationship between Gimbalans and their wives.
    b. an anthropological way of defining transvestism.
    c. the camraderie between those men who are exclusively homosexual for their lifetimes in a primitive society.
    d. a form of ritualized sex.

25. All of the following are forms of female circumcision except
    a. sunna.
    b. clitoridectomy.
    c. doce anos.
    d. infibulation.

T   1.   All people have some inherited sexual drive that occurs apart from learning or conditioning.

F   2.   Anthropology developed in Europe and the U.S. during the days of Prohibition.

T   3.   The sexual attractiveness of nudity is culturally determined.

F   4.   Anthropologists have written extensively about the occurrence of orgasm during sleep.

T   5.   In sexually permissive societies masturbation is rare.

T   6.   A society that approves of cunnilingus always approves of fellatio but not vice versa.

T   7.   Many societies publicly condemn premarital coitus but secretly approve of it.

F   8.   No societies have yet been discovered that allow men to marry male transvestites.

T   9.   Incest taboos exist to prevent complications of kinship, inheritance, and role conflict.

F   10.   Societal attitudes toward marriage are consistent and hardly vary at all.

T   11.   All societies are more tolerant of male extramarital activity than of female extramarital behavior.

F   12.   Most nonindustrial societies prohibit homosexual behavior.

T   13.   If a society is intolerant of homosexuality, the intolerance is greater for males than females.

T   14.   Some societies actually allow sex between children and adults.

T   15.   There is a strong sexual element in many religions.

Fill in the Blanks

1.   The majority of adults are not sexually attracted to individuals below the age of (puberty).

2.   A sharp sexual distinction between childhood and adulthood doesn't occur in many (primitive) societies.

3.   (Incubi) were male spirits believed to victimize women during sleep.

4. (Petting) is usually one's first heterosexual activity.

5. "A sexual union between two or more persons recognized by society, the persons involved; entailing legal obligations" describes (marriage).

6. That one cannot marry persons too closely related is part of the (incest) taboo.

7. A marriage with one male and one female is called (monogamous).

8. If one is married within one's group, this is called (endogamy).

9. Sexual activity with someone other than one's spouse is called (extramarital) activity.

10. (Ceremonial license) refers to rituals that allow sexual rules to be temporarily removed.

11. In many societies, marriages are arranged and are not based on (love).

12. The sexually attractiveness of nudity is (culturally) determined.

13. A society recognizes a potential sexual attraction between relatives and allows them to defuse this through humor. This is a form of ritualized sex called a (joking relationship).

14. Human sexuality can be modified by learning and (conditioning).

15. A good deal of sexual attractiveness stems not from physical appearance but from (behavior).

Discussion/Essay Questions

1. You are given unlimited funds to conduct the first study of sexual dysfunction in different societies. Which societies would you choose? Design the study.

2. Different cultures have very different notions of what is physically attractive and what sexual practices are desirable. What does this tell us about the issue of instinctive versus learned components of sexual arousal?

3. In some societies, all boys have homosexual activity during childhood. Then, at adulthood, the man chooses a wife and never again has a homosexual contact. What does this imply about the development of sexual orientation?

5. Compare clitoral and penile circumcision practices at puberty. What are some of the consequences of such operations? Describe some ritual pubertal ceremonies performed in the U.S.

6.   Explain exogamy and endogamy, and why they are regulated.

7.   What differences in the patterns of adult sexual behavior might you expect to find in a culture with open, permissive attitudes toward childhood sexuality compared to a culture that places strong restrictions on childhood sex?